Street scene in Anchorage, largest city in Alaska.

Alaska

A Reconnaissance Report on the Potential Development of Water Resources in the Territory of Alaska for Irrigation, Power Production and Other Beneficial Uses

By THE UNITED STATES DEPARTMENT OF THE INTERIOR

Oscar L. Chapman, *Secretary*

Sponsored By and Prepared Under the General Supervision of
the Bureau of Reclamation

Michael W. Straus, *Commissioner*

ALASKA DISTRICT OFFICE

Joseph M. Morgan, *District Manager*

JANUARY 1952

Contents

CONTENTS

PHOTOGRAPHS

CONTENTS

Letters of Transmittal

"*The place of Alaska in our present stage of development is most significant in two respects. It is important as an area for expansion and as a source of raw and finished materials. It is important, secondly, in any consideration of national security and defense of the United States. It is interesting to note that the military authorities feel that the military works being constructed in Alaska, however modern they may be, are not sufficient to provide local security or protection to the United States. Alaska must have more people, more railroads, more farms, more industries.*"

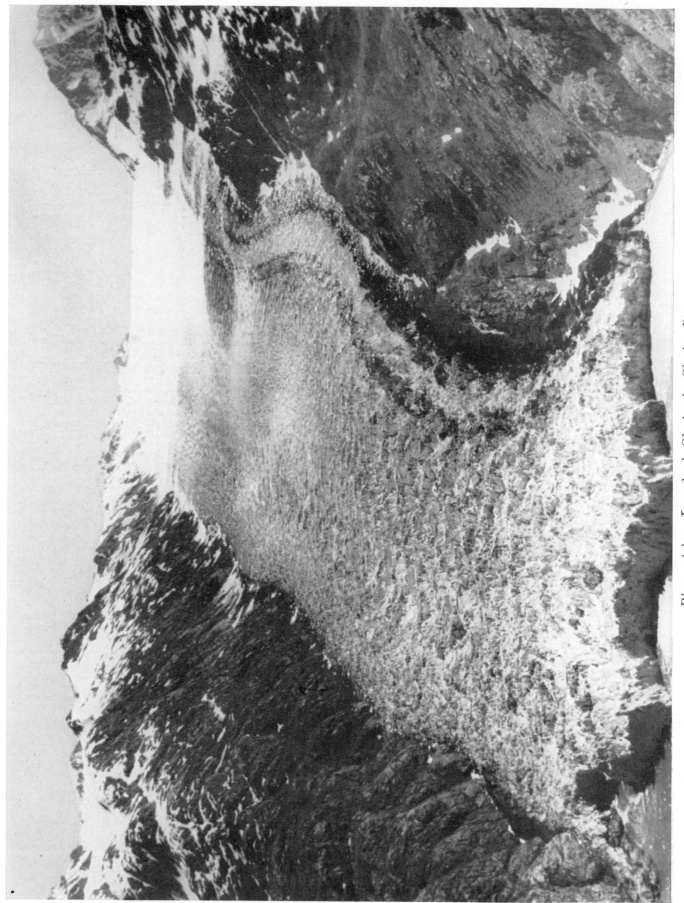

River of ice—Lamplugh Glacier in Glacier Bay.

Letters of Transmittal

UNITED STATES
DEPARTMENT OF THE INTERIOR
OFFICE OF THE SECRETARY

WASHINGTON 25, D. C.

JULY 3, 1951.

MY DEAR MR. SPEAKER: Transmitted herewith for the information of the Congress is my report on a reconnaissance of the potentialities for development of the water and related resources of the Territory of Alaska. The report was prepared under the sponsorship of the Bureau of Reclamation, with participation by other agencies interested in the development of Alaska, under authority of provisions in recent Interior Department Appropriation Acts, which authorized ". . . engineering and economic investigations, as a basis for legislation, and for reports thereon to Congress, relating to projects for the development and utilization of the water resources of Alaska . . ."

The report cites the need for the initiation of a program for detailed investigations of the potentialities for development of the water and related resources in Alaska.

The report was submitted to the President, and the Director of the Bureau of the Budget has advised as follows:

> "We consider the subject report as revised to be a reconnaissance inventory of conditions, problems, potentialities, and apparent trends in Alaska with suggestions for developments which possibly might be undertaken sometime in the future as may be determined by more thorough investigations and detailed studies. It is understood that it is now proposed to transmit this report to the Congress only for its general information and not as a request for legislation or authorization of projects. On that basis there would be no objection to transmittal of the report to the Congress."

Because of the widespread interest in the development of Alaska, it is recommended that the report be printed as a Congressional Document.

Sincerely yours,

(Signed) WILLIAM E. WARNE,
Acting Secretary of the Interior.

HON. SAM RAYBURN,
Speaker of the House of Representatives,
Washington 25, D. C.

UNITED STATES
DEPARTMENT OF THE INTERIOR
OFFICE OF THE SECRETARY

WASHINGTON 25, D. C.

MARCH 8, 1951.

MY DEAR MR. PRESIDENT: Enclosed is the report of the Department of the Interior on a reconnaissance of the potentialities for development of the water and related resources in the Territory of Alaska, prepared by the Bureau of Reclamation under authority of provisions in recent Interior Department Appropriation Acts, which authorized " . . . engineering and economic investigations, as a basis for legislation, and . . . reports thereon, relating to projects for the development and utilization of the water resources of Alaska . . ." The report of the Commissioner of Reclamation has been approved and adopted as the report of the Department of the Interior.

Copies of an earlier draft of the enclosed report were sent to the Governor of Alaska, the Secretary of the Army, the Secretary of Agriculture, the Chairman of the Federal Power Commission, and the Director, Office of Domestic Commerce, Department of Commerce, for their information and comments. The report has now been revised, taking into consideration the constructive comments received from these agencies.

The report contains recommendations for the initiation of a program for a detailed investigation of the development of the water resources of Alaska.

I shall appreciate having your advice concerning the relationship of the enclosed report to your program.

Sincerely yours,

(Signed) OSCAR L. CHAPMAN,
Secretary of the Interior.

THE PRESIDENT,
The White House,
(Through the Bureau of the Budget.)

UNITED STATES
DEPARTMENT OF THE INTERIOR
BUREAU OF RECLAMATION

WASHINGTON 25, D. C.

MARCH 1, 1951.

THE SECRETARY OF THE INTERIOR.

SIR: On June 1, 1949, the December 1948 report of the Bureau of Reclamation on a reconnaissance of the potentialities for the development and utilization of the water and related resources in the Territory of Alaska was approved and adopted as the report of the Department of the Interior. Since that time, the report has been under review by the other interested Federal agencies. After consideration of the helpful and constructive comments of the other agencies, contained in letters dated June 27, 1949, from the Governor of Alaska; August 30, 1949, from the Chairman of the Federal Power Commission; September 2, 1949, from the Secretary of Agriculture; November 7, 1949, from the Director of the Office of Domestic Commerce, Department of Commerce; December 21, 1949, from the Chief of Engineers. Department of the Army; and February 8, 1950, from the Assistant Secretary, Department of State; the report has been revised as of February 1950. A copy of the revised report is attached hereto.

The report cites the need for the initiation of a program for detailed investigations of the potentialities for development of water and related resources in Alaska. Since the completion of our report in the field, studies on the agricultural phases of development of Alaska have continued, and several progress reports on these phases have been issued, notably "Some Economic Aspects of Farming in Alaska, January 1950," and "Markets for the Products of Cropland in Alaska, July 1950," by the Department of Agriculture in cooperation with the Alaska Agricultural Experiment Station.

Information developed by these studies, as well as more recent information compiled during the 1950 census, has made some of the information contained in the attached report outdated, without, however, invalidating the basic premises of the report. Accordingly, I recommend that you approve the attached report and adopt it as the revised report of the Department of the Interior, and that you transmit it to the President and, subsequently, to the Congress.

Respectfully,

(Signed) G. W. LINEWEAVER,
Acting Commissioner.

Approved and adopted March 8, 1951.

(Signed) OSCAR L. CHAPMAN,
Secretary of the Interior.

UNITED STATES
DEPARTMENT OF THE INTERIOR
BUREAU OF RECLAMATION

WASHINGTON 25, D. C.

MAY 20, 1949.

THE SECRETARY OF THE INTERIOR.

SIR: This is my report on a reconnaissance of the potentialities for the development and utilization of water and related resources in the Territory of Alaska. The report has been prepared under authority of a provision in the Interior Department Appropriation Act, 1949. The purpose of the report is to present the results of the engineering and economic investigations made to date, for the consideration of the Congress as a basis for legislation.

My report is based on the attached report of the Chief of the Alaska Investigations Office of the Bureau of Reclamation, dated May 2, 1949. The latter report presents a description of the land and its people, its present development and apparent trends, and its needs for future development, including sufficient detail on essential problems to judge the necessity for the type of development which can best be fostered through projects and activities of the Bureau of Reclamation.

The report has been prepared with the cooperation of local, Territorial, and Federal agencies operating in the Territory and contains, in its substantiating materials, statements prepared by a number of cooperating agencies. Without their full and wholehearted cooperation, this valuable inventory of facts and potential developments could not possibly have been prepared. Our Bureau is particularly grateful for the splendid help that has been received in this connection, for this document will be useful not only to the present Congress in connection with its consideration of appropriate legislation for the Bureau of Reclamation, but to the public at large both in the United States and in Alaska, and to the many Federal, State, and local governments, industries, and commercial interests which are concerned with the future of Alaska.

This report permits us to be reasonably specific in discussing the potentialities for development. While it is not intended to make and does not make, recommendations with regard to particular projects or activities to be undertaken, it presents a sufficiently definite understanding of the individual types of resources and their whereabouts to permit us, with reasonable assurance, to avoid a number of generalizations about Alaska which have heretofore too often been necessary.

The place of Alaska in our present stage of development is most significant in two respects. It is important as an area for expansion and as a source of raw and finished materials. It is important, secondly, in any consideration of national security and defense of the United States. It is interesting to note that the military authorities feel that the military works being constructed in Alaska, however modern they may be, are not sufficient to provide local security or protection to the United States. Alaska must have more people, more railroads, more farms, more industries.

In stating his position with respect to the funds provided for preparation of this report, the Chairman of the Interior Department Subcommittee of the House Committee on Appropriations later stated that he had previously suggested that the Department of the Interior investigate the advisability of development of Alaska and felt pleased to know that something was being done about it. That this view was held not only by the Congress of the United States in making this initial appropriation, but by others even more intimately cognizant of the problems involved, is made apparent by the fact that the 19th Alaska Territorial Legislature memorialized the President, the Congress and the Department of the Interior by Senate Joint Memorial No. 5 approved by the Governor of Alaska on February 12, 1949, as follows:

> "Now THEREFORE, your Memorialist, the Legislature of the Territory of Alaska convened in Nineteenth Regular Session, respectfully urges that Alaska be included in the Bureau of Reclamation program with participation under the Reclamation Fund, and submits that such inclusion of Alaska would be to the benefit of all concerned."

A complete copy of the Memorial is attached hereto.

I recommend for your consideration and that of the President and the Congress, the initiation of a program which will facilitate the economic development of the Territory of Alaska through the reclaiming of unused land for agricultural purposes and the development of the unused resources of the Territory to provide low cost hydroelectric power and related types of developments. In connection with multiple-purpose projects, water supplies should be developed, where needed, for irrigation, municipal, and industrial use. The Bureau of Reclamation recognizes that its program is only one facet of a broader program which is needed and justified in Alaska, but its share of this program is an essential link in the development of Alaska in the interest of the whole of the United States.

I recommend that you approve and adopt this as your report and that you transmit it to the President and the Congress. In doing so, I hope that you will find it appropriate to recommend that the President and the Congress consider favorably the enactment of legislation for the carrying out of the Bureau of Reclamation's program in Alaska.

Sincerely yours,

(Signed) MICHAEL W. STRAUS,
Commissioner.

Approved and adopted June 1, 1949.

(Signed) J. H. KRUG,
Secretary of the Interior.

UNITED STATES
DEPARTMENT OF THE INTERIOR
OFFICE OF THE SECRETARY

FOR THE TERRITORY OF ALASKA

JUNEAU, ALASKA, FEB. 15, 1949.

COMMISSIONER OF RECLAMATION,
Bureau of Reclamation,
Department of Interior,
Washington, D. C.

DEAR MR. COMMISSIONER: At the request of the Nineteenth Alaska Territorial Legislature, now in session, I have the honor of transmitting to you certified copy of Senate Joint Memorial No. 5, passed by the Nineteenth Alaska Territorial Legislature and approved by the Governor of Alaska, urging the inclusion of Alaska in the Bureau of Reclamation program.

Yours very truly,

(Signed) LEW M. WILLIAMS,
Secretary of Alaska.

IN THE SENATE BY SENATOR ENGEBRETH

SENATE JOINT MEMORIAL NO. 5

IN THE LEGISLATURE OF THE TERRITORY OF ALASKA

Nineteenth Session

TO THE PRESIDENT AND THE CONGRESS OF THE UNITED STATES, THE SECRETARY OF THE INTERIOR, THE BUREAU OF RECLAMATION, AND THE DELEGATE FROM ALASKA:

Your Memorialist, the Legislature of the Territory of Alaska, in Nineteenth Session assembled, respectfully submits:

WHEREAS, Alaska as the continental corridor to Asia is of vital strategic importance to the United States; and,

WHEREAS, expansion of utilities and other services in Alaska with consequent acceleration of settlement would strengthen the Territory as a buffer area in the interest of national defense, in keeping with present programs of the Department of the Interior, the Army and the Navy and other Federal departments; and,

WHEREAS, the Bureau of Reclamation, through its Reclamation Fund, operating since 1902 in the Western States, has played a great part in developing those States in the fields of land reclamation and irrigation projects and has further developed those States, with augmented activity since 1939 in the field of hydroelectric power; and,

WHEREAS, projects handled through the Reclamation Fund (which is a revolving fund) have been self-liquidating, as would hydroelectric and land utilization projects in Alaska, if Alaska were allowed to participate under the Bureau of Reclamation program; but,

WHEREAS, Alaska has never been included under said program (except for a recent survey) for lack of statutory authorization by Congress; and,

WHEREAS, development of Alaska through participation in the Reclamation Fund would even inure to the long range benefit of the Western States which look to Alaska as an expanding market for their products, not to mention improvement of their position from the national security standpoint;

Now THEREFORE, your Memorialist, the Legislature of the Territory of Alaska convened in Nineteenth Regular Session, respectfully urges that Alaska be included in the Bureau of Reclamation program with participation under the Reclamation Fund, and submits that such inclusion of Alaska would be to the benefit of all concerned.

AND YOUR MEMORIALIST WILL EVER PRAY.

Passed by the Senate February 2, 1949.

(Signed) GUNNARD M. ENGEBRETH,
President of the Senate.

ATTEST:

(Signed) BONNIE JO GRONROOS,
Secretary of the Senate.

Passed by the House February 9, 1949.

(Signed) STANLEY McCUTCHEON,
Speaker of the House.

ATTEST:

(Signed) JOHN L. HEDDE,
Chief Clerk of the House.

Approved by the Governor February 12, 1949.

I certify that the within and foregoing is a full, true and correct copy of Senate Joint Memorial No. 5, passed by the Nineteenth Alaska Legislature and approved by the Governor of Alaska.

(Signed) CELIA THEILE,
Clerk Secretary's Office.

(Signed) ERNEST GRUENING,
Governor of Alaska.

Report of
The Chief

"...*Wealth is lost as long as the timber falls and rots, as long as the arable land remains unproductive, and as long as the rivers dissipate their energy into the seas.*

"*Stopping this waste and conserving these resources are momentous tasks that require a coordinated, well-founded, comprehensive plan. Continued effort will produce such a plan.*"

The Devil's Thumb, sharp spine of the Coast Range near the Stikine River.

Report of the Chief

UNITED STATES
DEPARTMENT OF THE INTERIOR
BUREAU OF RECLAMATION

ALASKA INVESTIGATIONS OFFICE

JUNEAU, ALASKA, MAY 2, 1949.

To: Commissioner
FROM: Chief, Alaska Investigations Office
SUBJECT: Reconnaissance report on potential development of water resources in the Territory of Alaska.

TRANSMITTAL

1. Herein is my report on the potential development of water resources in the Territory of Alaska for power production, irrigation, and other beneficial uses.

AUTHORITY FOR THE REPORT

2. This report is authorized by virtue of the Interior Department Appropriation Act, for the fiscal year 1949, which provided $150,000 to be expended by the Bureau of Reclamation on Alaskan investigations "for engineering and economic investigations, as a basis for legislation, and for reports thereon, relating to projects for the development and utilization of the water power resources of Alaska. . . ."

COOPERATION AND ACKNOWLEDGMENT

3. Federal, Territorial, and local agencies, and many individuals assisted by supplying essentially all of the information. Only their splendid cooperation and collaboration made the report possible. It is an example of the perfect cooperation found everywhere in the Territory, whenever the future development of Alaska is concerned.

4. The Alaska Development Board of the Territorial Government rendered invaluable aid by contributing general data and editorial assistance. Many Federal and Territorial agencies summarized their individual programs for inclusion in the report. Chapter VII of the substantiating materials is devoted exclusively to these programs. Cooperating Federal agencies were: Alaska Native Service, Alaska Railroad, Alaska Road Commission, Bureau of Land Management, Bureau of Mines, Fish and Wildlife Service, Geological Survey, and National Park Service, all of the department of the Interior; Civil Aeronautics Administration and Weather Bureau, of the United States Department of Commerce; Rural Electrification Administration, Forest Service and Agricultural Extension Service of the United States Department of Agriculture; and the Commander-in-Chief of the Alaskan Command of the United States Department of National Defense. Cooperating agencies of the Territory of Alaska were: Office of the Governor, Department of Agriculture, Department of Health, Department of Mines, and Alaska Development Board. Officials of electric utilities supplied much of the data on power supplies, markets and rates.

BASIC PREMISE

5. Except for the statements contributed by some of the cooperating agencies, the report was written in its entirety in Alaska about Alaska. The viewpoints are those of the vast majority of the citizens of Alaska. It does not record the viewpoints of a few who would befog the issues while they exploit the resources for their own personal gain. There can be no compromise when Alaska's future is at stake. Her natural resources must be conserved and utilized for the common good of the Nation. Nor are any viewpoints given herein that would serve to perpetuate the ideology of continued Federal domination over the land and the people. It is written on the basic premise that a government of the people, by the people, and for the people has a definite responsibility to help the people of Alaska develop their country along democratic principles for the greatest good of all.

THE LAND AND THE PEOPLE

6. It is a bigger country than most people realize extending nearly one-sixth of the distance around the

world at this latitude. So big is it that a wide variety of climate and topography can be found; the cool and humid fiords of the Panhandle; the fog-concealed active volcanic region of the Aleutians; the semi-arid temperate valleys of south central Alaska; the extreme 170 degrees temperature variations in the semi-arid rolling hills of the Yukon; and the flat, frozen, treeless tundra of the Artic areas.

7. Alaska was discovered only 200 years ago. Under the Russian flag, it was stripped of fur resources, then sold to the United States in 1867 as a worthless possession. The States did not value it highly for they neglected to establish any permanent form of government for 17 years. The District of Alaska was formed at that time, but changed to the Territory of Alaska in 1912.

8. In 1880 there were only 430 white people in a total population of 33,000. Today, the total population is nearly 3 times greater but only one-third are natives. The present number of people in Alaska is really unknown because of the rapid immigration. Estimates for Anchorage, the fastest growing city, vary from 19,000 to 35,000 people.

PRESENT DEVELOPMENT

9. In commerce, the fisheries industry with annual exports of $100,000,000 ranks first in importance, followed in turn by the mining and fur industries. Recreation is a big business. There are no Territorial taxes on property or on corporate or personal income. Exports and imports are almost in balance at about $120,-000,000 each per year.

10. "Wild life on the hoof" has an estimated value of more than $100,000,000 with an annual take of $4,-000,000 by trappers and hunters. The government-owned fur seal herd in the Pribilof Islands administered by the Department of the Interior comprises about 85 percent of the fur seals of the world. The herd contained more than 3,000,000 animals in 1947. Seal hunting is restricted to natives. Another native industry is that of raising and grazing reindeer. In 1948 there were about 40,000 head on the treeless ranges of northern and western Alaska.

11. Alaska can be reached by sea, by air, and by land. Transportation and communication facilities are inadequate in some areas and costly throughout the territory. Ships from the States ply coastal waters as far north as Nome with stops at intermediate ports. Alaska is a vital base for trans-world air flights between North America and the Orient. The Alaska Highway links Canadian and Alaskan road systems. Principal towns are connected by telephone, telegraph, and radio with the States and Canada.

12. Inside Alaska are more than 3,000 miles of waterway transportation routes. The Department of the Interior operates river steamboats for more than 1,000 miles on the Yukon and Tanana Rivers on a regular-summer schedule and also operates the Alaska Railroad from the ports of Seward and Whittier on the Gulf of Alaska north to Fairbanks, a distance of 471 miles from Seward. Air transportation is available on regular scheduled flights to all principal population centers. Chartered plane service is furnished by veteran bush pilots to virtually any place in Alaska. This is the favorite mode of transportation to remote and otherwise isolated areas. There are more than 1,800 miles of road in the highway system.

13. Forests cover much of the country and are valuable reserves for the Nation. Reserves of merchantable timber are estimated to exceed 180 billion board-feet. Southeast Alaska supports a dense growth of virgin hemlock, spruce and cedar. In the interior vast forests remain practically untouched although burnt-over timberland is extensive in some regions and considerable timber has been cut near settlements and mines.

14. Gold and copper have accounted for most of Alaska's past mineral production totaling almost a billion dollars. Silver, coal, lead, tin, mercury, platinum, and zinc have been mined and shipped in relatively small amounts. Some oil has been produced.

15. Agricultural lands are now chiefly developed in Matanuska Valley near Anchorage and in Tanana Valley near Fairbanks. Only about 12,000 acres in the entire Territory are being cultivated, although potential farm land totals many times that amount. Existing farms produce wheat, barley, oats, peas, potatoes, clover, alfalfa, carrots, rutabagas, cabbage, other hardy vegetables, and bush fruits. Livestock consists of beef and dairy cattle, horses, sheep, hogs, and chickens. Several farmers irrigate their crops.

16. Defense of the States has required fortification of Alaska. It is the back door invasion route to the States. Southeast of Fairbanks, 25 miles on the Richardson Highway, the Army Air Force has recently constructed one of the world's largest airfields. Extensive improvements are being made on other air bases at Fairbanks, Anchorage, and Nome. The Navy is exploring Petroleum Reserve No. 4 covering more than 35,000 square miles on the Arctic Slope.

17. Recounting Alaska's resources and activities gives no hint as to the existing economy of the Territory. Alaska has economic growing pains. A new country seldom, if ever, has a balanced economy during its evolution and Alaska is no exception. Settlement of agricultural lands has been slower than development of other industries and most foodstuffs are imported. Although possessing some of the finest forests in the world, Alaska imports a substantial portion of her lum-

ber. Imports of petroleum and related products exceed $10,000,000 annually, yet potential oil fields lie undeveloped. Electric power is in short supply in most areas while the energy of roaring rivers is dissipated into the sea and forever lost. "It's the freight," say merchants defending their retail prices. Most items cost half again more than in the States. Freight rates are high because ships return to the States empty. Even though substantial reduction in transportation rates were effected, this alone would not be the final solution. The economy and development of the Territory require that concerted impetus be given to full utilization of the natural resources. Constantly recurring shipping strikes force Alaskans to depend on air-lift operations for the necessities of life or do without. Even the air-lift is unsatisfactory; Juneau, the capital city, is served by only one airline from the States and sometimes 10 days elapse between flights. Inside Alaska there are more people than restaurants to feed them; houses and hotels to shelter them; and professional people and stores to serve them. During summer months the demand for skilled workers is terrific. This seam-bursting, lopsided frontier economy is expanding at such a dynamic rate it is hardly comprehendible.

18. Although development has been retarded by an almost exclusive dependency on extractive industries, the Territory has made great economic strides. The Armed Forces found Alaska's economy of great value in World War II. As the Western States found new life, the war also started a burgeoning in the north country. Vast military expenditures, plus scores of new service industries, resulted in a substantial increase in economic levels throughout Alaska, but its greatest contribution was people. New people with new ideas— more than 20,000 of them. Today people more and more want to work in the Territory throughout the year, to make their homes and live out their lives in Alaska. Development of Alaska's resources offers a challenge Alaskans want to meet. For the first time in its 81-year history under the American flag, a real feeling of permanency is being sensed throughout the Territory.

19. Alaska has much in natural wealth to contribute to the Nation despite the limited development in the mining industry. Alaska's mineral production since 1880 is valued at almost one billion dollars—140 times more than the original purchase price of the Territory.

FUTURE DEVELOPMENT

20. Alaska has a great future. The people of the world are looking northward toward all undeveloped countries and their untapped wealth of natural re-

sources. The Territory of Alaska, together with all such lands, faces an era of rapid development.

21. Here in Alaska lie needed crude resources: fertile land, undeveloped mineral deposits, forests, and potentialities for development of low-cost power. In addition, nature has provided a setting of recreational opportunities for the enjoyment of millions of people.

22. The high industrial demand of the past 10 years emphasized that the United States is deficient in respect to a number of metals and minerals essential to the national security and economy. Normally these minerals can be purchased and imported from other nations in sufficient quantities to supply commercial needs in the United States, but during a world crisis, shipments from foreign sources might be entirely cut off. Some of these minerals occur in Alaska in substantial or significant quantities.

23. Deposits of mercury, chromite, platinum, tin, tungsten, zinc, and antimony might, under more favorable economic conditions or through the continued development of greater reserves, make welcome contributions to American industrial requirements. There are possibilities for significant discoveries of oil and the Territory contains deposits of building and construction materials to meet many of its own growing needs.

24. Alaska's fisheries provide one of the great food resources of the world. Fish waste can be manufactured into many useful products: vitamin "A" and "D" units, oil for paints and varnishes, animal feed for fur farms, and fertilizer for agriculture. New methods of processing of many species of fish, other than salmon, would expand the industry still further, increasing its total annual production far beyond the $100,000,000 mark.

25. Alaska is rich in wildlife resources, but they have contributed little to the internal economy of the Territory, as almost all pelts are shipped out of the Territory for tanning and manufacturing. Establishment of these industries would advance the economy of several regions, providing employment for many Alaskan natives.

26. Southeast Alaska supports a dense growth of hemlock, spruce, and cedar from which 1,000,000,000 board feet could be harvested anually in perpetuity.

27. The United States now uses $2,000,000,000 worth of paper and paper products annually, necessitating the importation of huge quantities of paper and pulp. During any period of sustained high industrial production, however, imports are insufficient to supply the demand. Such shortages will be partially alleviated by development of the paper industry in Alaska. One mill is practically assured for Ketchikan and the construction of a second plant near Sitka will in all probability start at an early date. Others are sure to follow. Conversion of hemlock and spruce into newsprint

would make possible the additional production of one-fourth as much newsprint as is now consumed in the United States. It is anticipated that full development would be attained in 10 years and could be sustained in perpetuity.

28. At least 5,000,000 people could be sustained on Alaska's resources. Norway, Finland, and Sweden with the same latitude, but more fully matured economically, have a present population density 2½ to 5 times greater than Alaska would have with 5,000,000 inhabitants. In fact, it is easy to see that Alaska could support a greater population density than Norway. In Alaska after discounting 200,000 square miles of the treeless regions worthless for agriculture, although valuable for reindeer pasture and mineral deposits, there are 386,000 square miles of land in Alaska more habitable and fertile and with more natural resources than the average land in Norway, Finland, and Sweden. A potential population density, midway between that of Norway and Sweden, would result in a potential Alaska population of more than 12,000,000 persons. By this reasoning it is not unlikely that Alaska ultimately will have 10,000,000 inhabitants.

29. When the country matures, agriculture will assume an important role. No nation is sufficient unto itself from a standpoint of agricultural production. As an example, the States import the products from 50,000,000 acres of foreign soil and in turn export surpluses of other products. Likewise Alaska can never hope to be entirely self-sufficient in food production. Climate would preclude the production of many desired foodstuffs. With a population of 5,000,000 to 10,000,000, however, it would be highly desirable to a balanced economy to have 10,000,000 to 20,000,000 acres of land in agricultural production. The Commissioner of Agriculture of Alaska states that agricultural land suitable for crops or grassland is approximately 17,000,000 acres.

30. Ample low-cost power is a prerequisite to the development of a mature and balanced economy. It is a magnet which attracts industry, business, and people. Power is wealth. Fortunately, Alaska river systems could produce more than 50,000,000,000 kilowatt-hours of energy a year. This much power would give 10,000,000 people more than twice that now available to each person in the States. Nature has provided these power sites so lavishly that even the most remote corner of the country is easily within modern power transmission distance.

31. Geographic areas which have been given consideration as a result of a reconnaissance made of the potential water power sites are listed below. Emphasis is placed on the fact that not all streams and their power potentialities have been considered, which, for the most part, was due to lack of sufficient basic data to evaluate

their production capabilities. Potential power sites are shown in red on the accompanying map.

32. A summary of the potential hydroelectric power developments by regions and areas follows:

TABLE 1.—*Summary of potential hydroelectric power development by regions and areas*

Region and area	Installed capacity (kilowatts)	Annual firm production (kilowatt-hours)
Ketchikan area	133, 000	730, 000, 000
Wrangell area	218, 000	1, 250, 000, 000
Sitka area	58, 000	320, 000, 000
Angoon area	37, 000	210, 000, 000
Juneau area	1, 775, 000	9, 760, 000, 000
Subtotal southeastern region	2, 221, 000	12, 270, 000, 000
Gulf of Alaska area	1, 744, 000	9, 780, 000, 000
Cook Inlet area	1, 519, 000	8, 660, 000, 000
Subtotal south central region	3, 263, 000	18, 440, 000, 000
Kuskokwim River Basin	850, 000	4, 800. 000, 000
Upper Yukon River area	44, 000	250, 000, 000
Yukon Flats area	1, 500, 000	8, 800, 000, 000
Tanana River Basin	156, 000	890, 000, 000
Subtotal Yukon-Kuskokwim region	2, 550, 000	14, 740, 000, 000
Subtotal Seward Peninsula region	35, 000	200, 000, 000
Subtotal Arctic region	225, 000	1, 280, 000, 000
Total	8, 294, 000	46, 930, 000, 000

33. Food production in Alaska is a matter of great importance to the Armed Forces. Immediately following the Pearl Harbor attack, Alaska was so vulnerable that men and war supplies were rushed to her defense. Matanuska Valley farmers by almost superhuman efforts were able to furnish much of the necessary food supply in those critical days thus freeing additional shipping space for defense materials. Before any similar emergency again arises, additional agricultural lands should be brought under cultivation and production increased by irrigation wherever needed.

34. Additional crop acreage is required. Developments in communication, transportation, mining, industry, and commerce would bring still greater local demands for products which could be economically produced on Alaskan farms.

35. Increasing the acreage of cropland, however, is time-consuming and requires investment of considerable capital. Except for 10 or 15 acres, clearing the virgin land of timber has been beyond the financial ability of the average settler. After providing such essentials as a home, out-buildings, water supply, fences, farm machinery and a few head of livestock, the settler needs sufficient cash or credit to clear a minimum of 40

acres of land to have a going and self-sustaining farm. To clear 40 acres of land might cost $6,000.

36. The development of Alaska is as important and vital to the United States as was the development of our Western States. A balanced portion of the development must be in agriculture. The principal question, as was the case in our Western States, is, how can this be accomplished? The general pattern of the development of our great West with Federal assistance points the way by which Alaska can be developed, not at the expense of other portions of the country but by the returns from Alaska itself. Not only does the country need Alaska's development from the standpoint of an expanding economy but the individual people need settlement opportunities, places to make their homes, business opportunities, and all the other benefits that are associated with a frontier country. Certainly individuals can reclaim small areas within their abilities and financial backing but for agriculture to expand in Alaska, even to meet the present needs, will require aid and assistance by the Federal Government both in "know how" and financial support. Development of land by clearing, drainage, and irrigation should be financed, where private capital is unable to accomplish it, by the use of Federal funds, to be paid for out of the returns from the production on those lands. Government sponsorship of the type which has been provided in the Western States would provide the stimulant necessary for Alaska to catch up in agricultural production so vital to a sound development. The potential agricultural areas are shown in yellow on the accompanying map.

37. Well-supported organized efforts are necessary to achieve the substantial agricultural development needed to supply existing demands for foodstuffs in Alaska. Some indication as to quantities required can be obtained from examining the import figures for 1947 as shown in the following table.

38. Quantities of specified agricultural imports from the United States to Alaska in 1947 (excluding estimated imports to southeastern Alaska, assuming that that region will continue to be supplied chiefly from the United States and Canada), and an estimate of the acreages required to produce these products in the Territory are shown in the adjacent table.

39. The figure of 87,000 acres shown as needed area is only a rough estimate of the amount of agricultural land which should be brought into production in the near future. Detailed studies must be made to determine the extent to which the tabulated products can be economically produced under Alaskan conditions in competition with imports from the United States and Canada.

40. Alaska is one of the greatest undeveloped areas in a land-hungry, resources-hungry world. The Terri-

TABLE 2.—*Quantities of specified agricultural imports from the United States to Alaska*

Product	Quantity imported (1,000 pounds)	Live-weight equivalent of imports (1,000 pounds)	Live-stock needed [1] (number)	Area needed [2] (acres)
Milk, evaporated, unsweetened	4,600	------	1,300	9,100
Butter	980	------	4,000	25,800
Beef and veal, fresh or frozen	4,070	7,330	[3] 8,000	[4] 32,500
Pork, fresh or frozen	200	------	-------	-------
Ham and shoulder, cured	770	------	-------	-------
Bacon	720	------	-------	-------
Sausage, not canned	480	------	-------	-------
Animal oils and fats, edible	480	------	-------	-------
Total hog products	2,650	3,450	2,300	11,700
Eggs in shell (1000 dozen)	1,140	------	114,000	7,400
Poultry	610	920	[5] 28,000	280
Potatoes	4,050	------	-------	390
Fresh vegetables	3,630	------	-------	260
Total	------	11,700	-------	87,430

[1] Milk cows, beef cows, brood sows, laying hens, and broilers. Youngstock are not included in these numbers but the usual complements of youngstock were taken into account in computing livestock yields and feed requirements.

[2] Estimates of crop acres in Alaska needed to produce the equivalents of imported products. They are based on crop yields slightly higher than Matanuska Valley farmers' estimates of usual yields and appreciably higher than yields reported for 1947. These higher yields were used because improved practices, including increased use of fertilizer and irrigation, are expected to become more common in the future than they have been in the past.

[3] To produce beef in addition to veal and beef from dairy herds.

[4] Assuming 40 percent of feed from range.

[5] Broilers to produce meat in addition to that from farm poultry flocks.

tory cannot expect to further develop on gold and fish alone. Advancement of its economy is contingent on the full utilization of resources now undeveloped. No geographical entity has ever attained lasting industrial greatness through extractive industries alone. To whatever extent integration is possible—from the extraction of raw materials to the manufacture of semi-finished or finished products—to that extent will Alaska achieve a place in the industrialization of the North American continent.

41. Current information concerning agricultural development permits three broad generalizations: (1) subject to detailed investigation and analysis of economic feasibility, about 87,000 acres of new agricultural land are needed now; (2) there are hundreds of thousands of acres of uncleared or undrained land, the soil, topography, and climate of which may be as suitable for agricultural production as lands now being farmed; (3) agricultural growth should be geared to developments in industry, commerce, and national defense, with respect to both its location and magnitude.

42. Ultimately, Alaska will contribute billions of dollars a year to National income. This will only be possible when the natural resources are fully developed and utilized. It is a task too great for small groups of individuals or even for Alaska. It is a responsibility of the Federal Government to conserve and develop

these resources so that people can utilize them for the creation of wealth and the benefit of mankind.

43. For the immediate, investigations of the water resources for power and multipurpose benefits should embrace the Big Susitna River Basin; the trans-mountain diversion of water from the Lewes River (Yukon) drainage basin in Canada with its chain of lakes to the Taiya River outlet 10 miles north of Skagway, Alaska, and other potential power sites in the southeast where interested pulp industries are investigating the possibilities of establishing pulp mills. The study and investigation of water resource development is needed particularly in two districts, the Fairbanks-Dunbar-Chena District and the Matanuska-Anchorage-Spenard District. Municipal water supply studies are also of vital importance to Fairbanks, Anchorage, Cordova, and other Alaskan communities. In Fairbanks well water supply is contaminated by contiguous cesspools, epidemics are imminent, investigations, and improvements are critically needed.

CONCLUSIONS

44. It is concluded that:

A. The demand for electric power supply in the Territory is expanding so rapidly that new installations of hydroelectric power plants are needed:

(1) To supply emergency requirements for power as quickly as possible to meet urgent needs of the civilian and military population in the Anchorage and Fairbanks area.

(2) To supply power requirements of existing and additional National Defense installations in the vicinity of Anchorage, Fairbanks, and Nome.

(3) To provide power necessary for full utilization of the natural resources and for full realization of Alaska's industrial and commercial potentialities. Sizable quantities of low-cost power would materially aid the establishment of the pulp industry; one pulp plant is being constructed near Ketchikan and another is virtually assured near Sitka. Three or four other pulp plants are being actively considered for development in Southeast Alaska. Large quantities of power may be needed to expedite early development of the coal hydrogenation program in the rail belt area. Power

would also be needed if a cement plant were to be built in the area. Power supply could be made available to the aeronautical laboratories for conducting supersonic wind tunnel research.

B. Adequate agricultural production is necessary to the economic life and future development of Alaska. Present production is inadequate. To increase agricultural production:

(1) Immediate investigation should be made of the physical and economic feasibility of bringing into production as soon as possible approximately 87,000 acres of new agricultural land. Reports should be prepared on the engineering and economic feasibility of specific land clearing, reclamation by land drainage and irrigation projects which may appropriately contribute to this goal.

(2) In order to prosecute such a program, investigations should be initiated immediately for reports on the reclaiming of lands in the Matanuska-Anchorage-Spenard District, the Fairbanks-Dunbar-Chena District and on the Kenai Peninsula near Homer.

C. Municipal and industrial water supplies are urgently needed in several localities, particularly in the Fairbanks area where well water is contaminated by contiguous cesspools. These requirements should be included in future studies of multiple-purpose projects.

D. Flood control and navigation of inland waterways in Alaska will increase in importance as the Territory is developed. The investigations of water resources to be accomplished in Alaska by the Bureau of Reclamation would be complemented by the investigations in Alaska authorized to be made by the Corps of Engineers under the Flood Control Act of 1948. The Bureau of Reclamation and the Corps of Engineers should jointly consider these problems in connection with irrigation, power and other multiple purpose project investigations. The Federal Power Commission should also assist in joint consideration of power features of the potential projects.

E. Annual appropriations should be made to permit an efficient investigation of Alaska's land and water resources at a rate commensurate with the needs.

(Signed) JOSEPH M. MORGAN.

Substantiating Material

"Here lies America's greatest wealth of untapped natural resources . . .

"To conserve these great natural resources, men must forget immediate personal gain for the benefit of future generations . . . to develop these resources, they must plan great plans and the Congress must have faith and understanding . . . to utilize these resources, at least five million self-supporting Alaskans are needed.

". . . Ultimately, Alaska will contribute billions of dollars a year to National income, but this contribution will be possible only when the natural resources are fully developed and utilized.

"Additional investigative work is required."

Aerial view of Anchorage, largest and fastest growing city in the Territory of Alaska.

CHAPTER I

Purpose of the Report

What of the water resources of Alaska? Have they any value? Should they be developed? These and a host of other questions have long needed answering. Recognizing the problems, the Eightieth Congress directed the Bureau of Reclamation to investigate the water resources of Alaska. In compliance with this request a field reconnaissance was made and the findings are stated in this report.

The major purpose of the report is to present the results of the reconnaissance investigation of the potental water resource development of the Territory. A portion of the report is based on field and office investigations recently performed by Bureau personnel. The major part of the report is a compilation of information obtained over the years by Federal, Territorial, and local agencies. The reconnaissance nature of the report should be emphasized. The Bureau of Reclamation presents no recommendations or preliminary plans for development of any specific project. Limitations of present knowledge and available sources of information are pointed out, and recommendations are made for detailed investigation and analysis to determine the engineering and economic feasibility of each specific project as continued development becomes desirable and necessary.

Another purpose of the report is to emphasize the need for joint investigation by the United States and the Dominion of Canada of several hydroelectric power potentialities. An agreement would be necessary for full development of several rivers common to both Canada and Alaska. It is doubted that either country could independently develop these rivers within their own respective borders to produce its share of power at such low-cost as under joint development and operation. The United States should actively seek an extension of the agreement with the Dominion of Canada to extend activities of the existing International Joint Commission to include investigation of potentialities of water resources common to both the Territory of Alaska and Dominion of Canada. The Secretary of the Interior should be designated to represent the United States Government in this matter.

Prior absence of a complete inventory of Alaska's natural resources has been an almost insurmountable obstacle in coordinating their development. Although the major purpose of this report is to cite water resource potentialities, it also includes the most recent and complete economic evaluation possible of the Territory's resources. It is believed this investigation is now sufficiently complete to correlate the various potentialities into a comprehensive plan for orderly development of Alaska's natural wealth.

To place any comprehensive plan in operation would require the coordinated efforts of all Federal and Territorial agencies. For example, full development of water resources would inundate stretches of some proposed highways. However, it is not too late nor is the highway system so extensive but that these multiple activities could be coordinated in the future. Only by such cooperation could millions of dollars of future damages be eliminated. It is only natural that highways should be located on easy grades near streams or rivers. There is sufficient information in this report on the proposed location of new highways and multiple purpose dams and reservoirs to indicate the necessity for coordination of these activities at the earliest possible moment.

The construction of many of these dams is highly probable in view of future demands for power and water. Construction would require access roads, many of which, with proper foresight, could become links in a future highway network. Many of these highways could be located along the shores of what potentially would be some of the largest man-made lakes in the world. Agricultural districts outlined in this report would eventually need to be included in farm-to-market road systems.

Multiple-purpose development of water resources for optimum use requires correlation of fish and wild life conservation practices with construction of dams needed for other purposes. The fishing industry ranks first in importance in Alaska's economy. This position can only be maintained if man-made destructive elements are minimized. The Fish and Wildlife Service should be consulted to make certain that proposed structures for water resource developments do not hinder the "run" of salmon. The information in this report is intended to set forth the location of some of the more important structures so they may be critically reviewed by conservationists.

One of the reasons for high food prices in Alaska is the cost of fertilizer necessary for agricultural production. One of the purposes of this report is to point out the needs for fertilizer and that waste products from fisheries could be utilized for fertilizer production.

The fisheries industry is in need of low-cost power for quick-freeze and cold storage plants. It is hoped that several of the power potentialities mentioned in this inventory will be of assistance.

The various governmental agencies concerned in the development of the resources of Alaska must work closely together. Unless the work of these agencies is well coordinated, certain types of ore deposits might well receive only passing consideration and some large low-cost hydroelectric power potentialities may receive only cursory investigation. The combination of extensive low-grade ore deposits and plentiful low-cost electric energy can lead to establishment of large-scale mining and metallurgical operations to assist in supplying the nation with mineral products.

Unclaimed and undeveloped ore deposits are known to exist on public domain in several potential reservoir areas. The determination of their commercial and strategic values are functions of the Bureau of Mines. If the ore is of over-riding commercial and strategic value it should be mined before it is inundated.

Lack of sufficient funds has been a severe handicap in the collection of basic data for water resource development. So much country has not been mapped, so few streams have been gaged, and there is so little knowledge of the quality of water in Alaska, that the Geological Survey needs to know the plans for resource development in order to plan the program of collecting basic data to the best advantage.

There are several villages that would be inundated by potential reservoirs. If such reservoirs would permit utilization of large quantities of power for development of other natural resources, then these reservoirs might potentially have more value than the present village sites. Should these villages grow into cities then this potential wealth might be lost forever. Proper planning now would do much to alleviate future difficulties. Potential agricultural lands in reservoir areas should be surveyed as to their adaptability for agricultural production and a determination made as to the best use of the land; for agricultural production or for a reservoir for multiple-purpose developments.

High transportation costs, to and within the Territory, are another economic ailment. Much of this cost can be traced to the lack of back-haul for the Alaska Railroad and steamship lines. Everything is loaded going north, but empty returning south. Plentiful low-cost power would materially spur industrialization, which would provide a back-haul and thereby lower transportation costs.

Development of water resources must be accomplished in such manner that the natural scenic beauty of the area is not destroyed. Correlation of water resource development activities with those of the National Park Service would not only accomplish this, but new recreational areas could be created in conjunction with man-made lakes.

One of the most pressing problems in Alaska has been the fact that work is seasonal, resulting in large numbers of unemployed during winter months. This is particularly true of Alaskan natives. It is not too difficult for them to obtain employment during the summer in the fisheries or allied industries or construction projects. One of the purposes of this report is to point out that such a labor force is available, that they are highly skilled and adaptable for industrial work and that low-cost hydroelectric power would make such industrial opportunities for employment economically possible. However, this native labor force would require schooling and training, an activity of the Alaska Native Service, Office of Indian Affairs.

The Weather Bureau of the Department of Commerce supplies many of the records needed for investigation of potential water resource developments. It is willing and able to provide such records only if the location of such potentialities are known. It is hoped the information given in this report will be of some assistance to the Weather Bureau in its planning for new installations and collection of records.

The Department of National Defense is extending the defenses of Alaska. Most new installations will require considerable electrical energy. One such installation contemplated for the near future would require 200,000 kilowatts of installed electric generating capacity. The availability of low-cost hydroelectric energy is one of the determining factors for the location of this installation. It is hoped that information given in this report regarding hydro-electric power sites will be of assistance to the Department of National Defense. The Bureau of Reclamation of the Department of the Interior and the Alaskan Command of the Department of National Defense have worked together on these matters in the preparation of this report.

Alaskan development cannot come overnight, nor will it be a simple matter of outlining a plan and following it to a conclusion. Many limitations must be recognized and either eliminated, surmounted, or accepted. Problems dealing with the soil, with climatic conditions, with agriculture, with industry, with transportation, and with the damage already inflicted by a lopsided economy are detailed in this report. The economic

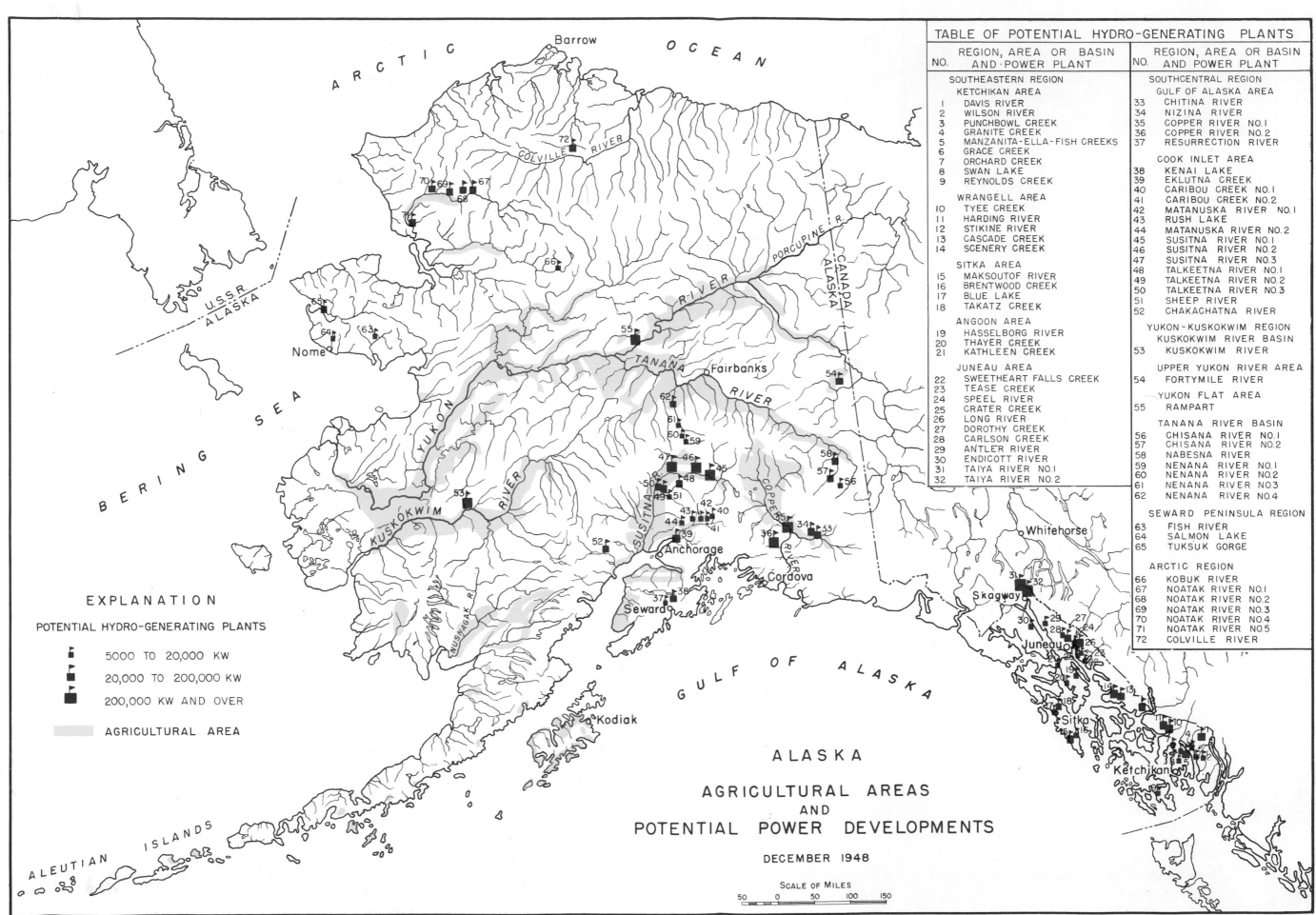

ALASKA

AGRICULTURAL AREAS

AND

POTENTIAL POWER DEVELOPMENTS

DECEMBER 1948

SCALE OF MILES
50 0 50 100 150

EXPLANATION

POTENTIAL HYDRO-GENERATING PLANTS

5000 TO 20,000 KW

20,000 TO 200,000 KW

200,000 KW AND OVER

AGRICULTURAL AREA

TABLE OF POTENTIAL HYDRO-GENERATING PLANTS

NO.	REGION, AREA OR BASIN AND POWER PLANT	NO.	REGION, AREA OR BASIN AND POWER PLANT
	SOUTHEASTERN REGION		SOUTHCENTRAL REGION
	KETCHIKAN AREA		GULF OF ALASKA AREA
1	DAVIS RIVER	33	CHITINA RIVER
2	WILSON RIVER	34	NIZINA RIVER
3	PUNCHBOWL CREEK	35	COPPER RIVER NO.1
4	GRANITE CREEK	36	COPPER RIVER NO.2
5	MANZANITA-ELLA-FISH CREEKS	37	RESURRECTION RIVER
6	GRACE CREEK		
7	ORCHARD CREEK		COOK INLET AREA
8	SWAN LAKE	38	KENAI LAKE
9	REYNOLDS CREEK	39	EKLUTNA CREEK
		40	CARIBOU CREEK NO.1
	WRANGELL AREA	41	CARIBOU CREEK NO.2
10	TYEE CREEK	42	MATANUSKA RIVER NO.1
11	HARDING RIVER	43	RUSH LAKE
12	STIKINE RIVER	44	MATANUSKA RIVER NO.2
13	CASCADE CREEK	45	SUSITNA RIVER NO.1
14	SCENERY CREEK	46	SUSITNA RIVER NO.2
		47	SUSITNA RIVER NO.3
	SITKA AREA	48	TALKEETNA RIVER NO.1
15	MAKSOUTOF RIVER	49	TALKEETNA RIVER NO.2
16	BRENTWOOD CREEK	50	TALKEETNA RIVER NO.3
17	BLUE LAKE	51	SHEEP RIVER
18	TAKATZ CREEK	52	CHAKACHATNA RIVER
	ANGOON AREA		YUKON-KUSKOKWIM REGION
19	HASSELBORG RIVER		KUSKOKWIM RIVER BASIN
20	THAYER CREEK	53	KUSKOKWIM RIVER
21	KATHLEEN CREEK		
			UPPER YUKON RIVER AREA
	JUNEAU AREA	54	FORTYMILE RIVER
22	SWEETHEART FALLS CREEK		
23	TEASE CREEK		YUKON FLAT AREA
24	SPEEL RIVER	55	RAMPART
25	CRATER CREEK		
26	LONG RIVER		TANANA RIVER BASIN
27	DOROTHY CREEK	56	CHISANA RIVER NO.1
28	CARLSON CREEK	57	CHISANA RIVER NO.2
29	ANTLER RIVER	58	NABESNA RIVER
30	ENDICOTT RIVER	59	NENANA RIVER NO.1
31	TAIYA RIVER NO.1	60	NENANA RIVER NO.2
32	TAIYA RIVER NO.2	61	NENANA RIVER NO.3
		62	NENANA RIVER NO.4
			SEWARD PENINSULA REGION
		63	FISH RIVER
		64	SALMON LAKE
		65	TUKSUK GORGE
			ARCTIC REGION
		66	KOBUK RIVER
		67	NOATAK RIVER NO.1
		68	NOATAK RIVER NO.2
		69	NOATAK RIVER NO.3
		70	NOATAK RIVER NO.4
		71	NOATAK RIVER NO.5
		72	COLVILLE RIVER

51654

988410 O—52   (Face p. 18)

feasibility of every step must be determined by careful study.

It is believed that the limitations which will be fully brought to light by careful investigation will be outweighed by the potentialities. Alaska is one of the greatest undeveloped areas in the world; its known potential wealth is greater than our national debt, although $3,000,000,000 already has been taken out by haphazard development under the absentee landlord system. Its national defense position is evident and its industry, agriculture, service trades, and professions must be developed to back up the defense plans of the Army, Air Force, and Navy. In the past and at present the Territory is being hamstrung by lack of a concentrated, thorough investigation of the best method of utilizing its resources and overcoming its known limitations.

There is a need for coordination of the activities of the various Federal and Territorial agencies involved in conservation and utilization of Alaska's resources. These agencies were asked for statements regarding their future programs. These are to be found in chapter VII of this report. It is hoped the information presented in the following chapters will provide the basis to plan intelligently for the orderly and comprehensive development of Alaska's natural wealth.

The Land and
the People

"The Yukon gold rush impelled Theodore Roosevelt to envision Alaska as 'a new Scandinavia in the Western Hemisphere.'...

"A polar-projection map shows Alaska to be strategically situated on world air lines....

"The interior of Alaska south of the Alaska Range has average winter temperatures similar to those of Montana, North Dakota, Minnesota, and Maine.

"... there are more frozen rivers and harbors in the United States than there are from the Aleutians to the Panhandle in Alaska."

Kodiak, oldest existing city in Alaska.

CHAPTER II

The Land and the People

The history of the United States is one of continual progress. As the westward march across the continent rolled onward, new States arose, new voices were lifted in the national councils and new economic tools developed to build prosperity and comfort for the Nation.

From the time of its discovery, Alaska's history has been much the opposite. Originally seized for plunder of its furs by Russians, it was sold by them as valueless because the sea otter and other prized animals had been wiped out. Historical records tell us America bought Alaska more to round out its geopolitical position on the continent than ever to use its lands and forests to make man happy. At least five times since its purchase in 1867, spirited Alaska booms have swept the United States. Orators rose on the floor of Congress to compare Alaska with Sweden in resources, Texas in area, and with the Western States in settlement possibilities.

However, Alaska remains a comparatively lonely wilderness. After eight decades of American ownership, Alaska has a population of less than 100,000 persons. The Yukon gold rush impelled Theodore Roosevelt to envision Alaska as "a new Scandinavia in the Western Hemisphere." Yet this land, larger than Finland, Denmark, Iceland, Norway, and Sweden combined, has fewer inhabitants than a couple of dozen square blocks in downtown Stockholm.

Many factors are responsible for this apparent lack of development in Alaska. The vastness of the country, ruggedness of its terrain, distances from markets, and lack of transportation facilities are not among the least of these. In order to make some analysis of Alaska's problems, then, it is necessary to understand not only the physical characteristics of the land but also something of the history of its people.

PHYSICAL LAND CHARACTERISTICS

The map of North America seems to depict Alaska as an irregularly-shaped northwestward extension of the continent that is essentially a compact land mass. But a cursory look does not give the true picture, for the 586,400 square miles of area—one-fifth that of the United States—are spread over an area nearly one-sixth of the distance around the world at this latitude and nearly two-thirds of the distance from Seattle to the North Pole. An island chain extends far into the Pacific and a "Panhandle" reaches far to the southeast alongside Canada.

The northernmost point of Alaska, like that of Norway is 1,250 miles from the North Pole. The southernmost island of the Aleutian Chain is 150 miles farther north than the United States, and is at the same latitude as London. The most southerly point on the mainland is at the same latitude as northern Ireland. Honolulu is due south of the mainland. The Aleutian Islands extend as far west as New Zealand.

A polar-projection map shows Alaska to be strategically situated on world air routes. The shortest air line from Minneapolis to Tokyo passes across the mainland of Alaska. Stockholm is only 3,600 miles from Fairbanks. Siberia is only 56 miles from Alaska.

Except for its contiguity to Canada on the east, Alaska is surrounded by water. It is bounded on the north by the Arctic Ocean, on the west by the Arctic Ocean, Bering Strait, and Bering Sea, and on the south by the Pacific Ocean. The coastline, including islands, bays, and inlets, is 33,904 miles long, more than the distance around the world. The island areas are in two main groups: The Aleutian chain with its hundreds of small islands; and the Alexander Archipelago with some 1,100 islands along the southeastern coast. Smaller island groups include the Kodiak group, south of the Alaska Peninsula, and Pribilof, Nunivak, St. Matthew, and St. Lawrence groups in the Bering Sea.

Mt. McKinley, 20,300 feet high, near the center of Alaska, is the highest peak on the continent and reaches the highest above its own base in the world. Equally impressive are the rugged mountain chains and islands of southeastern Alaska that rise abruptly from sea level. The mountains, plateaus, and lowlands are arranged somewhat similarly to those in the United States. While the mountains of the United States are arranged with roughly north-south trends, the mountains of Alaska occur in broad arcs with prevalent east-west trends. The Alaskan features have genetic relationship with the geologic structure of the western States.

The Pacific mountain system, most seen by tourists, parallels the coastline at the south and southeast. In Southeastern Alaska the Coast Range, extending southeast through British Columbia, continues northwestward into the Yukon Territory, where it loses definition. Near the northwest end of the Coast Range it almost merges with the St. Elias Range, with peaks as high as 19,850 feet, and containing the Chugach, Nutzotin, and Wrangell mountains as subsidiary ranges. In an echelon relationship with the St. Elias Range is the Alaska Range, extending from a point west of Mt. McKinley southwestward to merge with the Aleutian Range in the Alaska Peninsula. The Aleutian Islands are westward-extending remnants of this range.

Less known than the Pacific Mountain system is the Brooks Range, trending east-west across northern Alaska, all above the Arctic Circle. The Endicott and Baird mountains are the most important clusters in the range.

Between the coastal ranges and the Brooks Range lies the Yukon Plateau, containing the Yukon River, more than 2,000 miles long. It closely rivals the other great rivers on the North American continent, including the Mississippi, McKenzie, or St. Lawrence. Like the Pacific Mountain system, the plateau is arc-shaped, extending northeastward from the Bering Sea to the Fairbanks region, and eastward and southeastward through the Yukon Territory into British Columbia.

North of the Brooks Range the topography is essentially that of a coastal plain, more interesting for its oil-bearing prospects than topographic features.

GEOLOGIC HISTORY

The geological history of Alaska is similar to a political history of the world. There were periods of upbuilding, degradation, eruptions, revolutions, and quiescence. The record of events is found in the rocks—their character, relationship with one another, their vertical and horizontal distribution, and in the fossils they contain.

The oldest known rocks occur in the Yukon-Tanana region. They were once horizontally stratified sedimentary rocks, but through a period of more than a billion years the rock has changed in character to schist and gneiss. Furthermore, earth movements have folded and fractured the rock into complex structures, and the exposed portion has been slowly wearing away.

During the time primitive life was developing on earth, chiefly in the seas, almost the whole of Alaska was sinking below sea level. When land falls below sea level it forms a basin to receive sediments derived from adjacent land areas. It is probable all of Alaska

Veniaminof Volcano on the Alaska Peninsula is a possible power source. Power production from volcanic heat has proved practicable in Italy.

was not below sea level at one time. If the time span of 400 to 500 million years were speeded up, the surface of Alaska would look much like the top of a restless sleeper's blanket. These convulsions tied in closely with the remainder of the continent and other parts of the world. The sediments deposited in the seas during that period now form the largest portion of rocks exposed in the Territory, but were supplemented by granitic rocks that slowly entered the sedimentary rocks while still buried, and by volcanic lavas. Like the earliest sediments, the rocks of this period have changed in character, but not as radically.

During the last 50 million years most of Alaska remained above sea level, resulting in wearing away of

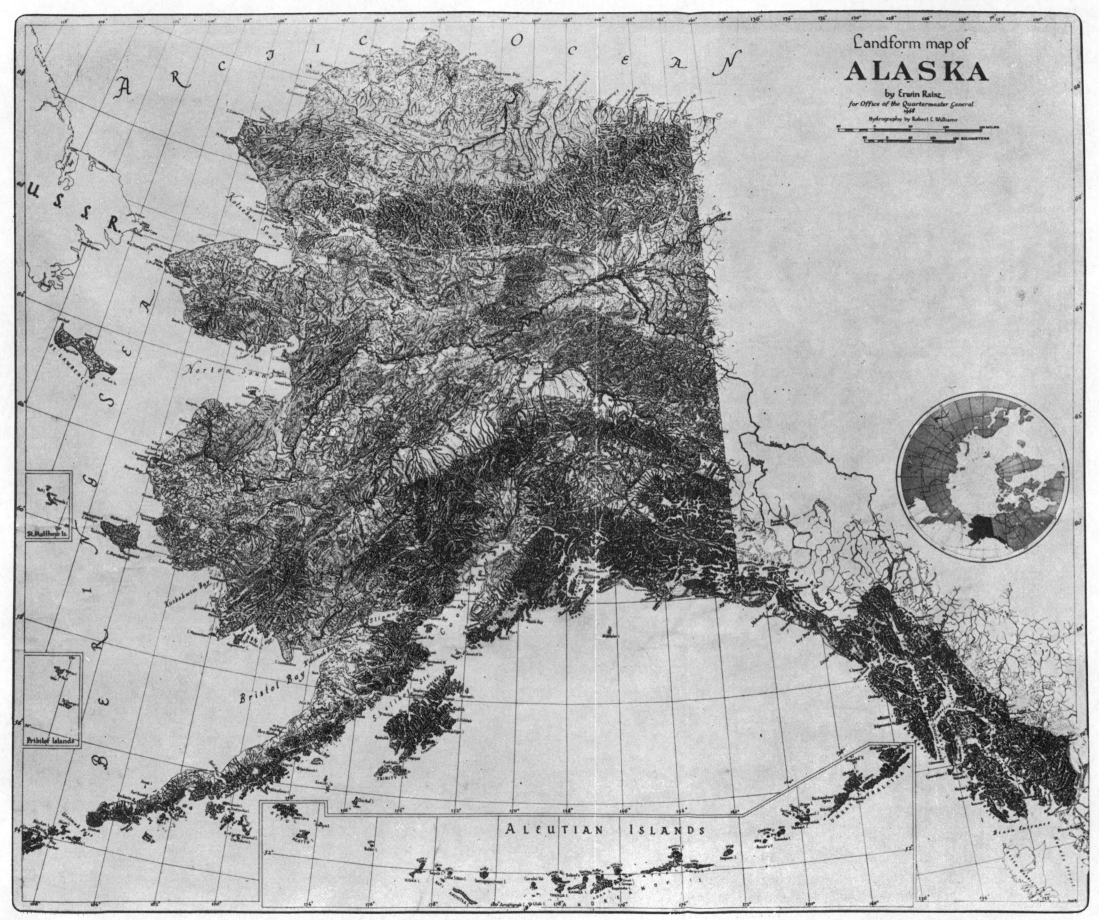

Landform map of
ALASKA
by Erwin Raisz
for Office of the Quartermaster General
1948
Hydrography by Robert L. Williams

ARCTIC OCEAN

U.S.S.R.

BERING SEA

Kotzebue Sound

Norton Sound

St. Matthew Is.

Pribilof Islands

Kuskokwim Bay

Bristol Bay

Shelikof Str.

ALEUTIAN ISLANDS

land areas rather than sedimentation. More profound than erosion was the face-lifting that occurred in the squeezing and folding of the rocks to form the major portion of existing mountain chains. Volcanism attended this mountain-building activity.

Like the northern part of the United States and most of Canada, Alaska was most severely glaciated during the Ice Age. About one-third of Alaska, chiefly the mountain areas, was covered with glaciers. They produced spectacular modifications in the character of the terrain, such as carving the maze of fiords and islands of Southeastern Alaska and the deposition of a thick fill of silt, sand, and gravel in the Yukon and other valleys. Existing glaciers are remnants of the Ice Age and are still large enough to portray graphically the effects of the larger masses.

The decrease in glaciation, the volcanic activity of the Aleutian chain, and the periodic earthquakes of parts of Alaska are vivid exhibits of our changing earth.

Alaska is a land of topographical extremes. Mount McKinley (20,300) is highest in the world above its own base Most of the interior is a vast plateau.

Valdez, coastal terminus of the Richardson Highway.

REGIONS AND RIVER BASINS

It is difficult to describe Alaska as one unit. The variety of landforms, climate, and resources make it desirable to divide the Territory into six regions for discussion: (1) Southeastern, (2) South-Central, (3) Southwestern, (4) Yukon-Kuskokwim, (5) Seward Peninsula, and (6) Arctic.

Southeastern Alaska includes a narrow strip extending 400 miles southeastward from the main portion of Alaska. The mainland portion is essentially the west slope of the snow-capped Coast Range. It rises sharply from sea level in forested slopes to 2,000 feet elevation and thence in relatively barren slopes to peaks as high as 10,000 feet.

The islands, collectively called the Alexander Archipelago, rise sharply from the sea to elevations of 3,000 to 5,000 feet. Different as the region is from continental United States, in many ways it is only a transition zone between the States and the "Northland."

South-Central Alaska comprises essentially those areas, except the Gulf of Alaska, draining into the Gulf of Alaska. It includes the Copper River area, Prince William Sound, Kenai Peninsula, and Cook Inlet areas northward to the ranges forming the Yukon Valley divide. The salient features of the region are its lofty mountains similar to the Southeastern region, but with their continuity broken by the wide valleys of the Copper, Matanuska and Susitna rivers as well as Cook Inlet. The islands are restricted almost entirely to Prince William Sound.

The Alaska Peninsula, Aleutian Islands, Kodiak Island group, and Bristol Bay areas comprise the *Southwestern Region.* The Alaska Peninsula is characterized by its well-known chain of volcanoes trending in a southwest-northeast pattern. These volcanic features are arranged chiefly on the southeast border of the peninsula. The northwest side, blending with the Bristol Bay area is a relatively level coastal region containing large lakes and indented by bays. The Kodiak group of islands is the largest of several groups off the coast. The Aleutian Island chain is a remarkably well delineated group of islands, arranged like stepping stones across a pond of water. World War II demonstrated their strategic importance.

The Yukon-Kuskokwim Region. Perhaps the most popular conception of Alaska by the "armchair tourist" is acquired from descriptions of this region. This region, consisting of the largest valleys of the Territory, is the typical tundra country. The low plateau is a monotonous series of meandering streams, shallow lakes, and rolling hills. The northern boundary is in the Brooks Range.

Seward Peninsula shared the spotlight during gold rush days in vindicating "Seward's Folly." This region consists of the plateau and mountain area which reaches westward toward Siberia; the coastal areas of Norton Sound to the south; and Kotzebue Sound to the north. The mountains of the region are less than 5,000 feet in elevation and were the only portions glaciated in the Ice Age. No glaciers exist at the present time.

Arctic Alaska includes most of the area north of the Arctic Circle. It consists of an extensive monotonous coastal plain, sloping gradually downward to the Arctic Ocean; the north slopes of the rugged Brooks Range, with peaks measuring 9,000 feet in elevation; and an intermediate dissected plateau area forming the foothills of the range. The region is too arid to support large glaciers.

A list of the more important streams of the Territory begins on page 28. Omissions from the list are chiefly those coastal streams with small basin areas and some with larger drainage areas, but with low discharge.

CLIMATE

Many persons believe Alaska is a frozen wasteland. The inhospitable land they envisage, however, exists in reality only partially between the Arctic Circle and Arctic Ocean. Alaska's proximity to the North Pole is about that of Scotland, Norway, Finland, and Sweden. The interior of Alaska south of the Alaska Range has average winter temperatures similar to those of Montana, North Dakota, Minnesota, and Maine. North of the Alaska Range, however, winter temperatures are somewhat lower. The southern coastal areas and the Alexander Archipelago, warmed by the fringe of the same ocean current that passes the coast of Washington and Oregon, are only slightly colder in winter than the Puget Sound area and the Willamette Valley.

Along the southern coast, variations of temperatures

Skagway, terminus of the White Pass and Yukon Railway.

TABLE 3.—*Important streams in Alaska*

Region	Major area	Stream	Principal tributaries
SOUTHEASTERN	KETCHIKAN	Salmon River	
		Davis River	
		Wilson River	
		Punchbowl Creek	
		Granite Creek	
		Chickamin River	Leduc River.
		Unuk River	Blue River.
		Reynolds Creek	
		Beaver Falls Creek	
		Orchard Creek	
		Grace Creek	
		Manzanita Creek	
		Ella Creek	
		Fish Creek	
		Falls Creek	
	WRANGELL	Tyee Creek	
		Harding River	
		Stikine River	
		Cascade Creek	
		Scenery Creek	
	SITKA	Maksoutof River	
		Medvetcha River	
		Takatz Creek	
		Brentwood Creek	
	ANGOON	Hasselborg River	
		Thayer Creek	
		Kathleen Creek	
	JUNEAU	Sweetheart Falls Creek	
		Whiting River	
		Tease Creek	
		Speel River	Long River
			Crater Creek.
		Dorothy Creek	
		Carlson Creek	
		Taku River	
		Antler River	
		Taiya River	
		Chilkoot River	
		Chilkat River	Klehini River.
			Tsirku River.
			Takhin River.
		Endicott River	
		Alsek River	
SOUTH-CENTRAL	GULF OF ALASKA	Copper River	Gulkana River.
			Tazlina River.
			Klutina-Nizina River.
			Chitina River.
			Bremner River.
			Tasnuna River.
		Power Creek	
		Duck River	
		Resurrection River	
	COOK INLET	Kasilof River	
		Kenai River	Snow River.
			Ptarmigan Creek.
			Trail Creek.
			Grant Creek.
			Cooper Creek.
			Russian River.
		Sixmile Creek	East Fork.
		Eklutna Creek	
		Matanuska River	Caribou Creek.
			Gravel Creek.
			Chickaloon-Boulder River.
			Kings River.
		Susitna River	Maclaren River.
			Tyone River.
			Oshetna River.
			Portage Creek.
			Chulitna River.
			Talkeetna-Sheep River.
			Yentna-Skwentna River.
		Beluga River	
		Chakachatna River	
SOUTHWESTERN	BRISTOL BAY	Togiak River	
		Nushagak River	Mulchatna River.
			Nuyakuk River.
		Kvichak River	Newhalen River.

TABLE 3.—*Important streams in Alaska*—Continued

Region	Major area	Stream	Principal tributaries
SOUTHWESTERN	BRISTOL BAY	Naknek River	
		Egekik River	
YUKON-KUSKOKWIM	BERING SEA	Kuskokwim River	Stony River.
			Holitna River.
		Yukon River	Lewes River.
			Fortymile River.
			Porcupine River.
			Chandalar River.
			Tanana River.
			Koyukuk River.
			Innoko River.
SEWARD PENINSULA	BERING SEA	Koyuk River	
		Fish River	
		Eldorado River	
		Nome River	
		Sinuk River	
		Kaviruk River	Kruzgamepa River.
			Kuzitrin River.
	ARCTIC OCEAN	Kugruk River	
		Kiwalik River	
ARCTIC	ARCTIC OCEAN	Kobuk River	
		Noatak River	
		Ikpikpuk River	
		Colville River	Killik River.
			Anaktuvuk River.

from season to season are scarcely noticeable; however, in the interior the summers are hotter and winters colder. Surprisingly uncomfortable are the hot summers near the Arctic circle in the Yukon River Valley.

Precipitation in most of Alaska is comparable to that in desert lands of the Western States. Average annual precipitation of 150 inches in the southeastern humid region quickly drops to 15 inches or less north of the Alaska Range and steadily decreases to 5 inches on the Arctic coast.

The most pronounced climatic difference between portions of Alaska and correspondingly similar portions of the semi-arid Western States is the amount of daylight in summer and winter. The long summer days in Alaska, particularly in the interior, are favorable for agricultural production and tend to offset the shorter growing season. The average frost-free period varies from about 140 days in southern Alaska to about 80 days in the Tanana Valley.

Despite the fact that Alaskan waters are hundreds of miles to the north, there are more frozen rivers and harbors in the United States than there are from the Aleutians to the Panhandle in Alaska. With the exception of Cook Inlet, which is little used for navigation because of high tides, Alaska has no freezeups east and south of Bristol Bay owing to the "Kiro Suwo", or Japanese Current, flowing eastward from the Asiatic coast.

Actually, Alaska has several climates, described in detail in chapter VII by the Weather Bureau, so it is technically wrong to speak generally of "the climate of Alaska."

Southeastern Alaska's climate is relatively mild. It is much like that of the Puget Sound region with fairly heavy rainfall diminishing sharply toward Haines and Skagway. Extreme temperatures are rare.

South-Central Alaska also has a comparatively moderate climate with heavy precipitation on the forested coast, but with considerably less rain and snowfall away from the coast. Anchorage, for example, has an average annual precipitation of only 15 inches.

Southwestern Alaska is a land of clouded skies and fog with only moderate precipitation.

The Aleutian Islands and Alaska Peninsula's major characteristic is the rapid changeability of prevailing weather conditions. High winds, low winter temperatures and foggy summers are common to the region.

The Yukon and Kuskokwim Basins and Arctic Slope comprise a region of slight precipitation and extreme variations in temperature (more moderate along the coast). Temperatures of 100° and minus 76° F. have been recorded in the upper Yukon Valley. The summers are warm to hot and the winters cold to frigid.

EXPLORATION

When an expedition of young scientists returned September 1948 from exploring the snow-capped Coast Range near Juneau, their findings helped broaden man's factual concept of America's "last frontier." But the United States of nearly a century ago was better explored than is modern-day Alaska.

The vastness, ruggedness, and isolation of "the Great

Nome, service center for Northwestern Alaska, is served by three airplane lines throughout the year.

Land" have definitely retarded investigation. The fact that Alaska was one of the last major land discoveries in world history can be held accountable in part for its incomplete exploration.

Not until July 16, 1741, was Alaska officially known to have been discovered. On that date, the Danish captain of the Russian Navy, Vitus Bering, sighted Mount St. Elias, 275 miles northwest of Juneau. Bering's men returned with $100,000 in furs—a cargo which signalized an immediate rush to exploit and, only incidentally, to explore the new land.

In their search for furs, the Russians first explored the Aleutian Islands and the Bering Sea, subsequently reaching eastward to Cook Inlet, Prince William Sound, and the Alexander Archipelago. Not one reached the mainland of Alaska (Chirikoff's men excepted) until 1761.

Meanwhile, other European nations began venturing to the Northwest coast of America. Spanish expeditions left bases in California during the latter part of the eighteenth century sailing north and west as far as Unalaska in the Aleutian Island chain. England's mariner, Captain James Cook, reached the Alaskan Coast in 1778 to sail as far as Icy Cape before being turned back by the Arctic ice pack. A French expedition veered from South Pacific explorations to the North Pacific, and was later followed by French traders who had heard the stories of rich furs. Yankee traders, too, followed the sea trails to the North.

Under the influence of Czar Alexander I, Russia somewhat belatedly, and with other nations now in the field ahead of them, followed up its initial advantage. Seeking new fur-producing territories, the Russian American Co. received exclusive control of Alaska in 1799.

Between 1803 and 1843, the Russians, Von Kursenstern, Golovnin, Etolin, Nasilof, and Zagoskin, contributed to coastal and interior exploration. A one-man trading post was established in 1836 on the lower Kuskokwim. In 1838 the Russians penetrated the interior, establishing a post at Nulato and exploring the Koyukuk and Yukon rivers above the post. Four years later they explored the Copper and Susitna River valleys. Hudson's Bay traders descended the Yukon and established Fort Yukon in Russian territory in 1847.

Britain's search for the fabled Northwest Passage was another economic motive that accounted for much of the early knowledge of Alaska's Arctic and Bering Sea shoreline. With a shorter route to the Indies as their goal, Frobisher, Davis, Weymouth, Knight, Hall, Beechy, Hudson, Baffin, Cook, and finally Franklin, who came within 90 miles of completing the passage in 1847, were but a few whose explorations resulted in the naming of Point Barrow, Icy Cape, Cape Prince of Wales, and other landmarks. One of Cook's lieutenants, George Vancouver, contributed an outstanding achievement to Alaskan exploration between 1791 and 1794 by charting Southwestern and Southeastern Alaska with such accuracy that it wasn't improved upon for more than a century.

Haines, seaport terminus of the new road to the interior. Haines may boom as gateway to the north

An incompleted plan of the Western Union Tele- graph Co. in 1865 to join Europe and America by tele- graph line from Oregon to Siberia precipitated new explorations of the interior. Construction stopped when the Atlantic Cable was successfully completed in 1867.

Gold first brought prospectors into the north as early as 1858 when pay dirt was discovered on the Fraser River in British Columbia, but it was not until the great rushes of 1898–1900 that large areas in Alaska were explored in the frantic search for gold.

The Geological Survey began explorations and sur- veys of the Territory in 1895. The Coast and Geodetic Survey began a sounding and mapping program of coastal waters. For the first time, detailed information on large areas of Alaska and its coast was published for general reference.

With the coming of the air age, exploration of Alaska took to the skies. In the late 20's the United States Navy undertook aerial photographic expeditions, in co- operation with the Geological Survey and the Forest Service. The photography obtained was later used by the Geological Survey in the preparation of planimetric and topographic maps. The American Geographic

Society conducted aerial surveys of a portion of the Yukon basin in 1936. The United States Navy com- pleted southeastern Alaska aerial photographic activi- ties during the summer of 1948.

SETTLEMENT

It has been said that "if the Nation had been settled at the leisurely pace which has prevailed in Alaska, our frontier would not yet have reached the Alleghenies."

Isolation has been the major reason for this lack of development. It should be remembered, however, that colonization did not begin until 1784—nearly 2 cen- turies after the founding of Jamestown (1607) and more than 4 centuries after the Spaniards established the oldest American colony at St. Augustine, Fla., in 1565.

Colonization of Alaska began on August 3, 1784, with the establishment of a trading post at Three Saints Bay, Kodiak Island by Grigor Shelekof, a Russian. The first settlement consisted of five log houses, blacksmith shop, barns for cattle and sheep, commissary, counting- house, farming implements, and most of the 192 men who comprised the embarkation party at Okhotsk.

Shelekof remained 4 years firmly establishing the colony and setting up an outpost named Fort Alexander on Cook's Inlet. He then returned to Russia to lay the groundwork for subsequent establishment of the crown-sanctioned Russian American Co. Almost all colonization for the next 50 years was under the auspices of this venture of the Czars to emulate in Alaska what Great Britain had accomplished with its British East Indies Co.

The Russian American Co. was formally chartered in 1799, but its foundations were laid from 1790 to 1799 by Alexander Andreevich Baranof, a Russian merchant employed by Shelekof to expand his fur-trading interests.

Baranof, in the face of great hardships, stabilized operations in Western Alaska and advanced Russian settlement 400 miles eastward along the mainland by establishment of a combined hunter-trader-agricultural colony at Yakutat in 1796. In 1799, he established Fort St. Michael on Sitka Island, about 6 miles north of the present Sitka.

When Baranof was replaced in 1818, he had succeeded in expanding Russian colonization of Alaska to 23 establishments. The Russian American Colony passed out of existence in 1863 without further colonization. The 1860 census showed the Russian colonists to number 576 men and 208 women.

Eleven years after the purchase of Alaska two salmon canneries were established at Sitka and Klawock. This was the birth of a new industry. By 1890 there were 37 canneries and salteries in Alaska. New settlements sprang up in coastal regions as fishing became a million-dollar industry and eventually in multimillion-dollar industry, employing thousands of men.

Gold, destined to become Alaska's second-ranking industry, brought thousands of persons to the North. Of those disappointed in prospecting, some remained to establish businesses, farm, fish, trap, cut timber, or live off the land by hunting.

Lack of laws regarding land tenure tended to discourage early settlers. It was not until after 1900 that effectual provisions for filing homesteads were made. Prior to that time neither land titles nor transfers were to be had, and town lots could not be legally held.

Rich companies controlling big money "crops" did little to encourage settlement. Fur companies used natives to gather pelts. Early fishing industries imported Chinese to do the work. Later they were to import cannery workers from the States.

In 1914 Congress authorized the President to locate, construct, and operate railroads in Alaska. The Alaska Railroad from Seward to Fairbanks was built, commencing operation in 1923.

Agricultural lands were settled along the railroad to the Matanuska Valley, adjacent to Anchorage, and in the Tanana Valley near Fairbanks.

Owing, in part, to excellent communication facilities and the remarkable role aviation has played in transportation, Alaska's social growth has probably outstripped its actual settlement. Historian Henry W. Clark accurately and significantly observes that ". . . while the outlying parts of the Territory present a picture of true pioneer life . . . with rigors ordinarily associated with the frontier, at the same time the centers of population are much further advanced than towns of corresponding size in the United States."

POPULATION

The magnetism of the North has pulled thousands out of their established orbits—from all parts of the United States—to Alaska since the end of World War II. Despite these high-pressure gains in population Alaska is still a comparatively vacant land with slightly more than 90,000 inhabitants. Compared to the United States average of 44 people per square mile, this is a meager one-seventh of a person per square mile.

A substantial population growth has been recorded since World War I. However, the biggest influx occurred during the past decade with thousands of veterans and war workers remaining or returning to Alaska after World War II. Until completion of the next census, the extent of this influx can only be estimated. The Alaska Development Board population estimate as of October 1, 1948, is 94,875, a 30-percent gain over the 1939 census figure of 72,524.

With a previous gain of about 13,000 persons in the 1930–40 decade, the 35,000 total represents a population increase of 60 percent in the past 20 years.

The first United States enumeration of Alaska's population, in 1880, stood at 33,426, of which only 430 were whites. Within 10 years the total population decreased by more than 1,300, but the total number of white inhabitants jumped to 4,298.

The gold rush of 1898 resulted in an influx of more than 30,000 persons. Continued mineral production, trapping, and development of commercial fishing were economic factors which played a major role in retaining much of the influx, as well as attracting many new residents to Alaska.

The decade beginning in 1910, was an era of depression for Alaska and was marked by a recession in population. During that period, more than 9,000 persons left the Territory. Population figures dropped from 64,356 in 1910 to 55,036 in 1920. Nome, for example, tallied 12,488 inhabitants during the "rush", but by 1920 its population stood at 852. Not all Nome's gold

Cordova, Prince William Sound fishing center.

seekers returned south. Many joined the surge into interior Alaska when gold was discovered in Tanana Valley in the early 1900's.

Density of population in Alaska, according to the 1939 census reports, was 12.7 persons per 100 square miles. Considerable variation in population totals and density in the four judicial divisions of Alaska is indicated in the following:

TABLE 4.—*Density of population*

Judicial division	Land area [1] (square miles)	Estimated 1949 population	Per 100 square miles
1st Division (Southeast)_____	34, 391	27, 000	79. 1
2d Division (Nome, Bering Sea, and Arctic)_____	147, 135	13, 000	8. 7
3d Division (Anchorage, Cook Inlet, Aleutians, and Bristol Bay)_____	142, 031	34, 000	24. 4
4th Division (Fairbanks and Interior)	247, 508	20, 000	8. 2
Total_____	571, 065	94, 000	16. 6

[1] Exclusive of inland water surface areas.

The native stock constituted nearly half of Alaska's population in 1920 and slightly more than half in 1929, but by 1939 the white population considerably exceeded the native. In that year there were 32,458 Aleuts, Eskimos, and Indians and 39,170 white persons. Eskimos comprise almost half the native stock and Indians more than a third. The balance are Aleuts. This trend has continued.

A summary of population figures by race obtained from past census enumerations follows:

TABLE 5.—*Summary of population by race*

Year	White	Native	Other races	Total
1880_____	430	31, 240	1, 756	33, 426
1890_____	4, 298	23, 531	4, 223	32, 052
1900_____	30, 493	29, 536	3, 563	63, 592
1910_____	36, 400	25, 331	2, 625	64, 356
1920_____	27, 883	26, 558	595	55, 036
1930_____	28, 640	29, 983	655	59, 278
1940_____	39, 170	32, 458	896	72, 524

Eskimos inhabit the north and west, the major concentration being along the coasts of the Bering Sea and Arctic Ocean. Aleuts are found principally in the

Aleutian Islands. The Athabaskan Indians are native to interior regions. Other Indian groups are found in southeastern Alaska.

Men outnumbered women almost 2 to 1 in Alaska's 1939 population. Since then it is believed the trend has been toward a more normal balance. There is a scarcity of males in the younger brackets. Less than half the white males over 15 years of age in Alaska are married as against three-fourths of the women in the same age group. Ninety percent of the white women over 20 are or have been married.

During the last census there were 141 Negroes in the Territory. Other nonwhites enumerated were: 403 Filipinos, 263 Japanese, and 56 Chinese.

Alaskan urban centers have recorded a steady growth during the past two decades. Most spectacular community growth has occurred in Anchorage which had an estimated population of 19,000 in 1948, as contrasted with 3,495 in 1939. Development of the Anchorage area as headquarters for the Alaskan defense theater, during World War II, was the main reason for this increase. Fairbanks, in the interior, has also experienced rapid growth for similar reasons, jumping from

3,455 in 1939 to an estimated 8,500 in 1948. Juneau, the capital of Alaska, increased from 5,729 in 1939 to an estimated 7,000 in 1948.

The population of Alaska's major communities in 1929, 1939, and 1948 follows:

TABLE 6.—*Population of major communities*

Community	1920	1929	1939	1948 [1]
Anchorage	1, 856	2, 277	3, 495	19, 000
Fairbanks	1, 155	2, 101	3, 455	8, 500
Juneau	3, 058	4, 043	5, 729	7, 000
Ketchikan	2, 458	3, 796	4, 695	7, 000
Sitka	1, 175	1, 056	1, 987	2, 000
Palmer			150	1, 500
Cordova	935	980	938	1, 500
Petersburg	879	1, 252	1, 323	1, 500
Wrangell	821	948	1, 162	1, 200
Kodiak	374	442	864	1, 200
Nome	852	1, 213	1, 559	1, 600
Seward	652	835	949	1, 000
Barrow	322	330	363	750
Skagway	494	492	634	650
Valdez	466	442	529	600
Total	15, 497	20, 207	27, 832	55, 000

[1] Estimated by Alaska Development Board.

Juneau Airport, one of many modern landing fields throughout air-conscious Alaska.

POLITICAL HISTORY AND GOVERNMENT

First hint of the sale of Russian America to the United States is found in Russian archives of 1854. Although it is known that Andrew Jackson was interested in the region as early as 1836, several reasons are ascribed for its actual purchase in 1867 by the United States Government for the sum of $7,200,000, or about 2 cents per acre. On Russia's part, they included decline in the colonies' economy, fear they might be seized by Britain and prospective costs of protecting and maintaining itself in America. On America's part, a dominant factor was the zeal of the then Secretary of State, William H. Seward.

The fact that Alaska was almost completely neglected during the decade following its purchase reflected the general opinion that it was of little worth to the Nation. Not until 1884 was anything done about governing the Territory on a permanent basis. Both the United States Army and Navy administered temporary government— the Army from 1867 to 1877 and the Navy from 1879— until the District of Alaska was created by Congress in 1884.

During the 2-year hiatus, 1877–79, Alaska lacked any form of government. Territorial residents actually had to appeal to the British Governor at Victoria, British Columbia, for protection from the Indians in a liquor traffic uprising. The District Act established the seat of government at Sitka, extending Oregon laws to Alaska, thus providing a court system and a civil and criminal code.

In 1906, Alaska was provided representation in Congress with one voteless delegate, and in 1912 the District of Alaska was abolished in favor of a Territorial form of government. Other legislation provided for incorporation of towns and transfer of the seat of government to Juneau. Thus a colorful era in Alaskan history ended as Sitka had been the "capital" of world commerce and social life in the North Pacific since 1799.

Ironically, the Organic Act which created Alaska's legislature in 1912 coincided with the explosion that summer of Mt. Katmai which threw volcanic ash over most of Alaska and created the Valley of Ten Thousand Smokes. Soon after, an earthquake rocked Fairbanks and in the fall of 1913, a hurricane almost destroyed Nome.

The first legislature, patterned after the Washington Territorial Act of 1853, consisted of eight Senators and 16 Representatives chosen equally from four Judicial Districts.

Wrangell, gateway to Stikine River, another old community in Southeastern Alaska.

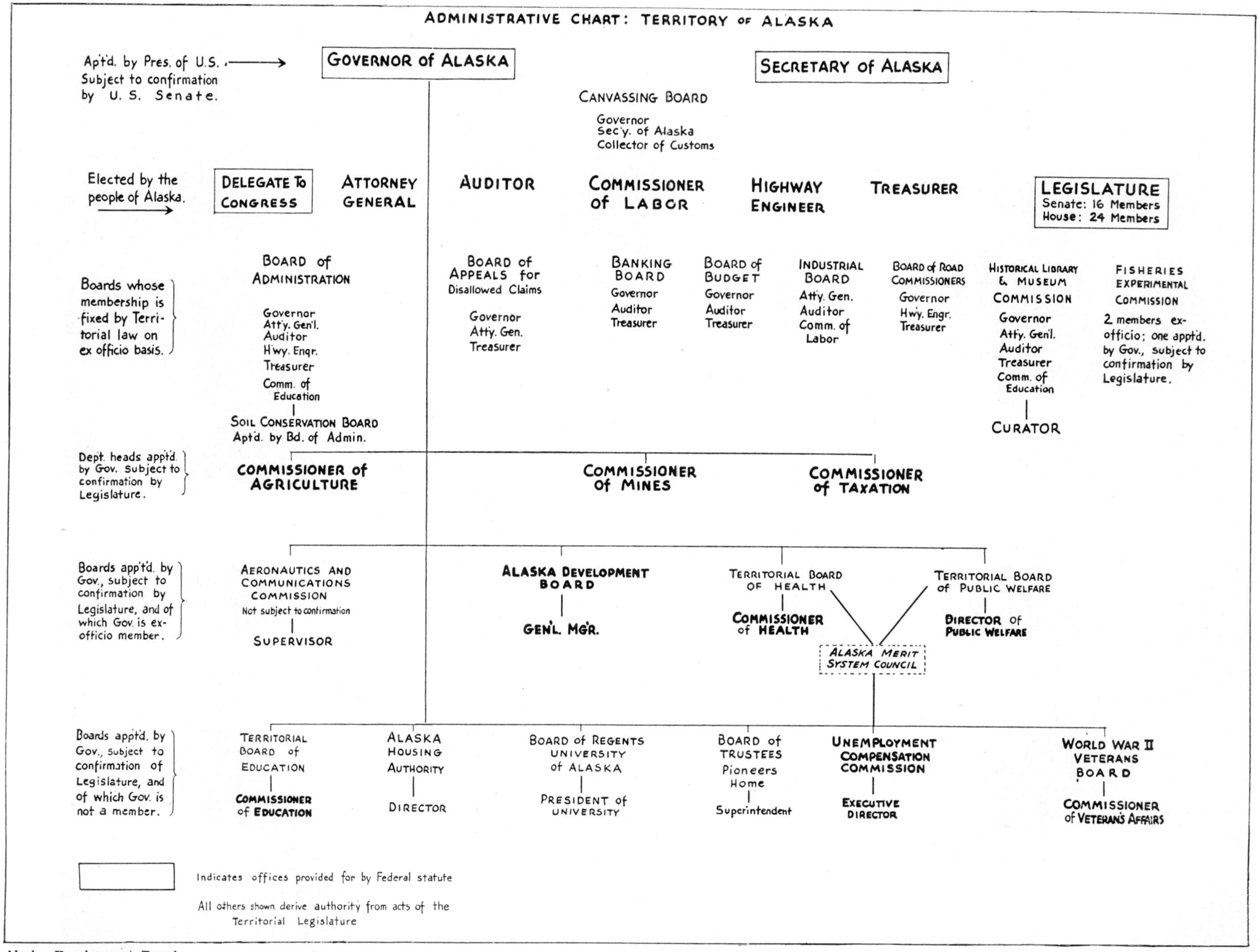

ADMINISTRATIVE CHART: TERRITORY OF ALASKA

GOVERNOR OF ALASKA

SECRETARY OF ALASKA

DELEGATE TO CONGRESS

ATTORNEY GENERAL

AUDITOR

COMMISSIONER OF LABOR

HIGHWAY ENGINEER

TREASURER

LEGISLATURE
Senate: 16 Members
House: 24 Members

Aptd. by Pres. of U.S.
Subject to confirmation by U.S. Senate.

Elected by the people of Alaska.

Boards whose membership is fixed by Territorial law on ex officio basis.

Dept heads apptd by Gov. subject to confirmation by Legislature.

Boards apptd by Gov., subject to confirmation by Legislature, and of which Gov. is ex-officio member.

Boards apptd by Gov., subject to confirmation of Legislature, and of which Gov. is not a member.

CANVASSING BOARD
Governor
Secy. of Alaska
Collector of Customs

BOARD OF ADMINISTRATION
Governor
Atty. Genl.
Auditor
Hwy. Engr.
Treasurer
Comm. of Education

SOIL CONSERVATION BOARD
Aptd. by Bd. of Admin.

COMMISSIONER OF AGRICULTURE

BOARD OF APPEALS for Disallowed Claims
Governor
Atty. Gen.
Treasurer

BANKING BOARD
Governor
Auditor
Treasurer

BOARD OF BUDGET
Governor
Auditor
Treasurer

INDUSTRIAL BOARD
Atty. Gen.
Auditor
Comm. of Labor

BOARD of ROAD COMMISSIONERS
Governor
Hwy. Engr.
Treasurer

HISTORICAL LIBRARY & MUSEUM COMMISSION
Governor
Atty. Genl.
Auditor
Treasurer
Comm. of Education

CURATOR

FISHERIES EXPERIMENTAL COMMISSION
2 members ex-officio; one apptd. by Gov., subject to confirmation by Legislature.

COMMISSIONER OF MINES

COMMISSIONER OF TAXATION

ALASKA DEVELOPMENT BOARD
GEN'L. MGR.

AERONAUTICS AND COMMUNICATIONS COMMISSION
Not subject to confirmation
SUPERVISOR

ALASKA HOUSING AUTHORITY
DIRECTOR

TERRITORIAL BOARD of EDUCATION
COMMISSIONER of EDUCATION

BOARD of REGENTS UNIVERSITY of ALASKA
PRESIDENT of UNIVERSITY

BOARD of TRUSTEES Pioneers Home
Superintendent

TERRITORIAL BOARD OF HEALTH
COMMISSIONER of HEALTH

TERRITORIAL BOARD of PUBLIC WELFARE
DIRECTOR of PUBLIC WELFARE

ALASKA MERIT SYSTEM COUNCIL

UNEMPLOYMENT COMPENSATION COMMISSION
EXECUTIVE DIRECTOR

WORLD WAR II VETERANS BOARD
COMMISSIONER of VETERANS AFFAIRS

Indicates offices provided for by Federal statute

All others shown derive authority from acts of the Territorial Legislature

Alaska Development Board

Today, the Alaska Territorial Legislature consists of 12 members in the Senate and 24 in the House, the members' salaries and transportation being paid by the Federal Government. They convene biennially in odd years for 60 days to legislate on Territorial matters not specifically prohibited by the Organic Act; adopt a biennial budget and pass on the Governor's appointments.

The actual government of Alaska is both Federal and Territorial. Both the Governor and Secretary of Alaska are appointed by the President, subject to confirmation by the United States Senate, for 4-year terms. In some instances the Federal and Territorial functions overlap; in others they are separate and distinct.

There are four Judicial Divisions in Alaska with headquarters at Juneau, Nome, Anchorage, and Fairbanks. A Federal District Judge, a United States Attorney and Marshal, all Presidentially appointed, preside over each. United States Commissioners, appointed by the judges, act as lower court magistrates, probate judges, and coroners in the larger communities.

Principal Federal departments operating in Alaska are the Department of Interior, Department of Agriculture, Department of Commerce, and Department of Labor.

The principal Territorial officers are the Attorney General, Treasurer, Auditor, Highway Engineer, Commissioner of Labor, and a voteless delegate to the United States Congress, all elected by popular vote. The elective officials also serve with the Governor and Secretary on eight boards or commissions whose membership is fixed by Territorial law on an ex-officio basis.

Department heads appointed by the Governor, subject to confirmation by the Territorial Legislature are the Commissioners of Agriculture, Mines, and Taxation.

Boards appointed by the Governor, subject to confirmation by the Legislature, and of which the Governor is an ex-officio member are the Aeronautics and Communications Commission (not subject to confirmation), Alaska Development Board, Territorial Boards of Health and Public Welfare.

Boards appointed by the Governor subject to legislature confirmation, but of which the Governor is not a member, are the following: Education, Regents, Trustees, World War II Veterans, Alaska Housing Authority, and Unemployment Compensation Commission.

Military services in Alaska have become increasingly important with awareness of the Territory's strategic value for National defense. In 1943, the Alaskan Department, now Alaskan Command of the Department of National Defense, was established with permanent headquarters at Anchorage. The Alaska Communications System, under the Signal Corps, operates a network of submarine cables, telegraph lines, and radio telephones throughout the Territory serving both Government and the public. The Navy Department in 1944 created the 17th Naval District in Alaska with headquarters at Kodiak.

There are 27 incorporated towns in Alaska governed by elected mayors and councils, with laws enforced generally by magistrates and local police forces. The incorporated communities levy taxes up to 20 mills, the maximum permitted by the Organic Act, and conduct their own schools with the help of some financial support from the Territory.

Alaskans are subject to all Federal taxes but as Territorial residents they elect no elector to the Electoral College, have no representation in the United States Senate and their elected delegate in the House of Representatives is voteless.

Present
Development

"Since the purchase of Alaska by the United States in 1867 for $7,200,000, the Territory has repaid its original cost almost 700 times in trade and commerce—and most of its wealth remains locked in the seas, on the land, and under the ground.

"Formerly Alaska had been thought of as a place to go, to work, to save money, and to leave. Today people more and more want to work in the Territory throughout the year, to make their homes and live out their lives in Alaska. Development of Alaska's resources offers a challenge Alaskans want to meet."

Sea-going vessels transport lumber to market.

CHAPTER III

Present Development

Since the purchase of Alaska by the United States in 1867 for $7,200,000, the Territory has repaid its original cost almost 700 times in trade and commerce—and most of its wealth remains locked in the seas, on the land and under the ground.

Although development has been retarded by an almost exclusive monopoly which the extractive industries have held on its economy, the Territory has made great strides in political progress. Suffrage for women in Alaska was enacted by its legislature in 1913—6 years before women were enfranchised in the States. Alaska was among the first to enact and enforce 8-hour day work laws, a Workman's Compensation Act, and efficient social security measures.

The Army and Navy found Alaska's economy of great value in World War II. It had supported air, rail and water transport, whose vessels and pilots the Armed Forces took over. Alaska alone had these tools to defend the frontier.

As the Western States found new life, the war also started a burgeoning in the North country. Vast military expenditures, plus scores of new service industries, resulted in a substantial increase in economic levels throughout Alaska, but its greatest contribution was people, new people with new ideas—more than 20,000 of them.

There has been a marked change in Alaska thinking during the past decade. The thought trend is no longer one of exploitation by the favored few, a handful of special interests who once dominated Alaska's economic and political life. Instead, it is rapidly becoming "development of Alaska by Alaskans."

Formerly Alaska had been thought of as a place to go, to work, to save money and to leave. Today people more and more want to work in the Territory throughout the year, to make their homes and live out their lives in Alaska. Development of Alaska's resources offers a challenge Alaskans want to meet. For the first time in its 81-year history under the American flag, a real feeling of permanency is being sensed throughout the Territory.

Alaska has much in natural wealth to contribute to the Nation, but in order to formulate an orderly and comprehensive utilization program of its resources it is necessary to have at hand the most complete evaluation of its potentialities possible, as well as the record of its past and present development.

FISHERIES

Little did the white men, who first dropped their nets and hooks into Alaskan waters about 1840, realize they were launching what was to become the Territory's greatest industry.

Following acquisition of the Territory from Russia, Alaska's isolation held the industry to meager proportions. Introduction of salmon canning provided the impetus the industry needed to grow. Beginning with two canneries in 1878, with a pack valued at $16,000, the industry has now mushroomed to over 100 plants with an annual pack worth more than $100,000,000.

Demand for other types of fish and shellfish has grown so that they too are now valuable additions to the industry. Alaska's fishery products were valued at more than $115,000,000 in 1948. The total value of production from 1867 to 1948 is estimated at $1,856,000,000—265 times more than Alaska's original purchase price.

The Pacific salmon comprises five species of salmon which are found in Alaskan waters. All are commercially important. In this discussion their individual characteristics are treated separately, but all have life histories similar in these respects: (1) They are anadromous, returning to fresh water from the sea to spawn; (2) they possess a generalized homing instinct, returning on their spawning migration to the same stream or locality in which they themselves were hatched or released as fry; (3) they mature, and spawn but once, shortly after which they die.

Sockeye or red salmon is the most valuable for canning purposes because its flesh retains its bright red color after processing. Occurring throughout Alaska, its greatest abundance is in Bristol Bay, Alaska Peninsula, Kodiak Island, and Cook Inlet.

Although the pack of pink or humpback salmon may exceed that of reds, its unit value is much lower. It is as nutritious and tasty as red salmon, but its meat is soft and pale and thus not as attractive in appearance. However, through sheer abundance they support extensive cannery operations in southeastern Alaska, Prince William Sound, lower Cook Inlet, Kodiak Island, and the Alaska Peninsula.

Principally used for canning, chum or dog salmon runs a poor third to sockeyes and humpbacks, both in quality and quantity. When canned it is usually watery, pale, and lacking in flavor.

The king salmon supports a fishery quite different than the canning species mentioned above. This type of fish is caught almost exclusively by trollers. Because of their fine flavor, attractive appearance, and individual care they receive in catching, "kings" command a premium price on the fresh fish market, or for a salting process known as mild curing. King salmon, ascend only the larger rivers, principally those of the mainland, and are not abundant. The large run is in the spring, appearing before any of the other species.

Coho or silver salmon sustains the troll fishery in southeastern Alaska during the fall, entering the fishery after the "kings" have gone. They also support gillnet fisheries off several of the larger rivers.

The halibut sustains a large spring fishery of unusual stability. It is a bottom fish of wide distribution on the banks and shoals of the Alaskan coast. They are marketed in either fresh or frozen condition.

Allied to halibut—in being caught by the same boats and with the same gear—sablefish or "black cod" is a comparative newcomer in the ranks of commercial species. Its acceptance on the market was a boon to the halibut fishery in Southeastern Alaska since sablefish can be taken when the brief halibut season is closed. Annual production is valued at almost $2,000,000.

Herring are used principally for reduction to meal and oil, although a small pack is salted for food purposes. They are regarded as a basic article in the diet for salmon and halibut and thus are a favorite bait with fishermen. The industry is centered in southeastern Alaska, Prince William Sound, and Kodiak Island.

The razor clam canneries at Cordova produces 1,500,-000 pounds per year. A small industry of canning butter clams has been consistently maintained in Southeastern Alaska during past years but was recently suspended because of rulings of the Food and Drug Administration concerning a possible toxic condition arising from the presence of a microorganism on which the clams feed.

The shrimp industry has been well-established on a local basis at Wrangell and Petersburg since 1920 and provides a significant off-season contribution to the

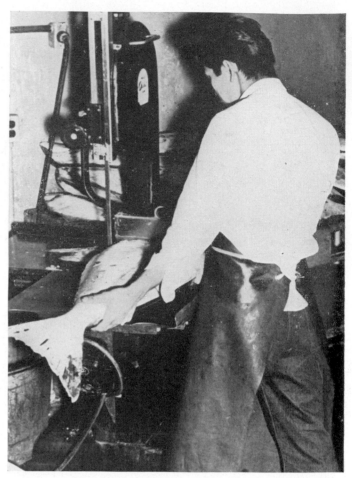

Halibut fishing, an important Alaska industry, employs about 1,200 men and produces about $2,000,000 annually in fish and by-products.

region's economy. The 1947 pack was valued at $326,-000 at the packing shed.

Two species of crab are found in Alaska: the common Dungeness and the not-so-common King crab. The Dungeness crab occurs mostly in Southeastern Alaska and in the vicinity of Cordova, where it supports a minor industry. The catch in 1946 was valued at more than $600,000. King crabs, ranging up to 18 pounds with a 5-foot spread, are taken in certain areas adjacent to the Alaska Peninsula, Bristol Bay, lower Cook Inlet, and the Bering Sea.

Inland and Local Fish of Utilitarian Value

In the watersheds of the Yukon and Kuskokwim Rivers as well as the smaller streams emptying into Bristol Bay and Cook Inlet, salmon have been a traditional mainstay in the economy of the resident native and white settlers. Unlike the big industry on the coast, there is no formalized commerce in the interior areas; salmon are taken and preserved for the personal year-round food supply of the people and their dog teams.

Ketchikan, salmon-packing capital of the world.

Each malemute sled dog requires approximately one whole fish per day for almost the entire year.

Trout and grayling, classed as game fish in the Alaska Game Law, provide a significant contribution to the food supply of settlers in remote regions of the interior. The Dolly Varden trout is overwhelmingly abundant in coastal streams. Steelhead trout, captured in small numbers incidental to salmon fishing in salt water, may be commercialized.

A picturesque and traditional method of obtaining food by the Eskimos is the catching of tom cod through the ice. This lowly species has not yet achieved any significance in commerce but by virtue of its accessibility and abundance during the winter it is important to isolated Arctic residents.

In Kotzebue Sound, natives take another species of fish known as the sheefish through the ice during the spring months. The sheefish is large, somewhat akin to both salmon and whitefish and of excellent food quality. Not much is known about it or its fishery.

The Fisheries Industry Today

Among the natural resources of Alaska, none has attained a greater state of development than the fisheries. The canned salmon industry dominates the economy of the fisheries. Only defense construction work has had a bigger payroll and more employees in recent years.

More than 20,000 persons are engaged in the Alaska fisheries industry each year. The majority are seasonal workers—employed only during the canning season. Approximately 50 percent of those employed are white, while Alaska natives account for 26 percent of the total labor force. A detailed breakdown of the labor force for 1943, follows:

TABLE 7.—*Summary of persons engaged in Alaska's Fisheries*

Persons engaged	Number
Whites	12, 825
Natives	6, 475
Chinese	43
Filipinos	3, 236
Hawaiians	13
Koreans	4
Latin Americans	53
Negroes	60
Puerto Ricans	15
Portuguese	1
Spaniards	24
Unknown	962
Total	23, 711

The total value of manufactured fishery products for that year was $66,516,357—of which $18,600,000 went to the fishermen. There were 6,654 fishermen, 10,957 shoremen and 1,532 transporters employed. Shoremen's wages were $7,720,798, and transporters' $2,088,366.

Petersburg, fur farming center of Southeastern Alaska.

During 1943, 83 canning plants were in operation. To supply these canneries it required 783 vessels of 5 tons or over, 287 launches, 65 power dories, 235 powered gillnet boats, 665 unpowered, 349 seine skiffs, 1,046 other rowboats and skiffs, 484 lighters and scows, 29 houseboats, 49 pile drivers, 9 pile pullers, 37 rigging scows.

To harvest this marine crop, 738 purse seines, 89 beach seines, 3,162 gillnets, 378 fish traps and an unknown amount of minor gear were required. The number of fish caught by each type of gear follows:

TABLE 8.—*Number of fish caught by each type of gear.*

Type of gear	Number of salmon
Seines	24, 716, 194
Gillnets	21, 838, 768
Traps	37, 801, 547
Lines	1, 279, 087
Wheels	211, 127

The salmon by-product industry was carried on at only two plants. Production consisted of 1,400,000 pounds of meal valued at $35,000 and 61,350 gallons of oil worth $52,148.

The herring fishery production was valued at $1,813,991. Scotch-cured herring amounted to $143,660; bait, $59,410; meal, $542,421; and oil, $1,084,000.

The halibut fleet, as those of the United States and Canada, operates under regulations of the International Fisheries Commission. Employed in the halibut fish-

ery in 1943 were 412 fishermen, 1,257 shoremen, and 92 transporters—a total of 1,716 persons. Engaged in the harvest were 84 vessels and 19 launches. Products, exclusive of liver and viscera, were valued at $2,277,975. Livers were valued at $343,437.

From brief statistical information available, increases in various branches of the industry are noted for 1945. That year Alaska produced 7,763 tierces of mild-cured salmon, compared with 3,122 in California, 1,209 in British Columbia, 1,790 in Washington, and 159 in Oregon.

Almost 10,000,000 pounds of salmon were frozen in 1943. In 1945, 15,473,092 pounds were frozen. Other fish freezings for the latter year follow:

TABLE 9.—*Fish freezings in 1945*

Type	Pounds
Bait and animal food	1, 872, 975
Cod	838, 131
Fillets	26, 678
Halibut	20, 572, 897
Lingcod	171, 935
Sablefish	5, 936, 572
Salmon	15, 473, 092
Others	31, 045
Clams	134, 176
Shrimp and crab	142, 555
Alaska total	45, 199, 556
Oregon total	17, 325, 895
Washington total	25, 686, 354

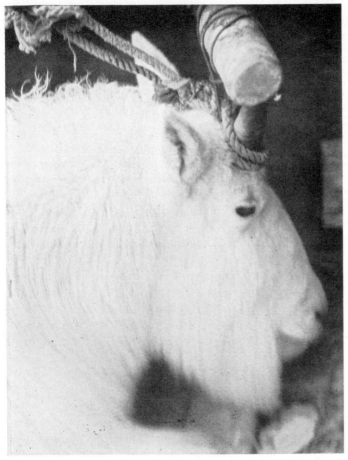

Male mountain goat. Arrangement on horns is to prevent injury to persons.

Halibut landings in 1945 totaled 21,049,000 pounds, compared with 19,630,000 in British Columbia, 13,676,821 in Washington, 793,000 in Oregon, and 300,000 in California.

The Territory of Alaska collected about $1,000,000 in taxes from the fishing industry during 1947 operations. Two-thirds of that amount is attributable to the pack tax on canned salmon. Taxes on fish traps, salmon cannery net income, clam canneries, salteries, cold storage plants, fish-oil plants, gillnet and seine operations, clam diggers, resident and nonresident fishermen accounted for the balance.

WILDLIFE RESOURCES

The population of Alaska dependent largely on wildlife as a mean of livelihood has been estimated to be 32,000. This is in addition to approximately 24,000 persons employed in commercial fisheries. Both activities are seasonal and there is some overlap between the two. The following statistics show the number of persons dependent on wildlife resources:

TABLE 10.—*Persons dependent on wildlife resources*

Judicial division	Population	Trappers and hunters (native and white)
1	27, 200	4, 000
2	12, 725	10, 000
3	34, 700	8, 000
4	20, 250	10, 000
Total	94, 875	32, 000

The majority of permanent residents in the Second Division, both native and white, are almost wholly dependent on wildlife resources for subsistence. Their food, clothing, dog food, and cash income is derived from fur and game animals and fish. In the interior the source is land mammals and birds. Along the coast sea mammals are food sources. In addition, they provide some of the material for handicrafts.

In the Fourth Division, embracing approximately the Yukon-Kuskokwim drainage plus the eastern Arctic coast, conditions are somewhat similar. With the exception of those employed in construction activities in the Fairbanks vicinity, many of the people are dependent upon wildlife for the necessities of life.

In the First and Third Division, comprising Southeastern Alaska, Alaska Peninsula, and Gulf of Alaska

Caribou bull in corral.

region, there is a greater urban population and commercial fishing is more important than game and fur. Even so, a large percentage of the native population derives much of its living from these sources.

White persons over 16 years of age are required to have a license for hunting or trapping. Eskimos and Indians are not licensed. The number of licenses issued during the past 3 years follow:

TABLE 11.—*Licenses issued for hunting and trapping*

License	Fee	1946	1947	1948
Nonresidence, big game	$50	232	411	484
Nonresidence, small game	10	234	773	1, 252
Resident hunting, trapping, and fishing	3	5, 075	5, 697	5, 343
Resident hunting and fishing	2	8, 867	8, 956	11, 749
Total		14, 408	15, 837	18, 828

Nonresident big game hunters are required to have registered guides on the hunt. Guiding and outfitting is an essential part of Alaska's business. In 1948 there were 104 registered and 14 assistant guides.

Money derived from licenses is equally distributed between the Territorial school fund and the United States Treasury. In 1947, licenses brought in more than $66,000. Cost of the license, however, is only a

Red and arctic fox pelts are traded at the Eskimo cooperative trading store at Point Barrow.

small part of the Territorial income from hunting. Statistics on total income are not available; but as an example it might be pointed out that the nonresident trophy hunter's expenditures for bagging a Kodiak bear have been estimated at $1,800.

Alaska has long been known as a producer of fine furs. Exploitation of fur seals on the Pribilof Islands was started by the Russians shortly after discovery of the Islands in 1786. Between that date and 1834 it is estimated that 1,800,000 seals were killed for their skins. These were taken without regard to sex and resulted in such depletion that restrictive measures were adopted in 1835 prohibiting slaughter of females. This resulted in a slow increase in the herd so that by 1867 the herd was estimated at about 1,000,000 animals, compared with an estimated 5,000,000 in its original, unexploited state.

As a result of numerous restrictions and international control measures enacted between 1868 and 1911, the herd increased by 1947 to an estimated 3,613,653 animals valued at more than $100,000,000. From 1910 to 1947 it produced a total of 1,146,556 skins having a gross value of $36,422,412. In addition, a by-products plant annually produces about $80,000 worth of oil and meal from the carcasses.

Under the international agreement, surplus male seals are killed each year by the Fish and Wildlife Service. The revenue derived from the sale of pelts goes to the United States, Great Britain, and Japan. Since the United States assumes the expense of maintaining the reservation and processing the skins, the largest share goes to America.

The raw pelts are shipped from the Pribilof Islands to St. Louis, Mo., where they are dressed, dyed, machined, and finished prior to the two annual public auctions. In 1947, 49,925 pelts were sold for more than $2,000,000.

The steller sea lions are large mammals which resemble the fur seals but have little commercial value at the present time. They are a despised nuisance on the commercial fishery grounds from Southeastern Alaska to Kodiak Island. Like the sea lions, harbor seals are pests to the fishermen and actually cause a direct economic loss by preying on salmon that are caught in gillnets. The Territory now pays a $3 bounty on this species.

The walrus, a traditional mainstay in the economy of Arctic Eskimos, provides food, oil, hides, and ivory. The latter product, however, once attained such commercial importance that walrus were slaughtered ruthlessly for their tusks and their total abundance was seriously depleted. The species is now protected by law and commercial exploitation is prohibited so the natives will be assured of their customary source of supply.

Feeding foxes on the front porch, Brother's Island.

Another valuable fur is that of the sea otter. This animal, once on the verge of extinction, has been protected since 1911 and has come back in such numbers that it will soon be possible to start a limited harvest of some of the animals.

Blue fox, white fox, lynx, wolverine, marten, and land otter are some of the more unusual furs taken in the Territory in addition to the more commonplace skins of beaver, muskrat, mink, and red fox. Furs shipped from Alaska in 1947 as reported in "Trade and Industry in Alaska" are:

TABLE 12.—*Furs shipped from Alaska in 1947*

Species	Number	Value
Beaver	26, 395	$834, 021
Fox, black and silver	3, 922	119, 204
Fox, red	3, 303	32, 085
Fox, white	2, 332	41, 946
Fox, blue	2, 275	59, 758
Seal (including hair seal)	61, 895	3, 561, 413
Marten	15, 071	586, 071
Mink	55, 584	1, 291, 400
Muskrat	195, 818	333, 987
Otter	2, 903	82, 312
Other	13, 233	80, 277
Total	382, 731	7, 022, 421

The Territory is at present divided into eight fur districts. This system provides considerable flexibility in the management of furbearing animals, particularly in determining season regulation. The Aleutian Islands have been classified for land use and those not reserved for military use, sea otter, or oceanic birds have been leased for blue fox farming.

Alaska big game has worldwide fame, attracting thousands of trophy hunters and photographers. Important species include brown, grizzly, kodiak, and black bear, moose, caribou, blacktail deer, mountain goat, and mountain sheep. Introduced species include musk oxen, bison, and elk, as well as the semidomesticated reindeer.

The important small game species are ptarmigan, grouse, and snowshoe hare.

Migratory waterfowl are of special importance to hunters of the remainder of North America. The Territory furnishes the nesting grounds for thousands of ducks and geese that provide outdoor sport for hunters in the States. Common species include the pintail, mallard, teal, wigeon, gadwall, bluebill, shoveler, canvasback, and goldeneye ducks; as well as the Canada, snow and white-fronted geese, and black brant. Less well-known species include the Emperor goose, eider ducks, and the whistling swan.

MINERALS AND MINING

To a large extent, development of Alaska's mineral resources has followed the pattern of North American frontier regions. As in the western part of the United States and Canada, most of the early explorations were made by fur traders and explorers—the men who cracked America's wildernesses. Discovery of placer gold by these early adventurers led to intensive searches which yielded numerous placer and lode gold deposits.

Although there were various discoveries of gold in Alaska by Russians and others prior to the purchase of the Territory by the United States, the first American discoveries were made at Sumdum and Windham Bay on the mainland between Juneau and Petersburg. These strikes yielded the first gold production in 1870, 3 years after the purchase of Alaska. Within a 10-year period, gold lodes were discovered near Sitka, Juneau, and on Douglas Island.

The Klondike discovery in the Canadian Yukon had the same effect upon the search for gold in Alaska as

Sea otter in kelp bed on Ogliuga Island. Otter is a valuable fur crop.

that in California in 1848 had upon the region west of the Rocky Mountains. By 1900, an estimated 50,000 prospectors roamed the upper tributaries of the Yukon River, both in Canada and Alaska. Along the Pacific Coast prospectors pushed north and westward to the Seward Peninsula. They were rewarded with many discoveries, the most outstanding being the beach placers of Nome and the river placers of Fairbanks.

It was during this gold-rush period, from 1895 to 1910, that the majority of known mineral deposits in Alaska were discovered. Little attention was paid by the prospector to minerals other than gold.

Numerous copper deposits were found in the Copper River, Prince William Sound, and Southeastern Alaska districts. The Bonanza, the most notable discovery, began production in 1911 when the 200-mile Copper River Railroad was pushed through to the slopes of the Wrangell Mountains. When abandoned in 1938, more than 1,250,000,000 pounds of metallic copper had been produced from this property.

Production of silver and lead has been limited largely to by-product recovery in gold and copper operations. Such recovery has met only an infinitesimal portion of

Idle bulls on Polovina rookery, St. Paul Island.

the demand for these metals and minerals in the United States.

Coal was first discovered in 1871 along the Arctic Coast, where it was mined for use on whalers and United States Revenue Cutter vessels. Little did the early explorers realize they were only scratching the surface of a few of the many deposits, which for all of Northern Alaska are estimated to contain 60 billion tons of subbituminous and 22 billion tons of bituminous coal.

Other coal deposits were found in various parts of the Territory during the "rush" era, but development of properties has been restricted to local market demands.

The combined coal resources of the railbelt and Homer areas are estimated as high as 24.4 billion tons of lignite or subbituminous, 2.3 billion tons of bituminous, and 1 billion tons of coking coal.

Petroleum has been developed at only one place in Alaska, the Katalla field, where seeps first attracted attention in 1898. This field yielded about 150,000 barrels of oil prior to 1933, when the refinery was destroyed by fire.

Despite limited development in the mining industry, Alaska's mineral production since 1880 is valued at almost one billion dollars—140 times more than the or-

Oil seep in Chilkat Creek, 1,000 feet from beach.

iginal purchase price of the Territory. A summary of Alaska's mineral production during this period follows:

TABLE 13.—*Alaska's mineral production (1880–1947)*

Gold	$635,515,000
Copper	226,569,300
Coal	25,252,500
Silver	14,144,400
Others	36,891,800
Total	938,373,000

Despite the fact Alaska has been a Territory of the United States for 81 years there has been little growth of the mining industry. Alaska is one-fifth the area of the United States but its total mineral production since 1880 is less than 1 percent of the National total.

Of the 33 metals and minerals now classified in the United States as strategic and critical materials, for which stockpiling is deemed the only satisfactory means

He's kneeling on a two-ton nugget of pure native copper.

of insuring an adequate supply for future emergency, 31 are known to occur in Alaska. The 33 strategic and critical metals and minerals are listed as follows:

Antimony	Cobalt	Lead
Asbestos	Columbite	Manganese
Bauxite	Copper	Mercury
Beryl	Corundum	Mica
Bismuth	Diamonds	Monazite
Cadmium	(industrial)	Nickel
Celestite	Graphite	Platinum
Chromite	Kyanite	Quartz Crystals
Rutile	Tantalite	Vanadium
Sapphire and Ruby	Tin	Zinc
Talc	Tungsten	Zirconium

All these metals and minerals, with the exception of bauxite and industrial diamonds, are known to occur in Alaska and deposits of some of them may be substantial. Recent reports from remote areas state industrial diamonds have been found. These occurrences have not been investigated, but Territorial Department of Mines engineers do not discount the possibility of their being discovered in Alaska.

Upper Yukon coal beds.

Evan Jones Coal Co. is one of the Territory's big bituminous coal producers. High quality coal is a great unde-veloped resource in Alaska.

TIMBER PRODUCTS

Conservative estimates place Alaska's coastal and interior forest lands at more than 375,000 square miles—almost twice as large as the combined forest lands of the four Scandinavian countries, where forest indus-tries constitute a major factor in their economy. How-ever, Alaska's forests have never played their proper role in the Territory's economy. From the time the first American sawmill, powered by boilers from the naval vessel *Jamestown*, cut the first log in Sitka in 1878, Alaskans have never cut more than one-thirteenth of the potential annual cut—one billion board feet in perpetuity.

Alaska's most productive forest region is the 16,000-000-acre Tongass National Forest, a long, narrow, island-dotted strip about 350 miles in length and 120 miles wide—in southeastern Alaska. Between 4,000,000 and 5,000,000 acres of this forest have been classified as merchantable timber. The volume of commercial timber in this area has been conservatively estimated as shown in table 14.

The average volume of commercial timber varies from 15,000 to 20,000 board feet per acre, but volumes of 40,000 to 50,000 board feet are common over a wide area. The majority of trees are from 2 to 4 feet in diameter and from 80 to 140 feet high. At least 75 per-cent of the commercial timber is within 2½ miles of tidewater. Only rarely do good stands extend inland more than 5 miles. The forest cover extends from tide-

TABLE 14.—*Volume of commercial timber in Tongass Forest*

Species	Board feet measure	Percent
Western hemlock	58, 000, 000. 000	74
Sitka spruce	15. 800, 000, 000	20
Western red cedar	2, 350, 000, 000	3
Alaska cedar	2, 350, 000, 000	3
Total	87, 500, 000, 000	100

water to about 2,750 feet elevation in the south and 2,000 feet in the north. At an elevation of 1,500 feet the commercial timber gives way to dwarfed, limby trees classified as noncommercial.

Almost the entire balance of Alaska's coastal forests are to be found in the Chugach National Forest of Western Alaska in the Prince William Sound region. This forest contains much the same type timber as Ton-gass National Forest, with the exception of cedar. The forest volume of the Chugach is estimated as follows:

TABLE 15.—*Forest volume of Chugach National Forest*

Species	Board feet measure
Western hemlock	4, 200, 000, 000
Sitka spruce	1, 900 ,000, 000
White spruce	100, 000, 000
Cottonwood	30, 000, 000
White birch	10, 000, 000
Total	6, 260, 000, 000

U. S. MINERAL POSITION—ACTUAL, IMPENDING, AND POTENTIAL

Based on known "commercial" reserves, outlook for noteworthy discovery, and the possibility that known submarginal resources can be made available by technologic progress and improved economic conditions

RELATIVE SELF-SUFFICIENCY

ACTUAL AND IMPENDING

(Based on present technologic and economic conditions and on known "commercial" reserves)

A. VIRTUAL SELF-SUFFICIENCY AS-SURED FOR A LONG TIME:

Bituminous coal and lignite	Magnesium	Fluorspar (metal)
Anthracite	Molybdenum	Helium (lime-lical)
Natural gas		Magnesite
		Nitrates
		Phosphate rock
		Potash
		Salt
		Sulfur

B. COMPLETE OR VIRTUAL DEPENDENCE ON FOREIGN SOURCES:

1. Small or remote expectation of improving position through discovery:

Chromite	Industrial diamonds
Ferro-grade manganese	Quartz crystal
Nickel*	Asbestos (spinning-quality)
Platinum metals	
Tin	

2. Good expectation of improving position through discovery:

Cobalt*	Graphite (flake)

C. PARTIAL DEPENDENCE ON FOREIGN SOURCES, ACTUAL OR IMPENDING:

1. Good expectation of improving position through discovery:

Arsenic*	Fluorspar (acid-grade)
Bismuth*	
Cadmium*	
Copper	
Iron ore	
Lead	
Mercury*	
Tantalum*	
Tungsten	
Zinc	

2. Little hope of improving position through discovery:

Antimony*	High-grade bauxite
Vanadium	Strategic mica

POTENTIAL

(If technologic and economic changes permit use of known submarginal resources)

A. VIRTUAL SELF-SUFFICIENCY:

Bituminous coal and lignite	Aluminum ores	Fluorspar (all grades)
Anthracite	Copper	Graphite (flake)
Natural gas	Iron ore	Helium
Petroleum	Magnesium	Magnesite
	Manganese	Nitrates
	Molybdenum	Phosphate rock
	Titanium	Potash
	Vanadium	Salt
		Sulfur

B. COMPLETE OR VIRTUAL DEPENDENCE ON FOREIGN SOURCES:

Platinum metals	Industrial diamonds
Tin	Quartz crystal
	Asbestos (spinning quality)

C. PARTIAL DEPENDENCE ON FOREIGN SOURCES:

Antimony	Strategic mica
Arsenic	
Bismuth	
Cadmium	
Chromite	
Cobalt	
Lead	
Mercury	
Nickel	
Tantalum	
Tungsten	
Zinc	

*Domestic production chiefly byproduct.

ESTIMATED "COMMERCIAL" RESERVES AS OF 1944, IN KNOWN DEPOSITS, COMPARED WITH 1935-44 ANNUAL RATES OF PRODUCTION & CONSUMPTION

Figures indicate only order of magnitude of estimated reserves. They do not imply that production at rates indicated could be maintained for the full period shown. Estimates do not include allowance for future discoveries.

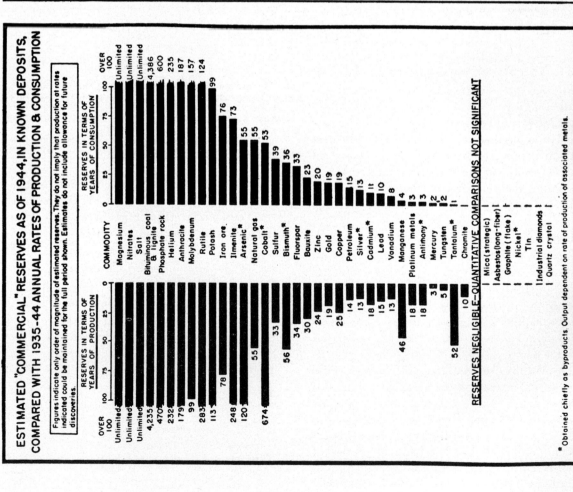

Lumbering in Alaska.

The interior forests of Alaska, composed mainly of white spruce and birch with a scattering of balsam, aspen, poplar, and tamarack, embraces an estimated 342,409-square-mile area along the Yukon, Tanana, Kuskokwim, and Copper Rivers. Maximum diameter of the trees in these forests is 24 inches. However, the majority range from 6 to 12 inches, and there are many areas of open woodland with scattered limby trees. A rough estimate places the volume of the interior forests at 910,000,000 cords.

Several small sawmills have been established in interior Alaska. These mills cut lumber and timber for mine flumes, home construction, and similar uses. There has been fairly heavy cutting around various settlements for wood-burning river boats, mine props, and home heating. Because of climatic conditions, growth of replacement timber is slow in the interior. Wide areas have been denuded by fire.

The 43,060-square-mile coastal forests, particularly the Tongass National Forest, have witnessed the greatest development because of their proximity to markets and low-cost transport as well as possessing a more favorable climate permitting almost all-year operation. Sitka spruce supplies most of the present sawmill requirements. It is manufactured into all the usual forms

of lumber and airplane stock. Western hemlock is used for a great variety of lumber products. Western red cedar is used for siding, high-grade lumber, shingles and poles, while Alaska red cedar is valuable for furniture manufacture, especially cedar chests and clothes closets because of its pronounced odor.

Most of the forest products manufactured in Alaska—fish boxes, barrels, and building materials—have been used within the Territory. Alaska lumber did not find its way into the export market until after World War I. From 1931 to 1940, shipments of Alaska forest products to the United States averaged $78,176 annually. In 1940, shipments of lumber valued at $11,960 were made to the Orient, Australia, and Hawaii. Exports of wood, lumber, and timber increased from less than $100,000 in 1941 to an average of more than $700,000 during 1946 and 1947; but lack of development in this industry is illustrated by the fact that during this 2-year period imports of forest products to Alaska totaled almost $10,000,000.

Alaskan logging methods are similar to those in Washington and Oregon. Machine logging with donkey engines and wire rope has proved most practical. A large amount of timber is logged directly into tidewater for rafting. Flat rafts are used in the pro-

Lumbering is big business for small operators.

tected waterways while Davis-type rafts are required for tows in wider, more exposed channels. Floating logging camps, easily towed from one logging camp to another, are in general use. The cost of towing timber has been estimated by the Forest Service at 1½ cents per 1,000 board feet per mile.

Virtually all timber, manufactured in Southeastern Alaska, is purchased from the National Forest. The minimum stampage prices for western hemlock is $1 per 1,000 board feet. Sitka spruce and Alaska cedar bring a minimum of $1.50.

Juneau and Ketchikan have modern electric-driven sawmills of 100,000 board feet capacity per 8-hour shift. Whittier, Sitka, Wrangell, Petersburg, Homer, Palmer, Fairbanks, and other communities have smaller mills. The yearly cut is now about 75,000,000 board feet, less than one-thirteenth the amount that could be cut without endangering a permanent supply.

Examination of production records show the growth of the industry during the past five decades:

TABLE 16.—*Sawmill production record*

Year	Number of mills	Total cut (board feet)	Shingles (squares)
1899	10	6, 571, 000	--------
1919	22	21, 673, 000	--------
1929	19	30, 393, 000	2, 943
1939	24	25, 885, 000	2, 471
1945	35	59, 056, 000	565

The majority of Alaska sawmills are small. In 1939, the most recent information available, nine plants listed production worth less than $5,000; six between $5,000 and $20,000; three between $20,000 and $100,000 and only three over $100,000. Total wages and salaries paid amounted to $341,526. Alaska mills usually cease operation during 1, 2, or 3 months in mid-winter for overhaul and repair of equipment and machinery. The effect on employment is shown by the fact that the industry employed 426 in July 1939, but only 106 in January 1940.

Copper mine at Nabesna, in the Copper River region.

The Alaska Unemployment Compensation Commission estimated that in 1945 there were 25 basic lumber industries and one furniture manufacturing plant, employing a total of 642 persons, operating in the Territory. Later figures and other data are not available.

For various reasons, 40,000,000 board feet of Alaska timber was rafted during 1948 to Puget Sound ports for manufacture in that area.

AGRICULTURE

Alaskan agriculture is still in its infancy, the first attempt at organized agricultural settlement being made less than 20 years ago. Agricultural experiment stations, established as early as 1899, have been so inadequately supported that basic agricultural knowledge is deficient in many respects. In addition, many farmers have had little experience in cultivating land in Alaska or elsewhere. As recent as 1939, half the farm operators reported they had occupied their land for less than 5 years.

Clearing the virgin land of timber, except for 10 or 15 acres, has been beyond the financial ability of the average settler. After providing such essentials as a home, outbuildings, water supply, fences, farm machinery, and a few head of livestock, the settler needs sufficient cash or credit to clear a minimum of 40 acres of land to have a going and self-sustaining farm. It might cost $6,000 to clear 40 acres of land, but one average potato crop coupled with normal market conditions would have a gross value exceeding $12,000. However, before the first sack of potatoes is ready for market, the investment in essential improvements and machinery, a normal complement of livestock, land clearing, plus seed potatoes, fertilizer, and labor would be more than $18,000.

Added to the excessive cost of clearing lands and the lack of sufficient funds to purchase necessary farm implements have been a deficiency of an adequate power supply for general farm use; the need for irrigation or drainage of some lands; the lack of roads and transportation facilities to transport products to market; and the strength of competition from Stateside producers.

Despite the above, agriculture has established a foothold in Alaska. Its development is relatively small when compared with the States, but still it is highly significant because of the substantial quantities of food which have been produced. It also gives substance to the promise of extensive future developments.

Agriculture Follows Other Developments

Agricultural development in Alaska, in contrast with common experience in the continental United States, has followed rather than preceded other forms of economic development. It began in small gardens near the cabins of prospectors, miners, freighters, fishermen, and on the clearings adjacent to missions. It constituted a secondary activity undertaken in part to supplement food obtained from fish, game, and importations. Frequently, as a hobby or to satisfy curiosity concerning the land's ability to produce, small gardens were started. This secondary position of farming explains, in part, the slow progress which has occurred.

There were 222 farms in 1910. They increased to 364 in 1920 and 500 by 1929. In 1939 there were 623 farms of which 164 were fur farms. Most fur farms were located in Southeastern Alaska. (Fur farming is discussed elsewhere in this report.) Other farms were largely in the south-central region, the majority being in Matanuska Valley, other farms were located near Anchorage, and on the Kenai Peninsula. There were also a few livestock farms on Kodiak and the Aleutian Islands. Farms in northern areas were established in the Tanana Valley. The increase in farms between 1929 and 1939 was confined to the south-central region, while decreases were noted in other areas.

Operation by owners, rather than by tenants or hired managers, was characteristic in Alaska. This is shown in the following data:

TABLE 17.—*Number of farms and type of operators in 1939*

Item	Total Alaska	Southeast region	South-central and southwest region	Northern regions
All farms (1939)	623	166	401	56
All farms (1929)	500	202	187	111
Fur farms (1939)	164	95	57	12
Farms other than fur farms (1939)	459	71	344	44
Full owners	339	58	249	32
Part owners	73	4	67	2
Tenants	28	6	13	9
Managers	19	3	15	1

Acreage and Crops

The acreage of harvested cropland increased from 3,875 in 1929 to 7,305 in 1939. The increase occurred in the south-central region, an appreciable decrease occurring in other regions. The low average acreage per farm indicates that many farms were very small. A farm, for census purposes, was defined as any agricultural property having 3 acres or more, or which pro-

Crisp cabbages weighing as much as 50 pounds are easily grown in Alaska.

duced products valued at not less than $250. Total cropland and acreage harvested per farm follows:

TABLE 18.—*Area of cropland (acres)*

Item	Total Alaska	Southeast region	South-central and southwest region	Northern region
Cropland	11,332	1,190	7,812	2,330
Cropland harvested	7,305	585	5,395	1,325
Cropland per farm	24	16	22	53
Cropland harvested per farm	16	8	15	30

Oats, peas, vetch, root crops, and other forage accounted for almost half the harvested acreage in that year. Perennial tame and wild hay boosted the forage crop total to 66 percent. Small grain production was confined mostly to Matanuska Valley, although some grain was harvested in Tanana Valley. Approximate percentages of harvested acres in the major crop groups were:

TABLE 19.—*Major crop groups* (*percent*)

Crop	Total Alaska	Southeast region	South-central and southwest region	Northern regions
Small grain and peas	26	1	32	13
Oats, peas, vetch and other annual forage crop	48	23	47	57
Perennial tame and wild hay	18	62	14½	17
Vegetables	2	6	1	3½
Potatoes	5	6	5	9
Small fruits	1	2	½	½
Total	100	100	100	100

Crop Yields

Influenced by farm practices and management, yields vary widely among farms. Approximate average yields per acre during recent years were: wheat, 22 bushels; oats, 35 bushels; hull-less barley, 25 bushels; annuals harvested for hay, 1¼ tons; annuals harvested for silage, 5 tons, and potatoes, 4 to 5 tons. Much

Strawberry patch at V. C. Spaulding's ranch near Juneau.

Cows in a meadow in Mendenhall Valley, Southeastern Alaska.

larger yields were obtained by farmers employing improved methods, including use of fertilizer.

Ordinarily Alaska's land does not produce heavy yields without applications of fertilizer. Because of the shortage of livestock on farms, greater dependence is placed on commercial fertilizers than on livestock manure. In 1947, 1,000,000 pounds of fertilizers and materials were imported. Assuming 10,000 acres of cropland were harvested, an average of 100 pounds of fertilizer per acre was used. Potatoes and truck crops, however, received a large portion of the total since application of 500 pounds or more per acre is a common practice.

Livestock

Distribution of livestock in Alaska farms was as follows:

Readily accessible waterways float timber rafts to sawmills.

TABLE 20.—*Number of livestock*

Kind	Total Alaska	Southeast region	South-central and southwest region	Northern region
Horses and mules	496	33	423	40
All cattle	3,749	651	2,943	155
Cows kept for milk	1,217	445	657	115
Other dairy stock (estimated)		206	400	40
Other cattle (estimated)			1,886	
Sheep and lambs	17,076	33	17,043	
Goats and kids	289	144	118	27
Swine	959	45	784	130
Chickens	18,374	4,274	13,696	404

There were differences in the importance of various kinds of livestock in each region. For instance, the majority of horses were in Matanuska Valley but dairy cows were important in all regions. There were some beef cattle in Matanuska Valley, but the majority, including sheep were on Kodiak and the Aleutian Islands. Swine were largely in Matanuska Valley. There were chickens and goats in all farming localities.

Livestock not located on farms were: horses and mules, 161; cattle, 140; goats and kids, 145; hogs, 63; chickens, 5,674; and work dogs 24,291. Dogs (work animals) not on farms had decreased from 37,287 in 1929.

Farm Production by Regions

Although there was little cultivated land in Southeastern Alaska in 1939, the value of agricultural products was substantial. Intensive agriculture was characteristic. This region led in greenhouse products, nursery stock, and dairy products and was important in vegetable, fruit, and poultry production. However, the majority of feed for dairy and poultry enterprises was imported.

There was little cropland in the southwest region, consequently the value of most crop production listed under the south-central and southwest regions in the table below was produced in the former region, mainly in Matanuska Valley. Dairy, poultry, and potatoes constituted the principal sources of farm income in 1939.

Farm income in northern regions, principally at Fairbanks, was similar to that in Matanuska Valley except that vegetables were of greater importance while poultry production was much lower. In most cases grain and hay was fed on the farms where grown and consequently did not enter into sales in volume in any region.

Values in dollars of the principal farm products sold from Alaska farms were:

TABLE 21.—*Value of farm products in 1939 (dollars)*

Product	Total Alaska	Southeast region	South-central and southwest regions	Northern regions
Hay	1,625	70	1,465	90
Potatoes	43,203	1,958	22,857	18,388
Vegetables	22,930	2,444	3,016	17,470
Fruit	4,612	1,569	1,928	1,115
Nursery Stock	1,320	1,075	95	150
Greenhouse products	13,095	10,000	1,045	2,050
Milk and cream	306,987	158,387	97,300	51,300
Eggs and poultry	47,720	10,583	34,540	2,597
Value of vegetables for home use	20,136	4,315	12,461	3,360

Cultivation of rich farm lands has boosted the population of Palmer from zero in 1930 to 1,500 in 1948.

Progress Since 1939

There has been appreciable development since 1939, but agriculture still retains much of its early characteristics. Gardeners and farmers are continually trying out a variety of practices, crops and enterprises, as well as commercializing on knowledge gathered through past experience. Agriculture remains a side-line occupation or hobby for the majority of persons actively engaged in farming.

Preliminary estimates made in 1948, indicate there are only about 125 farms which can qualify as full-time operations. The majority are in Matanuska Valley—the only place where substantial organized efforts to further agricultural settlement have been made in Alaska.

In 1929, the Alaska Railroad was instrumental in bringing families to Matanuska Valley. Additional families were brought in by the Alaska Rural Rehabilitation Corporation in 1935, and given assistance in clearing land, erecting buildings and developing farms. There are now about 80 full-time farms, many part-time farms and gardens in Matanuska Valley. Dairying is the leading farm enterprise. Approximately 40 grade "A" dairy farms furnish Anchorage and Palmer with fresh milk, but production is still far short of demand. Potatoes, vegetables, poultry, pork, and beef are produced. Some hogs are raised in the valley but

the greatest production is from three farms utilizing garbage from Port Richardson.

Matanuska Valley is the leading agricultural area in the Territory. According to the Agricultural Extension Service, an additional 2,000 acres of land were cleared in 1947. A number of silos were constructed in 1948. More dairy barns are being built; others improved to meet grade "A" standards. Marked interest is being displayed in improved crop and livestock practices.

In terms of acreage of cropland, the second most important farming area is Tanana Valley, in the Fairbanks vicinity. Milk is the leading agricultural product. In contrast with Matanuska Valley, all commercial milk at Fairbanks is produced by two dairy farms and the Agricultural Experiment Station herd.

Several farmers desire to enter the dairying field but lack of financial and mechanical means for clearing sufficient acreage has prevented them. For this reason, small farmers are forced to rely on potato and vegetable production. This type of farming carries high risks and is not conducive to soil improvement, or building a sound, stable, well-rounded agricultural program. Despite clearing handicaps, farmers in this area cleared about 1,000 acres in 1947, according to reports of the Agricultural Extension Service.

Farming in the vicinity of Homer and other points on Kenai Peninsula has made little progress since 1929.

Grade A dairy barn in Matanuska Valley.

Lack of facilities to transport products to market appear to have been the principal difficulty. Construction of a dock at Homer and completion of the road from Homer to Anchorage will remove some of the difficulties.

Southeastern Alaska still has little land under cultivation, but dairy and poultry production, based largely on imported feeds were valued at $500,000 and $50,000 respectively in 1946.

Value of Production in 1946

The approximate values of products produced on Alaska farms in 1946 were as follows:

TABLE 22.—*Value of agricultural products in 1946*
(1,000 dollars)

Area	Milk	Vegetables	Poultry and eggs	Beef, pork, and wool	Total
Southeastern Alaska	500	50	50		600
Matanuska Valley	525	500	150	157	1,350
Kenai Peninsula, Kodiak and Aleutian Islands					275
Tanana Valley	160	185	55		400
Total					2,625

Often the market for home-grown products is limited to the locality in which they are grown because of transportation difficulties. The recent increase in civilian population of many towns plus military purchases, has resulted in consistent shortages of perishables such as whole milk, eggs, and hardy vegetables.

Reindeer in Alaska's Agricultural Picture

Reindeer production is a livestock enterprise peculiar to the northern regions. In 1929, approximately 713,000 reindeer roamed tundra ranges from Point Barrow on the north, to Kodiak Island in the south and from the coastal belt bordering the Bering Sea and Arctic Ocean to Ophir in the interior.

Today, there are less than 40,000 reindeer in Alaska. A joint survey conducted in 1948 by the Alaska Native Service and Fish and Wildlife Service cited five major reasons for this large-scale depletion. They were: (1) slaughter of reindeer by wolves, (2) starvation through continued grazing of a single portion of the respective ranges, (3) poor herding and management, (4) excessive butchering, and (5) mixing and migrating with caribou.

Prior to 1937, reindeer were owned by both Eskimos and whites, the Eskimos owning about two-thirds of the stock. Surplus stocks permitted considerable export of reindeer products. The most important of these products were meat and hides. Reindeer hides provide a fine leather for manufacture of leather jackets and kid gloves. Skins are utilized locally in manufacture of winter garments—mukluks, parkas, mittens, socks, leggings, trousers, and sleeping bags. Export of hides increased from 8,000 in 1928 to more than 14,000 in 1930.

Meat for the export market was prepared under modern methods of slaughtering and shipping. Several cold storage plants operated along the coast and meat was shipped to the United States in refrigerated ships. Exports of reindeer meat jumped from 1,000,000 pounds in 1928, to 2,000,000 in 1929 and 2,500,000 in 1930.

Reindeer byproducts, the antlers, bones, and blood and viscera were used in the preparation of meals fed to dogs and foxes. Antlers were exported for use in the manufacture of knife handles and similar articles.

In northern Scandinavian latitudes reindeer milk is used for making of butter and cheese. No reindeer milking was or is now being done in Alaska. The animal was used to a slight extent as a beast of burden—for packing in summer and drawing of sleds in winter. Readily broken to halter, the average reindeer can haul a sled loaded with more than 300 pounds.

Past investigations reveal that the minimum-sized herd from which an individual owner can earn a living is in the neighborhood of 1,000 head. Tom Brower of Barrow, Alaska, estimates his annual income from 1,300 head is approximately $6,000.

There is every reason to believe that through proper direction and management the herds can be rehabilitated to their former status.

WHOLESALE AND RETAIL TRADE

Alaska has always been a good customer of the United States. In the decade prior to World War II, there were only about 10 countries in the world with which the United States did more trade. The Alaska trade surpassed that of the Central American countries combined, Norway, Sweden, Denmark, Belgium, Holland, the Balkan countries, Italy, and China.

By the end of 1947, the volume of trade between the United States and Alaska had reached a grand total of more than $4,500,000,000—625 times more than its original purchase price. Of this amount, almost $3,000,000,000 was the value of shipments of fish, minerals, furs, and forest products to the United States. Shipments of foodstuffs, clothing, machinery, and other

manufactures to Alaska accounted for about $1,500,000,000.

From mere examination of statistics, this balance of trade in Alaska's favor has been termed by some economists as being unfavorable to the United States. However, these figures do not present a true picture as this $1,500,000,000 balance of trade is more apparent than real. Much of it was in the form of profits and overhead expenses actually paid in the United States. Many of the mining, fishing, and other companies maintained office staffs and headquarters in the United States, paying in the States much of the overhead wages and costs and dividends. Consequently, such statistics as payrolls, Federal income and other tax payments, do not wholly portray development of trade and commerce in Alaska.

Actually, many States have been credited with Federal tax payments which were exclusively the result of Alaska production. That fact is often ignored when contributions of the Federal Government to Alaska are compared with Alaska's tax payments in return. In fiscal year 1948, however, internal revenue collections within Alaska alone totaled $18,885,047.

It is difficult to estimate the value of Alaska exports to foreign countries since its major commodity—canned salmon—is shipped to Pacific Coast States for warehousing, brokerage, and marketing. Although the United States exports about $30,000,000 in fish products annually, the amount attributable to Alaska manufacture is not known.

Prior to World War II, Alaska exported about $16,000 in wood products to the Orient. During this same period, exports to Canada's Yukon Territory amounted to $500,000 while imports from the area were only $200,000. Trade with British Columbia amounted to $100,000 in exports and $70,000 in imports.

Although postwar figures are not available, it is known that imports from British Columbia have increased substantially because of recurrent maritime tie-ups. In many instances, southeastern Alaska has depended on imports of meat, eggs, and other products from Canada as its sole source of food supply. Similar products were brought into interior Alaska from Edmonton, Alberta, over the Alaska highway.

Trade statistics between Alaska and the United States during 1947 show the total Alaska imports to be $123,002,041, while exports were $116,809,279. Accompanying statistics show the distribution of imports and exports among animals and fish, agriculture, forest, mineral, and manufactured products.

According to 1939 census figures there were 989 retail establishments, employing 1,636 persons. Gross receipts were $23,047,912. Included in retail trade establishments were the following types of businesses: beverages, tobacco, confectioneries, books, office supplies, drugs, foods, general stores, and trading posts, hardware, electrical, marine supplies, restaurants, tailor shops, wearing apparel, coal and wood, service stations, ice, lumber, monuments, furniture, and photographic supplies.

There were 105 wholesale concerns, which employed a total of 105 persons and did a gross business of $9,016,990. These wholesale firms included the following: foods, beverages, gasoline, hardware, electrical equipment, wearing apparel, furs, coal, feed, furniture, lumber, and cement.

There were 389 service establishments, which employed 702 persons and did a gross business of $3,391,131. Service establishments included: carpentry, boat-repairing, garages, metal-work, plumbing, barber and beauty shops, cleaning and pressing, shoe repairing, watch repairing, undertaking, photo finish-

ing, billiard parlors and bowling alleys, theaters, dance halls, roadhouses, and hotels.

It is to be noted that of over 900 retail concerns, only 25 reported gross incomes over $100,000 or more per year. There were 74 in the $50,000 to $100,000 bracket; 606 from $5,000 to $49,000. With a substantial increase in population since 1939, many new businesses have been established and it is undoubtedly true that more concerns are now in higher income brackets.

According to Alaska Development Board figures, Alaska bank deposits more than doubled from 1941 to 1948. Total deposits of 18 Territorial and National banks were listed at $22,110,699 on June 30, 1941, while total deposits of $59,948,989 were reported by the 20 banks in operation in the year ending June 30, 1948. In the same interval, bank capital increased from $985,000 to $1,175,000, surplus and undivided profits from $1,382,483 to $2,862,512.

TABLE 23.—*Value of in-shipments—United States to Alaska*

Year	Animals, fish and products	Agriculture products	Forest products	Mine products	Manufactures and miscellaneous	Total
1931	$3,199,899	$4,339,739	$1,188,100	$1,882,756	$11,881,580	$22,492,074
1932	2,321,172	3,629,565	1,067,809	1,758,641	10,844,048	19,621,235
1933	2,240,929	3,875,089	1,311,766	1,935,984	11,362,775	20,756,543
1934	3,180,354	5,753,920	1,795,680	2,382,181	17,261,295	30,373,430
1935	3,630,186	6,213,160	1,966,199	2,962,296	17,255,339	32,027,180
1936	3,798,344	6,800,795	2,477,931	3,690,387	22,324,263	39,091,720
1937	4,220,574	7,432,321	2,681,840	4,088,081	24,509,408	42,932,224
1938	4,306,950	7,432,370	2,358,884	4,385,608	24,260,254	42,744,066
1939	4,501,819	7,410,014	2,569,742	4,809,675	25,035,830	44,327,080
1940	4,818,942	8,161,938	2,974,345	5,205,033	26,969,320	48,129,578
1941 [1]						82,206,605
1942	8,558,682	13,766,625	6,770,455	10,007,647	50,394,212	89,497,621
1943	9,557,974	16,246,566	4,152,730	11,790,314	31,811,214	73,558,798
1944	8,153,674	16,283,441	3,510,702	6,272,623	27,821,923	62,042,363
1945	8,740,545	16,180,142	3,711,701	5,998,379	29,416,643	64,047,410
1946	10,699,168	15,797,059	3,130,705	7,212,301	38,165,996	75,005,229
1947	13,579,275	20,723,757	6,677,970	13,150,815	62,677,462	116,809,279

[1] Figures for respective imports not available.

TABLE 24.—*Value of out-shipments—Alaska to United States*

Year	Animals, fish and products	Agriculture products	Forest products	Mine products	Manufactures and miscellaneous	Total
1931	$39,135,330		$34,994	$11,567,081	$61,246	$50,798,651
1932	27,951,325		20,858	10,907,788	57,904	38,937,875
1933	31,783,289		43,480	9,995,113	14,505	41,836,387
1934	43,710,901		42,889	16,004,468	29,355	59,787,613
1935	32,544,029		80,028	18,824,230	25,986	51,474,273
1936	56,324,378		130,985	19,751,576	15,673	76,222,612
1937	52,864,583		100,835	25,667,871	67,382	78,700,671
1938	47,786,712		86,497	27,422,959	30,654	75,326,822
1939	38,648,510		124,449	21,343,719	27,541	60,144,219
1940	36,612,468		116,752	21,885,054	10,408	58,624,682
1941	63,773,965		92,672	19,099,575	207,199	83,173,411
1942	53,858,079		117,347	12,139,485	40,031	66,154,942
1943	67,945,364		145,177	2,000,388	27,261	70,118,190
1944	66,714,011		64,097	2,378,820	58,575	69,215,503
1945	67,994,492		114,439	1,752,140	378,747	70,239,818
1946	62,407,974		715,749	5,581,416	137,287	68,842,426
1947	115,274,166		744,011	6,652,958	330,906	123,002,041

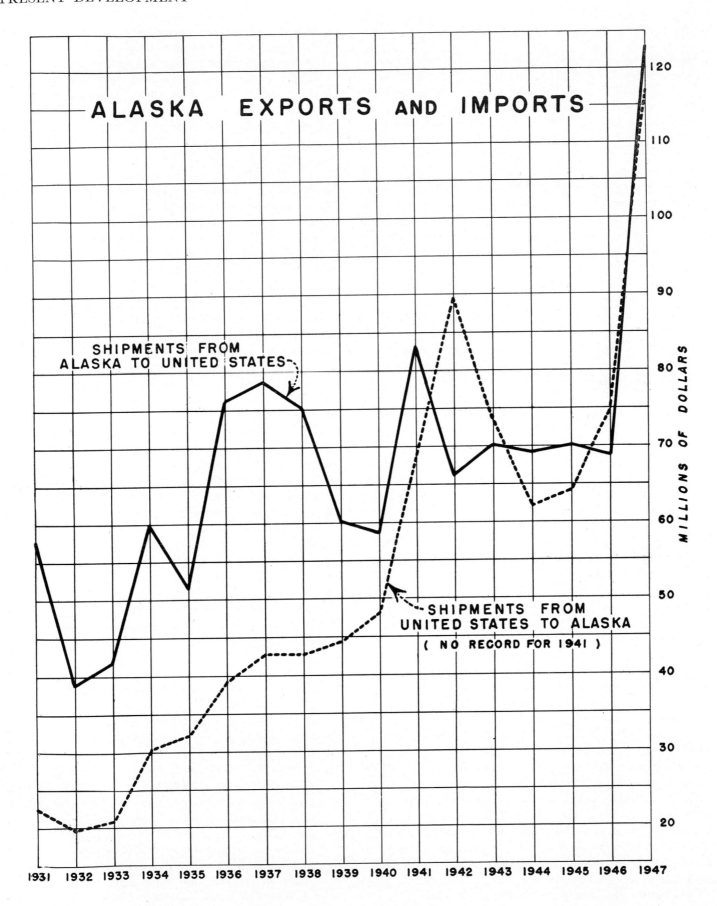

ALASKA EXPORTS AND IMPORTS

SHIPMENTS FROM ALASKA TO UNITED STATES

SHIPMENTS FROM UNITED STATES TO ALASKA

(NO RECORD FOR 1941)

MILLIONS OF DOLLARS

MANUFACTURING

Manufacturing on the Pacific Coast of North America was pioneered in Alaska. History tells that Sitka, capital of Russian America, was once the manufacturing metropolis of the Pacific Coast. Sitka had the first boat yard, the first sawmill, the first flour mills, and the first iron foundry. Products of its foundry are to be found in parts of California where mission bells cast in Sitka still ring.

With America's record for pioneering—cracking open its wildernesses and developing its resources—it would be natural to assume the industrial impetus given Alaska prior to 1867 would have continued on a larger and grander scale following its purchase. Unfortunately, this has not been the case.

In the 30-year period preceding the Klondike gold rush, there was only limited exploitation of Alaska's resources because of governmental policies. Development of manufacturing industries remained at a standstill. During this time the main enterprise in the Territory was the annual harvest of the seal rookeries—leased by the Federal Government to a San Francisco company.

Manufacturing was a relatively unimportant factor until the fishing industry entered Alaska in the late 1880's. According to 1899 census figures, there were 48 manufacturing plants, of which 36 were engaged in canning and processing fish, in Alaska. Total production was listed at $4,194,421, the value added by manufacture being $2,431,838.

Within the next 2 decades, the total number of manufacturing establishments had jumped to 147, the value of their products increasing to more than $40,000,000. More than 50 percent of the value of the raw material was added through manufacture.

Alaska, 60 times larger than the combined area of Hawaii and Puerto Rico—both junior territories by more than 30 years—ranks last in manufacture. According to the 1939 census the value of Alaska's manufactured products was $38,815,436, while Hawaii's was $134,005,263 and Puerto Rico's $111,499,641. Alaskans explain the Territory's lowly position in manufactures is due chiefly to the inadequate evaluation and limited development of its resources, plus the "absentee landlord" policy, established early in Alaska's history, of shipping raw materials to the United States for processing and manufacture.

The total value added by manufacture of Alaska's resources by 230 establishments in 1939 was $17,898,679, the cost of materials, fuel, and electric energy being $20,916,757. Wages during this period were $11,458,311, representing 16 percent of the total value of the manufactures.

The largest manufacturing enterprise was the fish canning and processing industry, which accounted for $36,367,663, almost 95 percent of the total manufactures.

Lumber and timber products ranked second in manufactures. There were 21 establishments, the total value of the product being $900,111. Manufacture added $590,695, or 65 percent to the value of the raw material.

There were four ice-manufacturing plants in Alaska in 1939. The total value of the product was $77,776. Manufacture added 87 percent to its value. Approximately $150,000 in marine equipment was manufactured in the Territory's boat-building enterprises. Other establishments included 24 bread and bakery concerns, 7 machine shops and 15 printing and publishing houses.

Among the above manufacturing concerns, 133 were corporations, 53 were individual proprietorships, 37 were partnerships and 4 were cooperatives. In total volume of business, 28 did less than $5,000; 47 from $5,000 to $19,000; 49 from $20,000 to $99,000; 85 from $100,000 to $499,000; 19 from $500,000 to $999,000 and 2 over $1,000,000. All 21 doing over $500,000 business were salmon canneries.

The 230 concerns employed a year around average of 5,467 persons, the peak being in July with 39,985 employees.

While these statistics are out of date, they are the most recent available and it is certain that the 1949 census will reflect substantial progress in Alaska in all fields of endeavor. It is known that with Alaska's estimated increase of almost 30,000 persons since 1939, that many new small manufacturing enterprises have sprung up in various parts of the Territory.

TRANSPORTATION AND COMMUNICATION

Lack of adequate land transportation routes between Alaska and the United States has had a profound effect on its development. The ruts of the ox cart and covered wagon; the rails and ties flung across American frontiers were forerunners of development in the western United States. But it was many years after much of the early pioneering had been accomplished that transportation routes—railways and highways—were blazed across the seemingly endless wilderness within Alaska.

From 1867 to 1942, the chief means of reaching Alaska was by a long ocean voyage, requiring a considerable outlay of capital for prospective settlers. Once reaching the Territory, there was no ready access to many productive areas because of its vast size and rugged terrain.

With the major market for Alaska's products at the end of a 700- to 2600-mile ocean haul, development centered only on products having a high unit value, such as gold, furs, and canned salmon. High freight rates—

Aerial Crossroad of the World

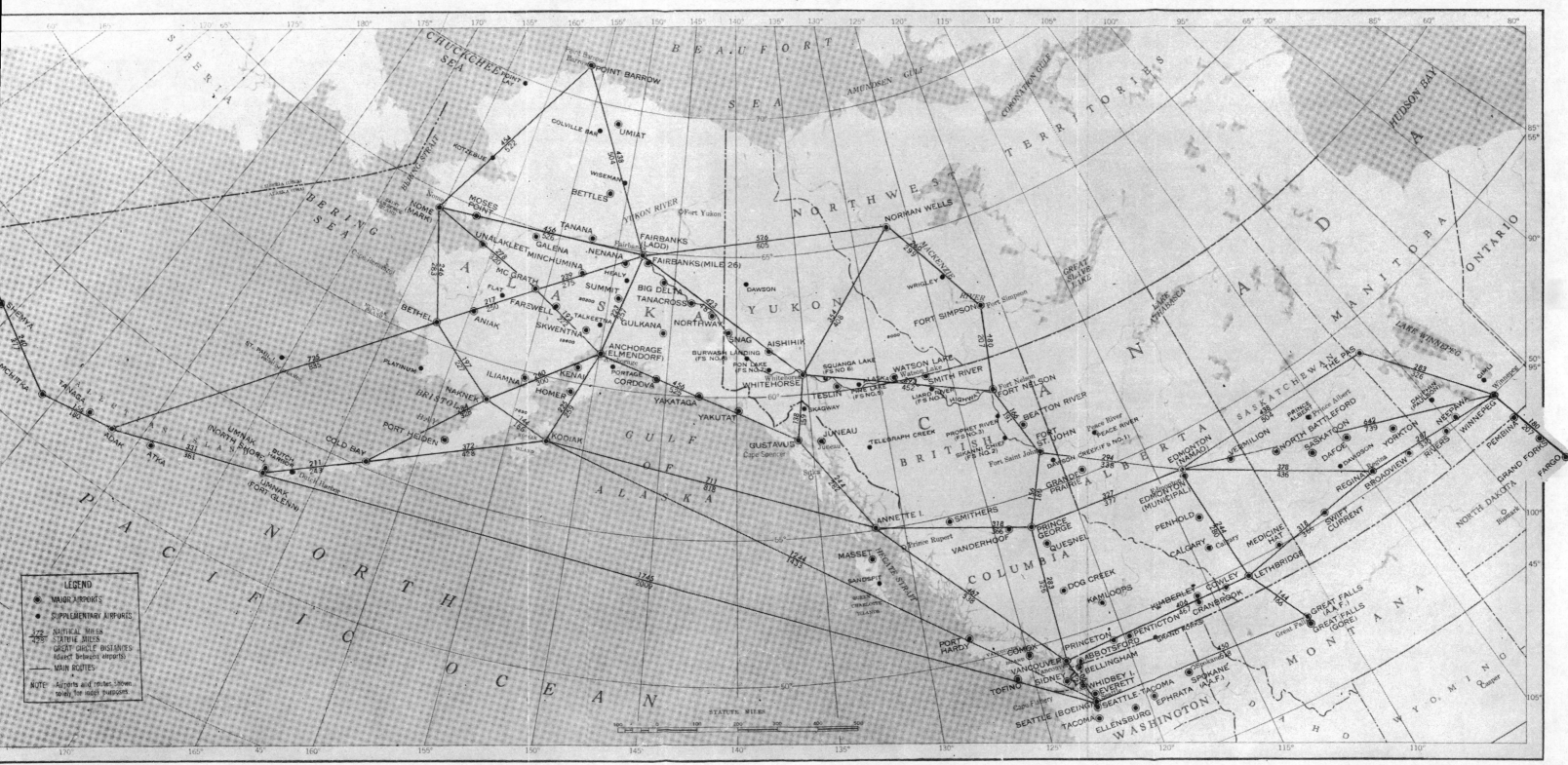

"Bush pilots" are indispensable to the economy of Alaskans who are termed the flyingest people under the American flag.

the highest in the world—blocked manufacture of many Alaska products which could have been marketed in the States. High freight tolls made it impossible for such manufactures to compete with imports from other countries.

Within Alaska, transportation was slow and tedious prior to the advent of the airplane. It was simply a matter of walking, dog team, power boat, or just plain rowing. Then came the Alaska Railroad and the interior highway system.

Because transportation is such an important factor in Alaska's economy—almost determining whether it lives or dies—its three chief mediums, air, land, and sea are discussed separately in this chapter.

Air Transportation

The airplane has been the covered wagon of Alaska. It played a major role in development of much of the Territory. Conversely, Alaska played an important role in development of aviation. Four United States Army planes, under command of Captain St. Clair Street, made the first flight from the United States to Alaska during the summer of 1920. The first air mail service within Alaska began in February, 1924. That same year Alaska was one of the "main-line" stops on the first round-the-world flight. The dirigible Norge, after a nonstop flight from Spitsbergen, was forced to land at Teller because of storms. Aviation pioneers such as Lincoln Ellsworth, Sir Hubert Wilkins, Carl Ben Eielson, Charles Lindbergh, Wiley Post, General

Henry H. Arnold, Howard Hughes, and dozens of others wrote Alaska's aviation history in deeds.

The feasibility of air traffic between Alaska and the United States was never demonstrated more clearly than during World War II. Following the Japanese attack on Dutch Harbor and occupation of Kiska, 10 airlines flew men and material to Alaska. In addition to Pan American, the sole prewar operator, United Air Lines, American Airlines, Northwest Airlines, Pennsylvania Central Air Lines, Trans-World Air Lines, Chicago and Southern, Western Air Lines, Braniff, and Panagra were engaged in the Alaska operation.

Because of vast distances and rugged terrain separating communities, the plane has been a boon to most Alaskans, whether they be fisherman, miner, logger, trapper, or trader. Nurses and doctors are transported to outlying districts to aid in control of epidemics, and sick persons are rushed to hospitals. Many Federal agencies make use of airplanes in Alaska. Large areas have been mapped by Navy planes. The Coast Guard uses planes to protect life and property; conservation agencies patrol fishing grounds by plane, and the Alaska Native Service depends on planes for movement of personnel and emergency supplies during winter months.

Prior to World War II, Alaska had 116 times as many planes, which flew 70 times as many miles, carried 23 times as many passengers, carried 1,034 times as much freight and express and 48 times as much mail as the United States on a per capita basis.

Today, only about 24 persons per 1,000 are estimated

to use air service in the United States. In Alaska the number of passengers carried has exceeded the total population every year since 1946. The Alaska per capita use of air freight and express is more than 200 times greater than in the States.

There were 29 air carriers in Alaska during 1948. They flew more than 7,000,000 miles, carried 129,616 passengers, more than 18,000,000 pounds of freight, and almost 2,000,000 pounds of mail all within Alaska. Between the Territory and the States there were 3,397 flights for a total distance of 4,236,357 miles. These planes carried 48,270 passengers, 9,441,511 pounds of freight, and 588,417 pounds of mail. Anchorage generates more air traffic than cities in the United States 100 times its size. Ketchikan and Juneau lead dozens of cities more than 20 times their size. Several Alaska towns of 500 population or less are linked by air with major communities on daily schedules, and the major communities in turn are linked with each other and the United States on similar schedules. One airline now flies the Great Circle route through Alaska to the Orient.

Land Transportation

Highways

It was not until 30 years following the purchase of Alaska that any effort was made by the Federal Government to explore routes for roads and trails. During this period, travel was limited largely to open waterways in summer and their frozen courses in winter. Mining machinery and supplies were transported from coastal or river landings over the snow in winter. Travel across the country during the summer was usually by foot or pack horse.

Actually, Alaska had no highway system prior to World War II. Excepting for the 371-mile Richardson highway, with its mining road extensions to Livengood, Circle, and Nabesna, the only roads were short stretches from towns unconnected with each other. Juneau's road system totaled 80 miles; Ketchikan's, 37; and other towns still less. A 75-mile road also extended northward from Seward, and Anchorage was connected by road with Matanuska Valley.

Construction of the 194-mile Glen highway during the war linked the Anchorage road with the Richardson highway; connected the Nabesna road to the Alaska highway—punched through the Canadian wilderness to give Alaska its first land link with the United States. The 42-mile Haines-boundary road was also extended to connect with the Alaska Highway. Alaska now has an interior highway system totaling 1,844 miles, of which only 350 miles receives winter maintenance.

Regular bus and limited truck services are now operated on the Alaska highway. Appreciable gains in bus and private auto traffic are recorded during the summer months when thousands of tourists flock to Alaska. Truck traffic increases during maritime tieups, when Alaskans send trucks to Canada for food supplies. During the long tieup during the winter of 1948, a limited amount of mail was trucked from Seattle to Fairbanks.

TABLE 25.—*Highway distances*

Alaska Highway	Mile	Elliott Highway	Mile
Dawson Creek	0	Fox	0
Fort St. John	48	Livengood	70
Fort Nelson	300		
Liard River	495	*Slana-Tok Cutoff and Nabesna Road*	
Watson Lake	635		
Teslin	804	Tok Junction	0
Norman Wells Junction	836	Slana	73
		Gakona	135
Carcross Road Junction	865	Gulkana	140
Whitehorse	917	Slana to Nabesna	41
Haines Road Junction	1,012		
Burwash Landing	1,090	*Edgerton Cutoff*	
White River	1,169		
Alaska-Yukon Border	1,223	Richardson Highway to Chitina	39
Northway Junction	1,265		
Tok Junction	1,305	*Glen Highway and Anchorage Roads*	
Tanacross	1,314		
Big Delta	1,423	Glenallen	0
Fairbanks	1,511	Palmer	143
Haines to Junction	166	Anchorage	193
		Palmer to Wasilla	14
		Palmer to Willow	50
Richardson Highway			
Valdez	0	*Steese Highway*	
Edgerton Cutoff	92	Fairbanks	0
Copper Center	102	Fox	11
Glenallen	116	Chatanika	27
Gulkana	128	Miller House	115
Paxons	191	Central	129
Rapids	233	Circle	163
Big Delta	280	Central to Circle Hot Springs	8
Fairbanks	368		

Railways

It was near the end of the era of America's railway builders, when financiers and statesmen were making every effort to draw the iron trails of commerce into fresh lands that a great north-south railway, extending from Alaska to the Panama Canal, was envisaged. Four governments—British Columbia, Canada, Great Britain, and the United States—entered into negotiations to discuss bridging of the rocky expanses between the American border and Alaska. For varied reasons the proposed line was never constructed.

At that time there was only one railroad in Alaska: the 111-mile White Pass and Yukon Route extending from tidewater at Skagway to Whitehorse in the Yukon Territory. Only 20 miles of this railway was in Alaska. It did, however, play an important role in development of interior Alaska. Prior to construction of the Alaska Railroad, the line, connected by river boat and winter

One of the several Diesel Streamliners in Service on the Alaska Railroad.

trail, provided a major outlet for the Fairbanks region. During World War II, it transported much of the supplies and equipment used in construction of the Alaska Highway, Canol Oil Project and other defense projects. The White Pass and Yukon Route is a privately owned corporation.

The United States Government authorized construction of the Alaska Railroad March 12, 1914. Construction began next summer, and within 3 years 354 miles of road was in operation. It was not until 1923 that the rail line was finally completed from the port of Seward to Fairbanks—a distance of 470 miles. In 1943 a 14-mile spur was constructed to link Portage with Whittier, another ocean port.

The Alaska Railroad broke open the door into interior Alaska. It carved a road to the coal mines of the Matanuska and the Healy River areas. It hauled dredges and heavy machinery to the mining districts and agricultural implements to the agricultural areas. It moved new settlers in. It brought building material for their homes. It carried food to sustain life. Along the path of the railroad, dozens of small communities have developed. Among these is Anchorage —now Alaska's largest city—which sprang up almost overnight into a tent city of 2,000 persons.

The railroad hauled over 1,000,000 tons during the year ending June 30, 1948. This tonnage is more than double the load carried during the war year of 1943.

In April, the railroad carried as much freight as it did during 6 months in 1929.

The economic value of the railroad is realized when examination is made of traffic figures for 1947. That year over 285,000 tons of mineral products; 46,000 tons of logs, ties, posts, lumber, and veneer; 138,000 tons of oil, gas, iron, and steel; 8,500 tons of mining machinery; 19,000 tons of cement; 4,000 tons of beer, equivalent to 109 bottles annually per capita; 179 tons of newsprint; 267 tons of canned food; 1,557 tons of canned fish; over 10,000 tons of groceries and 500 tons of prefabricated houses were hauled over the line.

The Alaska Railroad also plays an important role in encouraging development of the region which it serves. During the summer of 1948, the railroad conducted a survey of industrial potentialities of the region. This survey appears briefly in chapter VII.

TABLE 26.—*Railway distances*

Alaska Railroad

	Mile		Mile
Seward	0	Palmer	157
Portage	66	McKinley Park	348
Anchorage	112	Nenana	412
Eklutna	140	Fairbanks	470
Matanuska	151	Whittier to Portage	14

White Pass and Yukon Route

Skagway	0	Whitehorse	111

Water Transportation

Ocean Navigation

Nature has provided a sheltered waterway along the Pacific Coast extending almost 1,000 miles from the head of Puget Sound to Skagway and Haines, far up the Alaska Panhandle. It is the world's most sheltered and beautiful ocean waterway. The Inside Passage through Canadian waters is a symbol of the physical interdependence of the two great American nations in the North Pacific.

Owing to climatic conditions, year-round steamship service is possible only in Southeastern Alaska, the southwestern and part of the peninsula area. Bristol Bay can be serviced only from early spring to late fall. The Bering Sea region is open to transportation from June until October, and it is possible for vessels to make only one trip each year to Point Barrow.

Alaska's shipping lines were originally established to transport ore and canned salmon to the United States. Transportation of passengers was a minor consideration. The vessels were usually old before entering the Alaska trade; schedules were uncertain and service poor.

Prior to World War II, three American steamship lines—Alaska Steamship Co., Northland Transportation Co., and Alaska Transportation Co.—serviced Alaska. The two latter named companies were competitors in Southeastern Alaska only. Two Canadian lines, operating out of Vancouver, British Columbia, sailed into Alaska waters as far north as Skagway transporting mostly passengers and only a small amount of Canadian goods. Restrictive legislation prohibited them from transporting passengers between Territorial ports or moving freight originating in the United States to Alaska.

Because of heavy war traffic Seattle and other west coast docks were unable to handle the bulk of military traffic for Alaska defense bases. To alleviate this situation, the United States War Department constructed extensive dock facilities at Prince Rupert, British Columbia, northernmost coastal railhead and only 90 miles from the nearest Alaskan port. Vast quantities of equipment and material were shipped from middle west and eastern States across the northwest rail route to Prince Rupert, where it was loaded aboard barges for trans-shipment to Alaskan ports. The success of this venture is attested by the fact that almost 2,000,000 tons of military equipment moved through the port.

Speaking of this operation, General Dwight D. Eisenhower said, "It was this American installation in Canada which served as the hub of the new military supply route to the northwest—cutting the water

Mount McKinley from mile 202 of roadbed newly improved under the expansion program.

voyage to Alaska by one-third . . . it was through Prince Rupert that hundreds of thousands of tons of supplies and thousands of troops were dispatched forward to bolster the defenses of North America in the dark days when the Japanese were threatening the American mainland."

American vessels in the Alaska trade were requisitioned by the War Shipping Administration in April 1942. Following VJ-day, immediate consideration was given to returning the operation to private account. The operators immediately asked for a rate increase of 100 percent. This was denied. After lengthy hearings, the United States Maritime Commission entered into an agreement (Contract No. USMC–C–60, 018) dated May 15, 1947, with (1) the Alaska Steamship Co., owned by the Skinner-Eddy Corp. whose main activities are devoted to the brokerage of salmon and whose president is G. W. Skinner, and secretary, R. C. Anderson; (2) the Northland Transportation Co. owned by G. W. Skinner, R. C. Anderson, and David E. Skinner; (3) the Alaska Transportation Co., an Alaska corporation, whose president, Norman Clapp, owns 51 percent of the capital stock.

TABLE 27.—*Water (ocean) distance*

Seattle												
749	Ketchikan											
851	102	Wrangell										
1064	315	229	Sitka									
1004	256	170	183	Juneau								
1100	352	266	216	115	Skagway							
1544	798	712	529	564	592	Cordova						
1559	813	727	544	578	605	87	Valdez					
1586	840	753	568	605	634	170	169	Seward				
1446	935	848	642	700	729	325	327	204	Kodiak			
1961	1560	1474	1250	1326	1355	936	934	808	646	Unalaska		
2633	2222	2136	1908	1987	2016	1597	1595	1470	1308	760	Nome	
3219	2807	2721	2493	2573	2601	2183	2180	2055	1893	1346	658	Barrow

Prince Rupert is 108 miles south of Ketchikan, Haines 18 miles south of Skagway, Yakutat 290 miles west of Juneau, Seldovia 168 miles from Seward.

Under the agreement the Commission agreed to furnish Government-owned vessels to the carriers at an annual charter hire rate of $1. The Commission would bear the cost of marine insurance on both Government and privately owned vessels under this agreement until its expiration date June 30, 1948.

During this period of operation there were numerous requests for rate increases, some of which were granted; others denied. There were recurrent shipping tie-ups owing to labor disputes. Rates climbed 66 percent over prewar rates, which were then the highest under the American flag.

In the Alaskan Rate Investigation No. 3, Docket 661, before the United States Maritime Commission dated December 15, 1947, the following freight rate comparisons were made: ". . . witness for the Territory testified that present rates for the Puerto Rico trade were 34 to 37 percent over prewar as against 66 to 68 percent for the Alaska trade, despite Government subsidy and capital costs and insurance in the Alaska trade. . . .

In comparison of present rates between Seattle and Cordova and between New York and San Juan, both routes having a distance of approximately 1,600 miles, the rate of cement to Cordova is $17 per ton compared to $9 per ton to San Juan . . . potatoes and onions $23 per ton to Cordova against $12.40 per ton to San Juan.

". . . This exhibit compares freight rates between Seattle and Nome (2,500 miles) and between San Francisco and Honolulu (2,150 miles). Examples are: Cement to Nome under present rates, $22 per ton; to Honolulu, $9.30. . . . The rate to Nome on potatoes and onions is $28; to Honolulu $12.35."

Rail freight rate comparisons were also made. ". . . The rate on sugar from San Francisco to Seattle (906 miles) is 47 cents per hundredweight; from Seattle to Juneau (1,056 miles) the rate is 75 cents. . . . From Chicago to Seattle (2,100 miles) the freight rate on bathtubs is $10.66 per hundredweight; from Seattle to Kodiak (1,970 miles) the rate is $21.20.

"Alaskan trade appears to constitute a startling ex-

River steamers are operated on the Yukon and Tanana Rivers by the Alaska Railroad.

Freight being unloaded from ships in Skagway Harbor.

ception to the usual rule that carriage by water is mile-for-mile, cheaper than carriage by rail," this portion of the report concluded.

Labor disputes have continued to plague the industry. For long periods during the past few years Alaskans, with their lifelines severed, have had to depend on small fishing boats to bring supplies from Seattle or Prince Rupert, or use of the Alaska airlift which resulted in substantial dealer increases being placed on all commodities. It has been estimated by the Ketchikan (Alaska) Chronicle that shipping strikes have cost the Territory more than $20,000,000 in business lost during the last 3 years.

River Navigation

Settlement of Alaska began along the coast, then moved inland along navigable rivers. Trappers, traders, and prospectors were the first to use this method of transportation. Today there are 3,500 miles of waterways in interior Alaska.

The Alaska Railroad operates Yukon River steamboats to sustain the mining industry and villages along the river. During the summer of 1948 the 1,028-ton riverboat *Nenana* and the 237-ton sternwheeler *Alice* were in service. The ships are based at Nenana during the winter, where a marineways is maintained along the Tanana River, almost 400 miles from salt water.

These riverboats carry supplies and a few passengers. The *Nenana* travels from Nenana down the Tanana to the Yukon and down river to Marshall, a trip of 774 miles. The *Alice* makes the 530-mile round trip up river to Fort Yukon, as frequently as shipping demands dictate.

COMMUNICATION

On a bleak day in 1865 Hiram Sibley, president of the Western Union Telegraph Co., asked Colonel Charles S. Bulkley of the United States Army Engineers whether he thought he could survey the route of a proposed telegraph line across Northern British Columbia, the Yukon Territory, and what then was known as Russian America to the Bering Sea.

Colonel Bulkley replied: "Sir, if you give me the maps that are necessary, the tools that are needed and men with courage, we'll build your wire."

That was the start of the famed Telegraph Trail expedition. But Sibley was unable to comply with Bulkley's initial request; almost the complete contemplated route was uncharted. Of the tools of the day, Sibley agreed to supply whatever was needed, but when the expedition's various units got into their second month it was clear they might just as well have tackled the wilderness with their bare hands. To Bulkley's third request, Sibley was able to accede—men with courage were not wanting on the old Telegraph Trail.

Bulkley's expedition was doomed to failure. In the summer of 1867, the steamship *Great Eastern* contrived to complete the Atlantic cable and the United States Government called off the northern projects.

For the following 30 years there was no activity in developing electric communications in Alaska. In 1900 Congress authorized construction of military communications between Army headquarters at St. Michael and other military stations by establishing the Washington-Alaska Military Cable and Telegraph System. Communications were gradually expanded by this organization throughout Alaska.

In 1936 the name was changed to the Alaska Communication System. Under direction of the United States Signal Corps the "ACS" now has 32 different stations and 8 branch offices in Alaska, serving the military, Federal, and Territorial agencies and the general public. The latter includes coastal service to and from ships at sea, press service to newspapers, radio broad-casts to radio stations, and general messages. Full details of this organization's activities appears in chapter VII.

The Alaska Railroad operates 501 miles of telephone and telegraph lines on its system, providing service to railbelt communities.

POWER SUPPLY AND MARKETS

Alaska has grown so rapidly that now the demand for power exceeds the supply in most cities and communities. Use of electricity is comparatively large even though it is expensive.

Power Production Facilities

No appreciable amount of water-power capacity has been developed in the territory. In the Juneau area the Alaska Juneau Gold Mining Co. has developed hydroelectric facilities totaling 15,125 kilowatts. The Ketchikan Public Utilities has developed two plants aggregating 6,200 kilowatts. The Anchorage municipality operates a 2,000-kilowatt hydroelectric station

Existing power development near Juneau.

Tanker engines supply electricity to Anchorage. Alaska's power potential is less than 1 percent developed.

at Lake Eklutna. Numerous small privately owned hydro developments, the majority under 100 horsepower, are used in various types of small mining activities.

Steam power production is used by larger mining industries to back up hydroelectric production. The Alaska Juneau Gold Mining Co. maintains an 8,000-kilowatt steam plant. The Fairbanks Exploration Co. engaged in placer mining activities in the Fairbanks area operates a 9,500-kilowatt coal-fired steam plant. At the Alaska Native School on Japonski Island near Sitka, a 3,000-kilowatt oil-fired steam plant serves the Native Service requirements as well as the town of Sitka.

The United States Smelting, Mining, and Refining Co. at Nome operates a 5,170-kilowatt Diesel-driven plant for its gold dredging operations. Among the communities depending either wholly, or for the most part, on Diesel power as a prime source of electric energy are: Nome, Seward, Valdez, Cordova, Haines, Skagway, Petersburg, and Wrangell. Several cold storage and cannery plants in scattered sections of Alaska own and operate small Diesel plants independent of outside sources. Similarly lumber mills utilize refuse (hog fuel) from their operations to generate energy.

There has been no complete inventory made of the capacity installed in existing power plants in the Territory. From data which are available, the total installed capacity of hydroelectric power plants is esti-

mated at about 32,000 kilowatts. Similarly, the capacity of nonhydro plants, including chiefly coal and oil-fired steam plants, and Diesel plants, is about 45,000 kilowatts.

With the possible exception of two localities in Southeastern Alaska, commercial power supply facilities have been totally inadequate to meet the needs of military establishments even under peace-time conditions. In every instance, existing deficiencies made it necessary for the Armed Forces to install independent sources of power supply. Most of these installations are a combination of steam and Diesel power production.

Alaskan coal is used extensively in the Fairbanks area owing to its proximity to coal fields along the railbelt. During severe winter stock piling of coal is necessary. This pyramids the average cost above $12 per ton, while concurrently lowering the calorific value which does not average much more than 8,500 B. t. u.'s per pound of fuel at the mine.

Fuel oil supplies are entirely dependent upon shipments from California thus further depleting reserves in the United States.

The cost of fuel is excessive. There are instances where transportation costs exceed actual cost of the fuels. Diesel fuel oil in Nome costs $6 per barrel, whereas the price at Anchorage is $3.75 per barrel. Steaming coal in the Fairbanks area costs about $12 per ton. The cost of electric production often amounts to as much as 35 mills per kilowatt hour at the switchboard.

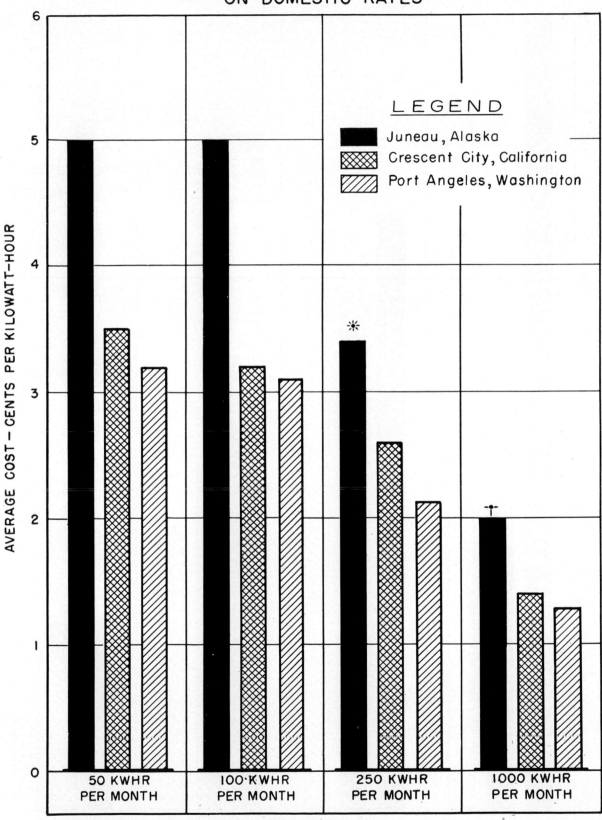

COMPARATIVE COSTS OF ELECTRICITY
ON DOMESTIC RATES

* Includes 150 KWHR at cooking and heating rate.
- Includes 540 KWHR at cooking and heating rate,
  and 360 KWHR at water heating rate.

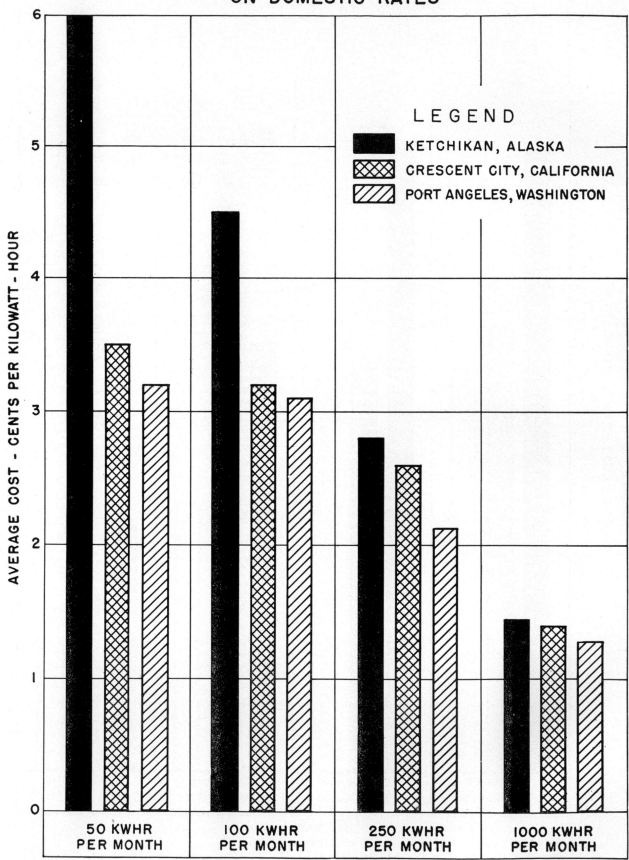

COMPARATIVE COSTS OF ELECTRICITY
ON DOMESTIC RATES

LEGEND
KETCHIKAN, ALASKA
CRESCENT CITY, CALIFORNIA
PORT ANGELES, WASHINGTON

AVERAGE COST - CENTS PER KILOWATT - HOUR

50 KWHR
PER MONTH

100 KWHR
PER MONTH

250 KWHR
PER MONTH

1000 KWHR
PER MONTH

Power Requirements

Throughout most of Alaska, domestic space heating, water heating, and cooking is accomplished by burning fuel oil or local bituminous coal. Much of the coal is low in B. t. u. content and difficult to handle during winter months. Fuel oil costs are excessive owing to the prevailing high transportation rates. In areas where hydroelectric power is available, rates are sufficiently low to permit electric cooking, water heating, and in well-insulated homes, even space heating. Where low-cost energy is available in Alaska the annual consumption in an average home is about 4,300 kilowatt-hours.

The cities of Juneau and Ketchikan are afforded hydroelectric service. It is interesting to note that in both these cities more than half of the total domestic and commercial customers served, operate electric ranges. This shows conclusively that electric energy is generally preferred as a source of fuel when low-cost power is made available.

Although the demand for electric service in the Territory during the past decade has been increasing at a rapid rate, the acceleration is considerably less in the areas where rates have been high.

Gold mining, both lode and placer, has been extensively carried on in areas contiguous to Juneau, Fairbanks, and Nome. In Juneau the Alaska Juneau Gold Mining Co. since 1914 has operated a lode mine, utilizing the natural water-power resources in the immediate vicinity which has contributed to an efficient "line-production" mining operation. Although not presently operating, a high degree of maintenance of equipment and structures continues.

Placer mining in Fairbanks and Nome areas is also electrically operated. However, at these two mines the source of power supply is produced from steam power plants. In the Fairbanks plant steam power is generated from coal fired boilers whereas in Nome, because of its geographic location, only fuel oil is used.

Coal mines presently operated are situated at Healy about 100 miles south of Fairbanks on the Alaska Railroad, at Jonesville in the Matanuska Valley and on a smaller scale in the vicinity of Homer on the Kenai Peninsula. Diesel electric power is used for the mine operations at both the Healy and Jonesville mines.

In Anchorage, electricity has been a critical commodity since 1941. From 1939 to date, electric consumption on the Anchorage municipal utilities system increased 570 percent. For its source of power supply, the city is largely dependent upon an abandoned, shipwrecked oil tanker, using the broken half which contains power production facilities.

In October, 1948 Anchorage voters approved purchase of a 1,000-kilowatt Diesel electric plant to alleviate the power shortage.

The Matanuska Electric Association is solely dependent on Anchorage for its power supply. In the 18 months period, January 1947 through July 1948, the number of customers served by the Association increased from 396 to 514. Two other rural electric cooperatives in the vicinity of Anchorage are critically in need of an additional source of electric energy because Anchorage is unable to fulfill their demands.

Fairbanks, largest community in interior Alaska, is 384 miles north of Anchorage by rail and 120 air miles south of the Arctic Circle. The principal natural resources in the Fairbanks area are minerals, fur-bearing animals, agricultural land and timber. The largest industry, exclusive of transportation enterprises and defense establishments, is gold mining. Lignite coal is mined commercially near Healy, about 100 miles south of the city.

The chief sources of cash income for Fairbanks residents are payrolls of Ladd Field, Eilson Field, the Alaska Railroad, several commercial airlines, gold mining, and various Government agencies which maintain offices in the city. It is also the commercial center of interior Alaska.

Farming is carried on chiefly along the Farmers Loop Road and along the Steel Creek Road lying north and northeast, respectively, from Fairbanks. A Rural Electrification Cooperative totaling more than 400 customers has recently been formed.

Juneau, Territorial capital, is situated at tidewater on Gastineau Channel, approximately 1,000 air miles northwest of Seattle.

Principal natural resources of the Juneau area are fish, minerals, and timber. In the early part of the century, Juneau was famous as the location of three large hard-rock gold mines, the Alaska Juneau, the Gastineau, and the Treadwell. Workings of the Alaska Juneau Mines are immediately adjacent to the city. At the present time none of these mines are operating.

In addition to the Alaska Juneau Gold Mining Co.'s mining properties, the company owns most of the power production facilities in the Juneau area and furnishes several million kilowatt-hours annually at wholesale rates to the Alaska Electric Light & Power Co. The latter company distributes the power to retail consumers.

One large sawmill is now operating in Juneau.

Juneau is the principal center of air transportation in southeastern Alaska. It is also a regular port of call for coastwise passenger and cargo ships of both United States and Canadian registry. Roads leading outward from the town extend only short distances to nearby suburban communities and rural areas.

COMPARATIVE COSTS OF ELECTRICITY
ON DOMESTIC RATES

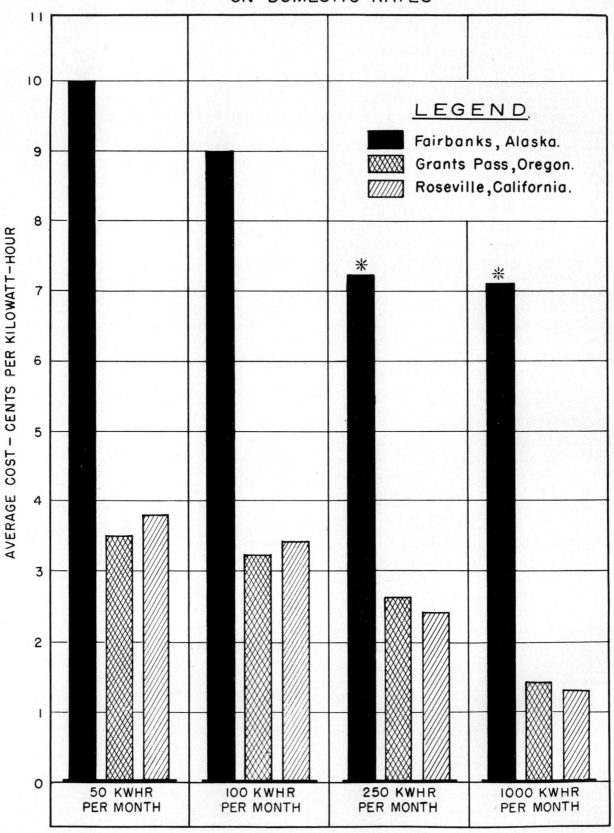

LEGEND.

■ Fairbanks, Alaska.
▨ Grants Pass, Oregon.
▧ Roseville, California.

AVERAGE COST — CENTS PER KILOWATT-HOUR

| 50 KWHR PER MONTH | 100 KWHR PER MONTH | 250 KWHR PER MONTH | 1000 KWHR PER MONTH |

✳ Includes 150 KWHR at cooking rate.

A large cold storage and quick-freezing plant in Juneau handles substantial tonnages of salmon, halibut, and other varieties of fish. There are several fish canneries in the immediate vicinity, but they are not an activity of major importance.

Agriculture consists chiefly of dairying and vegetable production for local markets. A rural electrification system now being constructed by REA will serve most of the farms in the Juneau area.

Among the sources of income on which the population depends, Federal and Territorial Government payrolls predominate, with the lumber and fishing industries employing fewer persons. Employment in mining is now only of a custodial and maintenance nature except for a few people operating the mining company's electric power system. Transportation enterprises and agriculture are dependent largely on government personnel for their income. There are several modern hotels and a number of curio stores, which rely in part on the sizeable summer tourist trade.

Ketchikan, with a population of about 7,000 persons, is Alaska's "First City," situated 600 miles north of Seattle on Revillagigedo Island. It is accessible by both American and Canadian steamship lines and three commercial airlines.

Uppermost among the natural resources in the Ketchikan area are pulp timber stands, unexcelled fishing beds, minerals, and elevated natural lakes facilitating economic development of hydroelectric power. Ketchikan enjoys a mild climate with precipitation some years approaching 200 inches annually.

One sawmill is now operated in Ketchikan and a 300-ton-per-day pulp mill is soon to be erected by a subsidiary of the Puget Sound Pulp and Paper Co. The Aluminum Company of America will soon resume mining operations on a limestone deposit in the vicinity. This lime is used in a new process to separate alumina from low-grade bauxite. The Permanente Metals Corp. is now operating a similar mine on Dall Island near Ketchikan.

Electric Rates

Electric rate structures are quite uniform throughout Alaska. The block form rate has been generally adopted by both municipal and privately-owned systems. The rate structure of the Alaska Light & Power Co. now in effect at Juneau is unusual. The oddity of this rate schedule lies in the fact that for general lighting, heating, and cooking service the rate is higher between November 1 to May 1 than is in effect from May 1 to November 1. This automatic rate increase is due to the lack of hydroelectric power during winter months. Consequently, the deficiency must be replaced by steam power production, which is more costly than hydroelectric power.

Rate levels differ widely throughout the Territory. The highest in Alaska are found at Nome with Fairbanks next in line. The lowest rates in the Territory are those offered by the Alaska Electric Light & Power Co. in Juneau for quantities consumed up to 75 kilowatt hours monthly. When electricity is used in excess of 75 kilowatt hours monthly, the Ketchikan Public Utilities, a municipal system, takes the lead. Its published rate for domestic lighting, cooking, refrigeration, and heating is:

First 50 kilowatt-hours at 6 cents per kilowatt-hour per month
Next 100 kilowatt-hours at 3 cents per kilowatt-hour per month
All over 150 kilowatt-hours at 1 cent per kilowatt-hour per month

Wide variations in rate charges are found to be due, for the most part, to excessive fuel costs. Lack of hydroelectric power development, and high shipping and handling charges for fuel and equipment account for this situation.

Recently the Territorial Government requested the Federal Power Commission to loan to the Territorial Government or municipal authorities its rate and valuation experts. Under the provisions of the Federal Power Act of 1935, in States (and Territories) where no regulatory commission exists, the Federal Power Commission may upon request of the Governor loan its "experts" for performance of service in the public interest.

On December 15, 1948, the Federal Power Commission agreed to make available members of its staff in connection with electric rates problems in Alaska.

It is expected this action will remedy several municipal situations of long standing grievances between the utility owners involved and the public at large.

The accompanying graphs compare average unit costs per kilowatt hour for consumptions of 50, 100, 250, and 1,000 kilowatt hours per month in Anchorage, Fairbanks, Juneau, and Ketchikan, with cities of comparable size in western States.

RECREATION

The first appraisal of Alaska's recreational resources was made almost 50 years ago by Henry Gannett, then Chief Geographer, Geological Survey, who reported:

"There is one other asset of the Territory not yet enumerated, imponderable, and difficult to appraise, yet one of the chief assets of Alaska, if not the greatest. This is the scenery. There are glaciers, mountains, and fiords elsewhere, but nowhere else on earth is there such an abundance and magnificence of mountain, fiord, and glacier scenery. For thousands of miles the coast is a continuous panorama. For the one Yosemite

COMPARATIVE COSTS OF ELECTRICITY
ON DOMESTIC RATES

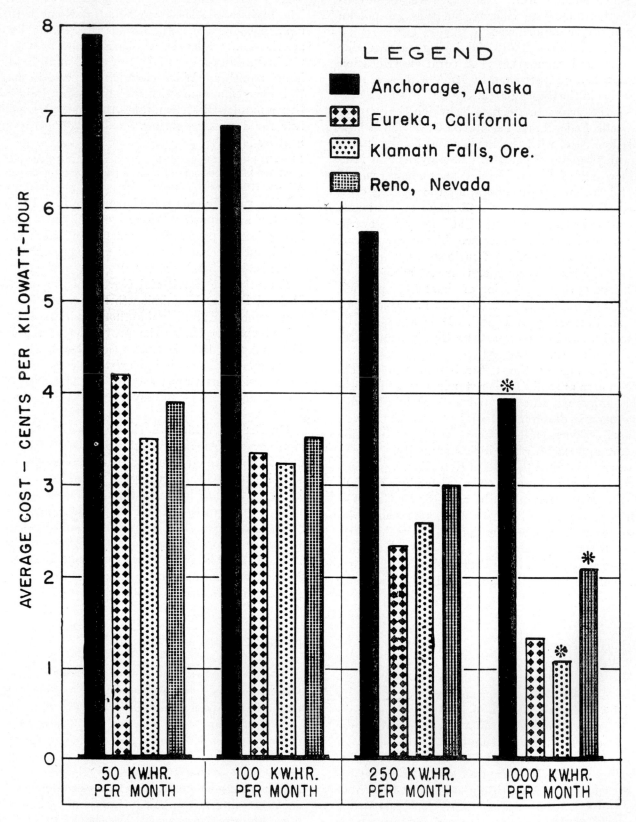

* includes 300 KWHR at
  controlled water heating rate

Camer-compelling scenery is common in Alaska. Entering Rudyard Bay—3,380-foot cliffs form part of Punchbowl Cove.

of California, Alaska has hundreds. The mountains and glaciers of the Cascades are duplicated and a thousand-fold exceeded in Alaska.

"The Alaska coast is to become the show place of the earth, and pilgrims, not only from the United States but from far beyond the seas, will throng in endless procession to see it. Its grandeur is more valuable than the gold or the fish or the timber, for it will never be exhausted. The value, measured by direct returns in money received from tourists, will be enormous; measured by health and pleasure it will be incalculable."

Despite this evaluation, comparative little use has been made of Alaska's recreational resources. No detailed survey has yet been made as to the potential value of its mountains, volcanoes, coastal waterways, rivers and lakes, glaciers, hot springs, and forests as natural recreational attractions.

Much has been written of the big game, fighting sport fish, and migratory waterfowl of Alaska. Hunters and fishermen have come to the Territory in increased numbers since the end of World War II to enjoy this form of recreation. The airplane has made it possible to reach remote areas in just a few hours,

where it formerly took days or weeks. Registered guides are available in all regions of the Territory.

At Ketchikan and Juneau, facilities are available to charter small boats with outboard motors for salmon fishing, or for use in connection with larger boats on hunting and fishing trips. A charter boat capable of river transportation was recently put into use in the Fairbanks area for hunting or sightseeing parties.

There is still a notable lack of resort and other housing facilities to accommodate any large number of tourists. The Alaska Railroad operates the McKinley Park Hotel in McKinley Park. There are no resort facilities in other National Parks and Monuments in Alaska.

Resident Alaskans make the most of recreational opportunities adjacent to their respective communities. Almost all Alaskans are ardent hunting and fishing enthusiasts and it is not unusual for a party of 3 or 4 businessmen to charter a plane early some morning, catch their limit of trout, and return to town in time to open their offices.

The majority of Alaskans living in the southeast portion of the Territory own their own pleasure boats. On Sundays and holidays many will picnic on nearby uninhabited islands, exploring beaches and inlets.

Harding Gateway leading to Seward.

Fishing for king salmon is fast gaining in importance as a salt water recreation. Fishing contests are held each summer in Juneau and Ketchikan. Trout contests are held in many other communities.

The majority of Alaskan communities have theaters, bowling alleys or roller rinks, gymnasiums, and other indoor type recreation. During the summer months a limited number of inter-city league baseball games are held in southeastern and the Fairbanks and Anchorage regions. In winter, an all-Alaska basketball championship tournament is now an annual event. Outdoor sports such as skiing and skating are favorites among Alaskans.

LAND OWNERSHIP

The United States Government holds title to 99 percent of Alaska's total land area of 571,061 square miles as compared with a grand total of 24 percent of the 48 States. The 1947 edition of the Statistical Abstract of the United States shows that in Alaska 364,995,705 acres—exclusive of the acreage of inland bodies of water—of the total area of 365,481,600 acres is in Federal ownership.

Included in the Federal lands figure is a large portion of the 21,009,209 acres granted Alaska for common schools and 438,250 acres for the University of Alaska, which as yet have not been specifically selected or designated. Homestead sites, which have not been perfected, are also included. Entries for homesteads from 1921 to 1946 included a total of 255,450 acres. Many homesteaders, however, let their entries lapse and over a

Angling near Cove Bay.

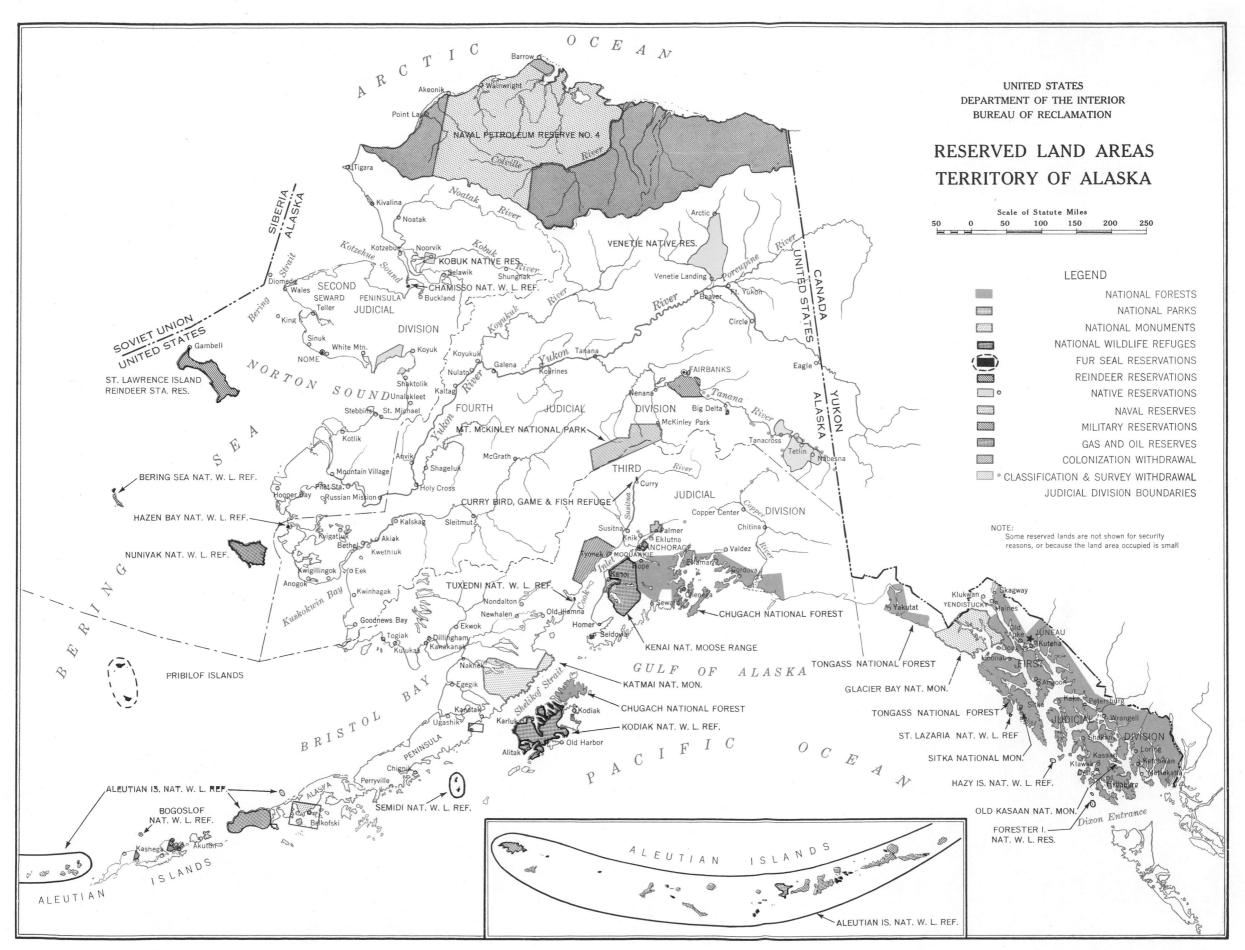

UNITED STATES
DEPARTMENT OF THE INTERIOR
BUREAU OF RECLAMATION

RESERVED LAND AREAS
TERRITORY OF ALASKA

Scale of Statute Miles

50   0   50   100   150   200   250

LEGEND

NATIONAL FORESTS

NATIONAL PARKS

NATIONAL MONUMENTS

NATIONAL WILDLIFE REFUGES

FUR SEAL RESERVATIONS

REINDEER RESERVATIONS

NATIVE RESERVATIONS

NAVAL RESERVES

MILITARY RESERVATIONS

GAS AND OIL RESERVES

COLONIZATION WITHDRAWAL

* CLASSIFICATION & SURVEY WITHDRAWAL

JUDICIAL DIVISION BOUNDARIES

NOTE:
Some reserved lands are not shown for security
reasons, or because the land area occupied is small

988410 O—52   (Face p. 80)

period of years several homestead entries have been made successively on the same tract of land.

These Federal lands have been placed under various agencies for administrative purposes; the Department of Interior having 309,710,394 acres, Department of Agriculture 20,849,187 acres, War and Navy Departments 34,382,425 acres and other agencies, 53,699 acres.

Approximately 30 percent of the total land area under Federal ownership, or about 109,000,000 acres, has been reserved or withdrawn for various purposes. Areas of the principal reserves and withdrawals, including the location of others are shown on the accompanying map. Because of security reasons, or areas insignificant in size, some reserved lands are not shown. In addition, there is in several instances, more than one type of reserve in a single specified area. However, the multiple-type reserve is not shown on the map in every case.

The classification of each reserve or withdrawal gives some indication of the present or intended future use of the land. National Forests in Alaska are principally timber lands, with no significant livestock grazing areas. National Parks and Monuments are intended to preserve, for recreational and other public purposes areas of unusual scenic or historic interest. Wildlife refuges and fur seal and reindeer reservations are administered in the interest of wildlife and game protection.

There are three withdrawals for colonization purposes. The withdrawal in the Palmer area was made in connection with establishment of the Matanuska Valley settlement in 1935. The majority of this land is now in private ownership or under purchase contract by valley farmers. This colonization withdrawal appears to have been instrumental in getting land into agricultural production as well as private ownership. Two other areas, one at Kenai and the other west of Fairbanks at Dunbar were withdrawn in 1948 for agricultural group-settlement investigation. Detailed studies of these areas are now under way to determine their suitability for agricultural development and settlement.

The green dots on the map indicate the location of small tracts which have been temporarily withdrawn while surveys are made to determine their suitability for parks, townsites and similar public purposes. These are located along the principal highways.

The uncolored portion of the map, with minor exceptions, consists of the vacant, unreserved, unappropriated public domain, totaling about 265 million acres. This region is administered by the Bureau of Land Management.

Present economic returns from the public domain and the majority of the land in the various reserves are the annual harvest of wild or natural products— game, fur, fish, timber and berries—as well as recreational benefits obtained by Alaskans and others.

Camping at Tolstoi Bay. Possibilities are unsurpassed for developing year-round recreation.

A Look at
Tomorrow

*"To tap its forests, its oil resources and its minerals;
to fabricate its timber, its furs, and its nonmetallic
minerals; to cultivate its millions of acres of land; to
build its roads, its airports and its private homes; to
harness the billions of kilowatts now running wild
through its canyons, Alaska will need millions of
new citizens. . . ."*

Prize-winning display at Matanuska Valley Fair, showing wide variety and remarkable size of Alaska farm produce.

CHAPTER IV

A Look at Tomorrow

Once Alaska's vast resources are evaluated, it is possible to envision its future world role. It is not beyond the realm of probability to state that once development of the Territory's natural wealth is given proper impetus its present population will increase tenfold within a decade; or even fiftyfold to a total of at least 5,000,000 persons within the next century.

There can be no questioning the importance of Alaska to the Nation; the value of orderly development of its resources.

"In this world of tomorrow, Alaska is assured a position of great importance. Upon Alaska our future may well rest." These were the words of General Henry H. Arnold, who like his predecessor, Billy Mitchell, termed Alaska the "most strategic place on earth."

Alaska's national defense position is plain to all. Its industry, agriculture, service trades, and professions must be developed to back up the defense plans of the Army, Air Force, and Navy.

Of equal importance is Alaska's economic future: the great contribution it can make to the Nation, to every citizen of these United States.

Its forests, arable lands, fish and wildlife, oil and minerals, recreational paradises, hydroelectrical power sites represent wealth beyond man's comprehension—potential wealth greater than our national debt. Already $3,000,000,000 has been taken out of the Territory by haphazard development under the absentee landlord system, dollars that have not been returned to lay the foundation for the Alaska of tomorrow.

No man knows the value of Alaska's hidden mineral wealth; however, Alaska's billion board feet of timber that could be cut in perpetuity, the hundreds of thousands of acres of crops that could be harvested, and the 50,000,000,000 kilowatt-hours of energy that could be produced by river control systems represent a loss to America of more than $1,000,000,000 every year.

Graphs showing the complete potential development pattern for Alaska resources were prepared for this report by various Federal and Territorial agencies. Their purpose is to portray graphically the industrial structure for a self-sufficient and self-supporting geographic area. That the groundwork might be laid for

acquiring a high degree of self-sufficiency in Alaska, these graphs, which are to be found in chapter VII, were prepared from the standpoint of the Territory's ability to provide the required raw materials.

The responsibility for formulating a comprehensive development program and its speedy enactment rests squarely on the shoulders of Congress. In reporting to the House Committee on Public Lands in April 1947 the Honorable J. A. Krug, Secretary of the Interior, said: "The past delay in Alaska's development proved exceedingly costly when the world was plunged into global war. To fortify and protect our giant North Pacific frontier during World War II, we spent about 25 times the amount we originally paid for Alaska. Much of this expense could have been saved had Alaska been a fully developed community."

Tomorrow, in view of the new concepts of polar strategy, the cost might be catastrophic.

The Nation has already witnessed the migration of industry westward during the past decade. As war emergency measures, new industries sprang up almost overnight along the Pacific Coast. Since the end of World War II, industry has, to a certain extent, shifted to the Pacific Northwest where low-cost power is available. Now, the eyes of industry have turned northward and Alaska is directly in line with their sights.

THE NEXT 10 YEARS

Alaska is an economic island. Geographically separated from the United States by hundreds of miles of Canadian wilderness, the Territory is dependent upon the vagaries of sea shipments, implemented by emergency airlift operations, and extremely limited trucking services over the Alaska Highway.

Development of Alaska is largely dependent on shipping at a more reasonable cost. The airplane and highway cannot take care of the heavy movement that is going to be the backbone of Alaska development. Construction of a railway, however, would provide a more substantial means of land transport of greater capacity and reliability.

The present economy of Alaska is out of balance, having been based almost wholly on extractive industries. The Territory cannot expect to further develop on gold and fish alone. Advancement of its economy is contingent on full utilization of resources now undeveloped.

Statehood for Alaska is another factor which would speed development of its economy. As a Territory, its legislature is extremely limited in the scope of its activities. For example, it is unable to undertake long range programs since it cannot authorize bonded indebtedness, nor create any debt; it cannot even assume indebtedness for the actual running expenses of the Territory in excess of the actual income for a given year.

During hearings for Alaska statehood before the House Committee on Public Lands, the Honorable J. A. Krug, Secretary of the Interior, emphasized: "If we were to defer the grant of statehood to Alaska, we would retard development of an area which cries for development. We must allow Alaska to become self-sufficient, not only for its own sake, but also so that it can pay its own way and take over the present administrative responsibilities of the Federal Government in the Territory . . . Alaska has suffered for many years under what is virtually a colonial system that has encouraged absentee exploitation of its natural resources without leaving enough social and economic benefits for the Territory. If Alaska is granted statehood, its people will have more to say about their economic as well as their political destiny. Absentee interests . . . will find it more difficult to dominate the economy of the area.

"I believe that admission of Alaska to the Union as a State is essential to the welfare and to the security of every one of us in the States . . . Alaska needs a tremendously increased population to develop its resources . . . but we cannot get several million people to go to Alaska if we are to deprive them of their rights as citizens when they step across the boundary."

Regarding Alaska's future population, the Federal Inter-Agency Committee on the Development of Alaska in a February 1948 report commented:

"It is not practicable to estimate now the population that Alaska can support when fully developed. Far too little is known definitely about many of the factors that will affect its population capacity. Appraisals have been made, however, of the increase that may be expected in the next few years under a suitable plan and program for Alaskan development. The results are indicated for the several divisions of Alaska on two bases—an assumed minimum basis and an assumed maximum basis.

"The growth actually made in the period indicated (1940–52) will depend in large part on the scope and vigor of the action taken by the Government in support of Alaskan development. Inadequate support would restrict growth. Vigorous support, in keeping with the national interests at stake, might permit growth in 5 years beyond the upper limit assumed.

"Estimated distribution of population in Alaska assuming both a 100,000 increase and a 200,000 increase in population during the period 1948 to 1952 is projected as follows:

TABLE 28.—*Estimated distribution of population*

Area	Distribution assuming a 100,000 increase		Distribution assuming a 200,000 increase	
	Increase	*Total*	*Increase*	*Total*
First division_____	27, 000	54, 000	52, 000	79, 000
Second division_____	3, 000	16, 000	8, 000	21, 000
Third division_____	40, 000	74, 000	80, 000	114, 000
Fourth division_____	30, 000	50, 000	60, 000	80, 000
Total_____	100, 000	194, 000	200, 000	294, 000

An inventory and possible utilization of Alaska natural wealth to sustain a tremendous increase in population appears on the following pages. Once development is given the proper impetus, thousands of pioneers, the men and women who will develop its resources, will move westward to Alaska. Old cities will grow larger and new cities will spring up where formerly only totems stood.

FISHERIES

The North Pacific Coast fisheries of North America, shared by the United States and Canada, represent one of the great food resources of the world. The potential of this fishing area, the majority of which lies in Alaska, is immense. It is a commendable and fortunate circumstance that in its exploitation and development these two nations have coordinated their administrative and conservation effort to set a pattern of international cooperation.

This spirit of international cooperation is of the utmost importance to the future of a great portion of Alaska's fisheries, since the International Fisheries Commission regulates not only halibut fishing seasons for various areas in the North Pacific, but also limits the total catch as well as the size and character of fishing appliances.

The International Pacific Salmon Fisheries Commission was formed with its immediate objective being development of the sockeye salmon fishery in and tributary to the Fraser River. Prior to regulating this area, salmon catches dropped from more than 2,000,000 cases in 1913 to about 300,000 in just 20 years. Although this fishery is located in Canada, it is important since it is shared by both Canadian and American fishermen.

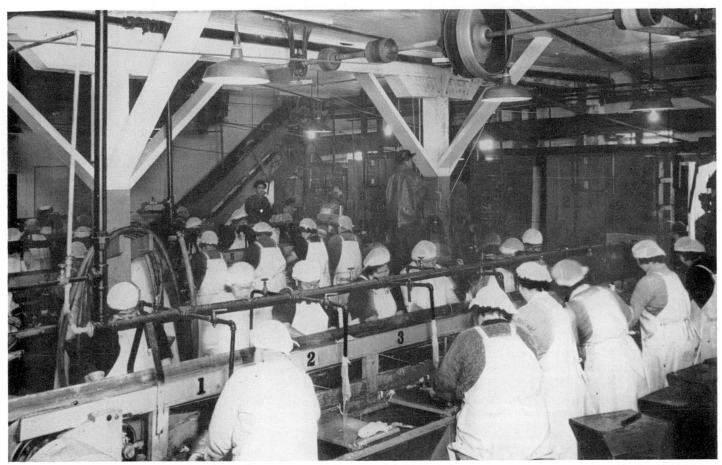

Indian women cleaning salmon at Metlakatla.   Salmon by-products now wasted are worth millions of dollars a year.

many Alaska fishermen participating in its harvest. Not all problems have been solved or are capable of ready solution, but the success of steps already taken augurs well for the future of North Pacific fisheries. The fishing areas are far flung. They stretch from the coast to Oregon to the tip of the Aleutian Islands and beyond to the Bering Sea, and into the unexploited waters of the Arctic Ocean.

The administration of sea fisheries is a Federal responsibility, and in various parts of the world nations have associated in agreements and undertakings for purposes of scientific investigations, but nowhere, except in the fishing regions of the Pacific shores of Canada and Alaska, have two nations so successfully collaborated in the regulation and utilization of their basic fishery resources.

The importance of this international cooperation to Alaska's economy is emphasized by the fact that fisheries have attained the greatest degree of development of any of the Territory's vast resources.

Some economists have stated that Alaska's fisheries have reached the stage of over-development; that the industry is capable of no further expansion. Despite this pessimistic attitude, close examination of capabilities of the industry reveals further expansion is not only possible, but desirable for new canning and other manufacturing processes. Certain enterprises are now possible with only limited capital.

It is true there is little likelihood the canned salmon pack, the fisheries' largest industry, will increase. Many new boats, technological advancement in canning, improved methods of transportation and supply, and an eager market for salmon in all forms have contributed to intensive exploitation that has progessively depleted the various salmon runs. The task now is one primarily of restoration and management in order to bring back a supply more nearly commensurate with normal levels.

However, the majority of formulas now used by the industry in canning salmon are not only archaic but also unreasonably wasteful from the standpoint of national economy. According to present methods and processes, about 30 percent of the fish parts, including heads, tails, intestines and fish eggs are thrown into the sea. This waste amounts to an estimated 120,000,000 pounds annually.

Part of the waste material would be suitable for canning of fish chowder, outlined in detail in the agri-

Indian cannery at Klawock.

cultural section of this chapter, and much of the remainder for badly needed fertilizers for farm use. Dried meal is a rich source of nitrogen and phosphorous, two elements most essential for growing Alaska crops.

It has been estimated that there are sufficient vitamin "A" units contained in fish waste material to supply one-tenth of present United States requirements, and enough vitamin "D" units to supply one-twentieth. In addition, oil extracted from this waste has considerable commercial value in manufacture of paints and varnishes, tanning processes, oil cloths and linoleum, and as a lubricating agency in the cutting and cooling of metals. Experiments made in 1948 indicate the waste, when ground and frozen, makes an excellent animal feed for fur farms.

Fish eggs—the roe of salmon, rock cod, gray cod, and herring—now have little commercial value. These items would find a lucrative caviar market in the eastern United States. Salmon roe makes an excellent caviar and although good reports were received on the few shipments which have been made, this phase of the industry has never been fully developed. Opportunity also exists in the salmon egg field for preparation of bait for sport fishermen.

Immense quantities of salmon heads are discarded each year, leaving open the possibility for canning these heads. Experts have pronounced them most tasty. National markets would have to be developed since squeamishness is felt in most sections of the United States regarding use of fish heads. They would be suitable for export to the majority of foreign countries where their use is common.

Alaska's herring fisheries offer much opportunity for development. Less than 5 percent of the Nation's domestic consumption is supplied by Alaska. In 1938, the United States imported 75,000,000 pounds of pickled, salted, smoked, and kippered herring valued at $6,000,000 from Scotland, Norway, Iceland, Newfoundland, and Canada. That year, Alaska's herring catch, almost identical in weight, reduced to oil and meal, was valued at only $2,000,000. It is estimated that revival of the herring industry to 1915–20 levels would provide 500 saltery workers with employment, 40,000 man-hours annually for longshore labor, 500 man-hours in salt handling, 10,000 man-hours in salt manufacturing 50,000 man-hours in manufacture of containers, about $175,000 to transportation companies, and a substantial amount for gear manufacture and boat repair and building.

Some indication of potential development in this industry can be seen by examining British Columbia fisheries, where herring ranks second to salmon. In the Canadian Province about 1,000,000 cases of herring are canned annually in 20 coastal canneries. No herring is canned in Alaska.

Other opportunities for development are as prominent in Alaska's fisheries. Quick-freezing may revolutionize the industry by developing more attractive packaging; making new species available or old species more tasty, including development of specialty products.

Present demands by exclusive hotels, clubs, and similar establishments warrant further development of salmon specialties such as smoked salmon and its associated products. Fancy packing and special merchandising, including careful selection of high quality fish would permit a product of this type to be marketed at over-market prices. This would also apply to smoked sablefish or black cod.

Another possibility is the canning of fish balls, prepared from halibut, salmon, flounder, black cod, and others, as a specialty item.

Little has been accomplished in developing the bottom fishing industry for cod, red snapper, sole, flounders, and others. This field offers exceptional opportunities for future expansion as tremendous quantities of these fish are to be found over a wide area. Through proper merchandising, these species could be packaged as a quick-freeze food product.

Octopus tentacles are exceptionally tasty and it is possible that through proper promotion a market could be established for this product. Quick-freezing, attractive packaging, and a special trade name would be important factors in marketing such a product.

The basking shark is another unexploited resource in Alaskan waters. Possessing an enormous vitamin-rich liver, this shark is gaining recognition with marked reductions in soupfin shark catches off the coasts of Washington, Oregon, and California. Its meat is also palatable, and although a few years ago one concern planned to market 1,000,000 pounds of Alaska shark meat per month, actual entrance by the company into the industry never occurred. The opportunity to develop this fishery is still open.

Expansion is also possible in crab, clam and shrimp industries since these shell-fish are found in abundance in most regions of Alaska. The Government now encourages growers to experiment with oyster culture by granting leases to tidelands desired for this purpose. Results of several attempts to cultivate Pacific (Japanese) oysters have been disappointing in Southeastern Alaska. The water, it is believed, is too cold for natural spawning and the rate of growth of planted meat is too slow to be profitable. Improved techniques may eventually produce better results as initial efforts have not been too determined.

Considering the zeal with which abalone is sought in California, excellent opportunity exists for exploitation of this marine delicacy. Abalones are very numerous along the rocky shorelines of Southeastern Alaska which are removed from all dilution of fresh water. These "Green" abalones are smaller than the California species but they possess the same fine flavor.

Various types of shells can be utilized in manufacture of curios, souvenirs, buttons, and other products. Demand for these products would grow proportionately with Alaska's tourist trade.

A valuable crop to be harvested from the sea is seaweed. Rough estimates place the area of Southeastern Alaska seaweed beds at 150 square miles, capable of producing 600,000 tons of potash annually. In addition to potash, iodine, agar-agar, and other products can be manufactured from seaweed. Seaweed is now being harvested in British Columbia.

A virgin field for pickled specialties such as pickled salmon, herring, kelp, and sea cucumbers is open for development. Many Alaskan women preserve kelp pickles and relishes which are not only delicious but also easy to prepare. However, here again is another case where a market would have to be developed.

Whaling, which once flourished in Alaska, went into eclipse with the advent of petroleum, steel, and plastics. As a result, whales have regained a measure of their former abundance in Alaskan waters and fishery experts state they now could support a sizeable operation if the market offered sufficient incentive. Interest in whaling on the Pacific Coast is actually reawakening with the opening of one whaling station in northern California and another on the Queen Charlotte Islands in British Columbia.

The high market value of salmon made possible the early utilization of their runs wherever found, but extreme isolation of the more northerly and westerly points made unprofitable the development of lesser fisheries. New cold storage plants on the Alaska Peninsula and Kodiak Island are now expanding the halibut fishery farther westward. Several concerns are pioneering the area with refrigerator ships that can stay on isolated grounds until a full cargo of fish or crabs is caught.

The Fish and Wildlife Service has sponsored exploratory fishing expeditions into northern and western waters and demonstrated that commercial quantities of king crab and bottom fish exist over much of the region.

The Bering Sea is an extensive, shallow sea with a muddy bottom, receiving a great amount of discharge from the land and is therefore well-suited to a tremendous production of fish life. No commercial fishing is now carried on in this area.

With the inevitable growing demand for seafood products and the gradual solution of problems of transportation and storage, there can be no doubt that important fisheries will ultimately develop in these remote areas.

What portends to contribute greatly to the entire fishing industry is trawling which is just coming into prominence in the Pacific despite the fact it is one of the oldest fishing methods on the Atlantic Coast. The quantity of trawl-caught fish off the coasts of Washington and Oregon has increased more than 200 times during the past 15 years. The Bering Sea has been described as the largest trawlable body of water in the world. The Gulf of Alaska has barely been touched. It has been estimated that 1,000,000,000 pounds of fish per year could be trawled from the North Pacific. A Fish and Wildlife Service expert reported several years ago that trawling "may be one of the major, if not the major, fishing industry in Alaska waters in the future."

New methods, new products, new fisheries, and new areas hold promise of boosting the value of Alaska's fisheries far beyond its present $115,000,000 annual mark, creating additional employment as well as more permanent employment for thousands of Alaskans.

WILDLIFE RESOURCES

Although contingent on many things, Alaska's wild-life resources can make a valuable contribution to the Territory's economy. For continued production of an annual wildlife crop, better management is the foremost need. Only extensive management, however, is feasible for the greater part of Alaska. In broad terms, there does not appear to be a place for the intensive type of wildlife management now practiced on the quail planta-tions of the Southern States or the grouse moors of England and Scotland.

Since management must be on an extensive basis, the success of any program is largely dependent on educa-tion. Conservation education is needed for young and old alike. Today's grade-school boys will be tomor-row's active hunters, fishermen, and trappers.

Not all adults are good conservationists. The good trapper, for example, has learned to trap his line con-servatively year after year. The poor trapper takes everything he can from the trapline and has to move to a new location the following year.

The major requirements for effective conservation of wildlife are outlined below:

(1) An extensive type of management of the wildlife resource, adapted to the needs of the resource and the people, is needed.

(2) Conservation education, including visual aids such as slides, cartoons, movies, charts, and teaching aids for use in schools, should be initiated.

(3) Because of Alaska's increased civilian and mil-itary population an aggressive and well-coordinated enforcement program for control of the human element, is required. Additional field stations have been planned by the Fish and Wildlife Service at Kotzebue, Bethel, Barrow, Fort Yukon, Ruby, Cold Bay, Tok Junction, Nome, Kodiak, Palmer, Glenallen, and Yakutat.

(4) Better utilization of the wildlife crop can be attained through elimination of waste with animals taken for sport, fur, or special uses. More attention should be paid to harvesting many species of this crop when their numbers are at the peak of a cycle. For example, many more grouse or snowshoe hare could be taken at cyclic peaks of abundance. The utilization of certain age or sex groups of various animals should not be overlooked. For example, some bull elk and bachelor bull bison contribute nothing to the herd and could be harvested.

Processing and Manufacturing

Commercial tanning and processing of pelts in Alaska should be explored. Native-tanned furs, though interesting to the tourist and satisfactory for many pur-poses, are objectionable to commercial markets because of their odor. Alaska pelts must now be sent to the United States for soft tanning and then shipped back to the Territory for manufacture. The Alaska Native Service has made a start in this direction by training young natives in commercial tanning methods.

Possibilities for extracting tannin from Alaska trees such as western hemlock, Sitka spruce, and black spruce barks should also be investigated. This has been con-sidered by the Forest Service, although it would not be a large item in proposed logging and timber utilization program. Bark from logs rafted in salt water loses much of the tannic acid, so it is possible interior Alaska forests will be found more suitable for this purpose than those of Southeastern Alaska.

Manufacture in Alaska of finished fur garments, gloves and slippers, and other products is another eco-nomic opportunity now only partially developed. The difficulty of competing with established "name" con-cerns in the field of fine furs in the United States mar-kets might be overcome through proper promotion of a "Made-in-Alaska" trademark. Processing of rough furs such as moose, caribou, wolf, and coyote also ap-pears feasible.

Establishment of special areas of critical importance to the wildlife resource have been proposed for more intensive management. Requiring land withdrawals, they will be similar to wildlife refuges. However, as management units they will not become inviolate sanc-tuaries for all species, but only for those requiring pro-tection. Proposals include the Morzhovoi Bay area near the tip of the Alaska Peninsula, an important waterfowl area, the Innoko River area, the Big Delta area, and Simeonof Island, a sea otter island.

The wolf and coyote control program may require expansion in critical areas such as reindeer, mountain sheep and caribou ranges. Competition between other species must be evaluated and an action program initi-ated where necessary. Examples of this type of com-petition include beavers and salmon, Kodiak bears and salmon, reindeer and muskoxen, and moose and black bears.

Alaska is an excellent geographic area for fur farm-ing. At the present time the 75 fur farms in the Terri-tory produce about 2 percent of the ranched fur crop of the United States and its possessions. Expansion of the industry is wholly dependent on market conditions.

Alaska has made several attempts to have part of the proceeds from annual sales of Pribilof Island fur seal pelts by the Federal Government returned to the Terri-tory but have always been unsuccessful, although Great Britain returned its share to Canada many years ago. In 1947 the pelts were sold for more than $2,000,000. More significant than just a share of the returns to

Alaska, would be establishment of the tanning industry in Alaska to process the pelts.

It appears incongruous to have a resource, taken in the most westward region of Alaska, shipped thousands of miles to the central portion of the United States for processing. Establishment of this industry in Alaska would be a valuable addition to further development of the Territory's economy.

MINERALS AND MINING

There are numerous reasons why such little progress has been recorded in this industry. Principally, inadequate transportation facilities to and within the Territory have resulted in such a high-cost operation that only the highest grade properties can be worked profitably.

Because of its high unit value, gold has been the major metal produced. Production of other metals and minerals is needed to stabilize the industry. With gold being the major metal produced, the mining industry is not now on a sufficiently firm basis to maintain a permanent economy.

A second reason for this comparative nondevelopment of the mining industry is the lack of knowledge of geological conditions and other data and information concerning mineral deposits. Only 0.3 percent of

Prospecting is hard work and uncertain of rewards but vital to the Nation.

More prospecting. Prime needs are access roads and an incentive system.

988410—52——8

Alaska has been mapped on scales sufficient to permit detailed analysis of geological features that pertain to mineral exploration. Only an additional 3.2 percent has been mapped on a scale adequate for even semi-detailed analysis of such features. Exploratory geologic maps cover about 45 percent of Alaska, but 51 percent has not yet been mapped geologically. This area is comparable in size to Maine, New Hampshire, Vermont, Massachusetts, Rhode Island, Connecticut, New York, New Jersey, Pennsylvania, Ohio, Michigan, and Illinois combined.

It is only natural that the principal role in advancing the mining industry should fall directly upon those who are engaged in mining activities. The continued responsibility for developing new mineral deposits falls directly upon private enterprise. Present market prices of many metals and minerals justifies their development and private industry should consider with due diligence their production in Alaska.

Viewed in the light of long-term needs, one hope of replenishing and augmenting national mineral resources lies in the discovery of new mining districts by geological, geophysical, and geochemical methods. Improvements in mining and metallurgical techniques have made possible the handling of low-grade ores and tailings that would not have been considered a few years ago.

Because gold has always been the predominant factor in development of the mining industry, many other valuable minerals have been passed over in the course of prospective activities. This type of prospecting has contributed little to the overall mineral knowledge of Alaska.

The prospector is to mining what the farmer is to agriculture. Without him the industry cannot endure. A serious situation faces the industry in Alaska today: the prospector has virtually vanished due to lack of encouragement. The Territorial Department of Mines is keenly aware of this need and has drafted several prospector incentive programs. However, with exception of a trial amounting to experiment during the war, none has been placed in operation for lack of funds. In the immediate future the exploitation of many minerals may be hastened by industrial expansion along the Pacific Coast—Washington, Oregon, and California—or until development within Alaska makes possible their local utilization.

Development and availability of low-cost hydroelectric power would assist in unlocking some of Alaska's vast mineral resources. Low-cost power would enable the mining and refining of raw materials in Alaska for subsequent shipping by boat to Pacific Coast markets to compete favorably with transcontinental rail deliveries.

No geographical entity has ever attained lasting industrial greatness through extractive industries alone. To whatever extent integration is possible—from the extraction of raw materials to the manufacture of semi-finished or finished products—to that extent will Alaska achieve a place in the industrialization of the North American continent.

It is to be noted that in 1945 Alaska imported $5,998,000 in nonmetallic mine products and exported none. It imported $8,298,000 in iron and steel manufactured products such as bars and rods, structural steel, pipe, nails, etc., and exported no ferrous ore. It imported $125,000 in copper and manufactured products and exported $1,000 in copper ore. It imported $1,788,000 in chemicals and exported none.

It is likewise significant that during this same year the United States imported $337,407,000 in nonmetallics. Ferro-alloy imports amounted to $59,979,000 and nonferrous imports at $481,084,000.

The shortage of ferro-alloys and nonferrous minerals in the States is depicted in export statistics. Export of ferro-alloys dropped from $13,392,000 in 1940 to $3,701,000 in 1945, while nonferrous exports dropped from $137,421,000 to $110,810,000 during the same period.

NONMETALLICS

It is difficult to over-estimate the importance of the mineral industry to the general welfare and development of Alaska. The success of many new industries may be directly contingent upon local development of minerals previously deemed valueless. For instance, there will be an immediate interest in paper clays (barite), talc, sulphur, and other raw materials when the pulp and paper industry is developed in Southeastern Alaska. Few persons are aware that to produce this sheet of paper requires the use, in some way or another, of limestone, salt, gypsum, talc, and even the lowly sandstone and clay.

Alaskan agricultural scientists have pointed out the critical need for fertilizers if Alaska is to make the best use of its agricultural land and show a substantial increase in crop production. Phosphates are particularly in demand. A diligent search might reveal sources of raw minerals for fertilizer manufacture. Alaskan imports of 5-10-10 fertilizer in 1947 totaled about 1,000,000 pounds, an average of approximately 100 pounds per acre of cropland harvested. An average application of 200 pounds per acre would be twice the present use, but only half the amount recommended by agricultural authorities. On the basis of 200 pounds per acre and one acre of cropland per capita, total fertilizer requirements for land to supply a population of

Juneau gold mill, Alaska's biggest lode operation.

100,000 would be 20,000,000 pounds each year, and for a population of 600,000 would be 120,000,000 pounds each year.

There is a possibility that Alaska lignite deposits can also be used for agricultural purposes. Black coal dust spread over snow-covered fields accelerates thawing of snow and facilitates preparation of ground, advancing planting from 10 to 14 days, according to experiments conducted by Dr. Basil M. Bensin, agronomist. In addition, lignite dust could be applied to garden crops during the growing season to increase absorption of heat by the soil and stimulate the growth of plants.

Some of the nonmetallics such as building stone, gravel and road ballast, limestone and clays, which have low unit value in proportion to their weight, have already been developed on a limited commercial scale. Ultimately these almost inexhaustible materials may even become more valuable than all of the other mineral products.

Low-cost fabrication of these nonmetallics into building materials would provide the impetus so badly in the construction field in Alaska today. Production of such materials would increase the demand for more and better homes and businesses as well as civic improvements—all of which encourage permanent rather than seasonal residences. Production of building materials in Alaska is a paramount need of both military and civilian interests. If Alaska industry is to expand on a healthy economic basis, full utilization of these resources is necessary.

A modern cement plant should be constructed immediately in Alaska. Currently, Alaska uses 250,000 barrels annually. This figure is conservative as it does not consider that the high cost of cement compels builders in the railbelt to substitute less expensive construction materials. Present cost of cement delivered to users in Anchorage ranges from $52.50 to $55 a ton. In Fairbanks the cost is $56 a ton in carload lots. A single sack costs $4.

Federal and Territorial agencies in a recent preliminary study determined that the most promising location for a cement plant is near Mile 323 of the Alaska Railroad on the Alaska Range divide. The availability of suitable raw materials in the immediate vicinity is now being investigated. With an initial plant capacity of 350,000 barrels, selling price would vary between $25

Gold placer mining with dredge and hydraulic stream.   Gold is Alaska's second major industry.

and $35 a ton depending upon degree of total capacity used. If cement is made available at these prices, the demand would far exceed total capacity of the contemplated plant.

Petroleum is yet another untapped resource of Alaska. The United States first learned of the possibilities of oil fields in the Arctic in 1886 when oil seepages were reported at Cape Simpson, 50 miles east of Barrow.

Reports of oil in the Arctic regions of Alaska caused President Warren G. Harding to sign a directive in 1923 creating the 35,000-square mile Naval Petroleum Reserve No. 4—the world's largest oil claim, half the size of the State of Oklahoma. Faced with a serious outlook on the national petroleum scene, the United States Navy commenced exploratory and developmental work in the area in August 1944.

The first extensive report of the Navy's petroleum operation to be made public was presented to a special subcommittee on Petroleum of the Armed Services Committee of the House of Representatives early in 1948 by Commodore W. G. Greenman, USN, Director of Naval Petroleum Reserves.

"We have not found oil in commercial quantities in the Reserve, although almost everywhere we have gone with the drill we have penetrated sands containing oil," Commodore Greenman reported. "In addition to the numerous oil and gas seepages widely scattered over the Reserve, we have found oil sand in three wells on the Umiat structure in the southeast, one of which produces 24 barrels per day of extremely rich oil, and also in a third well and in several core holes at Cape Simpson, 150 miles to the northwest of the Arctic Coast."

Commodore Greenman optimistically concluded his statement: "Indications are all as favorable as have been found before drilling in the majority of the oil fields that have been found in the world. If explora-

tions had not been pushed under such conditions, then none of the oil fields of the world would have been found."

Dr. W. E. Wrather, Director of the Geological Survey, confirmed the Commodore's statement with: "The Geological Survey is of the unequivocal opinion that Naval Petroleum Reserve No. 4 offers possibilities for developing significant quantities of oil. This opinion is based upon the information acquired through the relatively generalized exploration to date and the analogy of conditions thus far determined with major oil-producing provinces elsewhere."

In the event that pools of sufficient size to warrant development are found, engineers have already roughed out pipelines, highways, and possible railways linking the fields with interior Alaska, and eventually the ice-free coast of the Gulf of Alaska.

Oil shales, assaying from 50 to 100 gallons and over per ton, are known to occur near the mouth of the Noatak River. Investigation of the extent of the shale bodies has not been sufficient to determine the probable quantity of shale oil that could be extracted from the deposits.

Director James Boyd of the Bureau of Mines recently pointed out that the United States is using more oil today than the entire world used in 1938 and in 1947 consumption reached 608 gallons for every man, woman and child in the country. The United States now depends on foreign sources for much of its oil. In event of an emergency, it is entirely possible that these life-lines could be severed overnight. Alaska would be in an especially tight position for oil supplies.

The importance to Alaska of production of petroleum and petroleum products cannot be over-emphasized. Alaska's present consumption is almost 13,000 barrels per day. Estimates for several years hence, exceed 30,000 barrels per day for civilian and military consumption. It is expected that only one-third of the demand will be in Southeastern and Southwestern Alaska including the Aleutian Islands while the principal demand will be from Kenai Peninsula northward including Anchorage and the Fairbanks area.

So vital are these requirements that production of synthetic oil and gas from Alaska coal is now being considered by Federal agencies. Three areas in general are being considered, namely, near Homer, on the Kenai Peninsula, Matanuska Valley, and Healy Creek near the north boundary of McKinley National Park. There may prove to be justification for construction of at least one plant.

Although Alaska's total coal resources are in excess of 110,000,000,000 tons, mostly in the lower rank coals, Alaskans imported $464,000 in coal during 1945. However, to a limited extent Alaska has taken advantage of this resource. Coal production ranks third in produced wealth of Alaska's minerals.

Another of the nonmetallics of importance is the production of precious and semiprecious gems and manufacture of jewelry. Appreciable deposits of jade and small deposits of other gems may be found in Alaska. The value of gem stones to the mining industry as a whole can be seen in the fact that during 1945, the United States imported $127,293,000 in precious stones and imitations and $19,572,000 in finished jewelry and plated ware. Nothing was exported from Alaska. A prime example of the value that could be added by processing raw materials in Alaska is the cutting and polishing of jade. Alaskans export raw jade and receive about $6 a pound. Cut into small pieces and polished for mounting into jewelry, it is worth more than $250.

In the Kobuk River region, north of the Arctic Circle, tremolite and chrysotile asbestos have been discovered. Investigations in the area have not been conclusive enough to determine extent of the reserve. One ton of long slip fiber chrysotile and 47 tons of high-grade tremolite were exported to the United States early in 1946. Other deposits have been found in central and southeastern Alaska.

METALLICS

In the metallic field, Alaska has much to contribute to the national wealth. Of known domestic occurrences of tin and highgrade chromite, the most promising are in Alaska. Alaska provides the major domestic source of platinum for the United States.

In addition, there are occurrences of copper, lead, zinc, antimony, titanium, mercury, molybdenum, graphite, iron, tungsten, and others throughout Alaska.

Although placer mines outnumber lode operations in Alaska, recovery of byproduct metals and minerals from river and sea beaches has not yet reached a stage comparable to similar operations in the States. Dredges and hydraulic operations have been concentrated on gold recovery and have paid little attention to byproduct recovery of other valuable metals. Among these metals and minerals which are found in placer sands are: silver, copper, mercury, cassiterite, chromite, chrysoberyl, columbite, ilmenite, magnetite, monazite, tungsten, and a wide variety of gem stones. Thus it is apparent that the value of Alaska's mineral output should increase appreciably when more attention is paid by present placer operations to byproduct recovery of other minerals.

The controlling factor in operation of placer properties is availability of water. Low streams in the late summer months force many operations to close from days to weeks before freezeup. Vast quantities of water are needed in the permafrost regions—the sub-

Hydraulic placer operation. Gold mining is a thirsty business in Alaska.

Frozen ground being cold-water thawed for dredging.

Arctic and Arctic areas of Alaska. In order to work these permanently frozen properties, the ground must be thawed a year in advance of operations. Alaska mining engineers have learned that the best method of preparing the ground is by the use of cold-water thaw. In this method, cold water is pumped into a series of holes which have been drilled to bedrock. Use of steam and other methods have proved unsatisfactory.

The importance of placer operations in the general mining picture of the Territory cannot be discounted. Low-cost power would permit dredges to work low-grade ground which now must be passed over in view of the high cost of operation. Equally as important is the storage of water in these placer areas and its diversion to major operational locations.

Rare metals such as tantalum and columbium are known to occur in the Territory. With the United States taking rapid strides into the Atomic Age, the possibility of Alaska as a source for radioactive materials cannot be ignored.

Alaska's mineral wealth awaits orderly development. The United States, faced with a dwindling supply of strategic metals and minerals, is largely dependent on foreign sources for a supply of these materials. Any one of several factors—war or political powers unfriendly to the United States—could cut off supply of the "have-not" minerals. Alaska may eventually supply some of the wants of the Nation. A higher degree of processing or manufacture in the Territory should

be encouraged. It must be borne in mind that strengthening Alaska's economy is as important to the United States as its defense bases which ring the continent.

TABLE 29.—*United States (excluding Alaska) imports and exports of nonmetallics and metallics*

[In thousands of dollars]

	Imports		Exports	
	1940	1945	1940	1945
Nonmetallics, total_____	137, 176	337, 407	466, 369	1, 090, 167
Coal and related fuels_____	4, 426	3, 024	66, 745	198, 188
Stone, cement, lime_	3, 564	7, 534	2, 528	16, 543
Petroleum and products_____	47, 654	152, 340	345, 619	751, 584
Clay and clay products_____	9, 515	7, 544	9, 449	22, 406
Glass and glass products_____	6, 102	1, 263	10, 310	36, 193
Others_____	21, 466	38, 408	31, 718	65, 254
Precious stones and Imitations_____	44, 034	127, 293	(*)	(*)
Metallics, total_____	209, 283	541, 063	150, 813	114, 511
Ferro-alloys_____	25, 513	59, 979	13, 392	3, 701
Nonferrous_____	183, 770	481, 084	137, 421	110, 810
Chemicals, total_____	79, 662	144, 222	153, 099	414, 314
Coal tars_____	15, 501	11, 882	16, 297	35, 164
Medicinal_____	4, 847	9, 966	20, 208	115, 844
Industrial_____	19, 036	37, 894	32, 888	90, 873
Pigments, paints___	1, 605	1, 053	20, 638	30, 799
Fertilizers_____	35, 250	41, 327	17, 676	18, 259
Explosives_____	621	37, 703	7, 203	16, 430
Soap, toiletries_____	2, 801	4, 396	9, 007	28, 529

*Included above.

A billion board feet of lumber a year could be harvested in perpetuity.

TABLE 30.—*Alaska imports and exports of nonmetallics and metallics*

[In thousands of dollars]

	Imports	Exports
Nonmetallics, total	5, 998	None
Coal	464	
Petroleum and products	4, 655	
Cement	113	
Glass	243	
Clay and clay products	211	
Others	312	
Metallics:		
Copper and copper products	125	1
Iron (bars, pipe, nails, etc.)	8, 298	None
Chemicals	1, 788	None

TIMBER PRODUCTS

Among Alaska's various sources of national wealth, its forests offer a potential for immediate development. There are approximately 1,000,000,000 board feet of commercial timber each year ready and waiting for the fallers' ax in Alaska's southeastern coastal forests.

Production of Alaska's forest products is awaited by an ever-growing market. There is a tremendous demand for wood products in the United States and abroad. Demand within a growing Alaska itself is no small item. Newspapers, magazines, and printing establishments must now depend, to a large extent, on foreign pulp production to meet their paper require-

ments. Demand for pulp for other uses, including rayon and plastics is also steadily increasing. To meet this mounting demand, American capital has been invested in Canada to build pulp and paper mills as the Pacific Northwest and other United States forests have been cut far more rapidly than they can be reproduced. Now, because of Canadian forest conservation policies, production of present pulp mills and establishment of new ones is limited. Canadian efforts fall far short of supplying demands within the United States. Against this fast-dwindling supply Alaska offers its huge coastal forests, now rotting for want of use but capable of providing a billion board feet of timber annually— now and forever. United States imports of wood and paper products from foreign sources increased from $261,779,000 in 1940 to $393,812,000 in 1945.

Establishment of the pulp and paper industry in the Tongass National Forest offers an immediate opportunity for development. Preliminary investigations indicate there is sufficient timber and waterpower available to supply five or six pulp and paper mills of 500-ton daily capacity. It has been estimated that this forest can furnish enough timber and waterpower to manufacture 1,000,000 tons of newsprint every year in perpetuity, on a sustained forest yield basis. The Forest Service has already approved a contract for establish-

Timber that falls and rots—millions in wealth lost forever.

ment of a pulp mill near Ketchikan. Active interest is also being shown in the location of similar mills at Sitka, Thomas Bay, and other points in Southeastern Alaska.

The total annual production of Tongass National Forest would supply almost 25 percent of the annual newsprint requirements of the United States press. In addition, large quantities of paper are needed annually by the Government Printing Office. In 1947, the Joint Senate-House Committee on Printing reported that in the last quarter of 1946 it was estimated that the Public Printer would need 40,000,000 pounds of paper to meet actual known demands for that period as compared with 21,500,000 pounds for the last quarter of 1939. The enormous Government demand is further illustrated by the fact that income tax forms for 1947 required printing of 665,705,000 blanks of various sizes requiring a total of 5,620,000 pounds, or 40 carloads of paper. At the time of making its report, the committee pointed out that Alaska offered the sole remaining untapped source of newsprint under the American flag.

Once the hungry domestic market is satisfied, there is the growing literacy of the Orient—which will demand more paper for books, magazines, and newsprint. As it has been previously pointed out, Alaska is closer— closer by hundreds of miles—to the markets of the Orient than is the continental coast of the United States proper, including the paper-producing regions of British Columbia.

Gulf state markets and other sections of the Atlantic seaboard can be reached from Alaska by water shipments through the Panama Canal.

Establishment of the pulp and paper industry in Alaska would give great impetus to the economic development of the Territory. Its operation would mean wise and profitable use of one of Alaska's vast, untapped natural resources. With an industry providing year-round employment, many Alaskans would be insured a regular rather than seasonal income. The enterprise would attract new and permanent settlers to Alaska. Population would grow in a way that is not now possible. It has been estimated that establishment of 6 pulp and paper mills would result in 16,800 new jobs and a population increase of more than 50,000 persons in Southeastern Alaska.

The pulp and paper industry would require an adequate network of roads and general improvements in all transportation facilities. More service and recreational industries would follow. There would be more interest in developing Alaska's agricultural potentialities; an unwillingness to depend longer on imported foodstuffs and other necessities.

It is evident these general improvements would not come overnight. The establishment of a single industry would not simultaneously bring prosperity and a balanced economy over the entire Territory. But the initial operation and its success would encourage other industrialists to examine the huge and valuable resources Alaska has to offer.

Geologists expect that pulp wood logging operations will make possible the discovery of important mineral deposits now likely to be hidden in the dense forests by vegetation.

Extensive cutting of pulping timber would make it possible to log all sorts of timber at once—thus immeasurably cutting the logging costs for such specialty timber as Alaska cedar. It would make it possible to produce cedar poles for power and communication lines at lower cost.

High freight rates to Alaska would provide a ready-made tariff for the local producer of furniture. As Alaska's population expands, more and more furniture will be needed. Good furniture can be made from hemlock, spruce, and cedar in Southeastern Alaska and from white birch in the interior.

The possibility also exists for manufacture of woodenware such as bread boards, cutting boards, ironing boards, drain boards, stepladders, bowls, rolling pins, plates, handles, smoking stands, hall trees, et cetera.

Prefabricated log houses would be a valuable addition to new forest industry manufactures. Log buildings are not only adapted to climatic conditions of Alaska, they conform also to the setting. There would be a considerable demand for this type of housing not only for permanent housing but also for tourist resorts and summer cabins.

Although 28,000 squares of shingles were used in Alaska in 1936, only 9 percent were manufactured in Alaska, where the western red cedar is ideal for shingles.

There are almost 6,000 small numbered boats registered in Alaska. In addition, it is estimated the fishing industry uses 287 launches, 349 seine skiffs, 1,046 rowboats and skiffs, 484 lighters and scows, 29 houseboats, 49 pile drivers, 9 pile pullers, and 37 rigging scows in gathering its annual harvest. There are hundreds more vessels, from rowboats to cruisers, owned by the resident population of Southeastern Alaska. Many of these boats could be repaired in Alaska instead of being sent south as is now being done. Hundreds of new skiffs, gillnet boats, seiners, and other type vessels are required annually by the fishing industry. These could be built on Alaska marineways and in Alaska shops. Boatbuilders could use Alaska cedar for decking, planking, et cetera.

Lightweight Sitka spruce could be used for the manufacture of oars, paddles, garden tool handles, broom handles, gaff-hook handles, pike pole handles. and many other purposes.

Sawmills utilize only a fraction of the potential forest yield.

Manufacture of barrels and tierces for packing mild-cured salmon and salted herring would be another potential industry. Currently, these barrels are manufactured in the United States. In prewar 1939, about 11,000 such barrels were used. Spruce and hemlock are ideal for manufacture of this type of barrel.

Toys, curios and novelties made from Alaska wood is another manufacturing possibility which cannot be overlooked. The expected increase in tourist business to Alaska would warrant profitable production of these items in the Territory.

Establishment of a wood preservation plant would be economically feasible. About 60,000 linear feet of treated piling and 2,250,000 board feet of treated lumber are now required annually in the Territory. Treated piling is used in construction of wharves, foundations for industrial waterfront buildings, dolphins, bridges, and trestles. Treated lumber is used for wharf superstructure, bridges, culverts, mining timber, and capping and railroad ties. Potential large users are the Alaska Railroad, White Pass & Yukon Railroad, road building agencies, mining companies, contractors, and others.

Power line cedar poles, now in demand throughout much of the United States, have about reached the vanishing point in the Pacific Northwest. Because of its extreme durability in contact with the soil, western red cedar is one of the best species for poles. The demand would not only make it possible but profitable to export these poles from Southeastern Alaska by boat to the nearest railhead at Prince Rupert, British Columbia, and thence by rail to the Middle Western or Eastern States where such poles are in the greatest demand. Power transmission lines now being studied for construction in Alaska would require within the next few years more than 20,000 poles with a total length exceeding 1,200,000 feet. By 1958, Alaskan power transmission and distribution pole requirements should exceed 10,000 each year.

The potential value of Alaska's forest resources can be seen by examining production and exports of the four Scandinavian countries—Norway, Sweden, Finland, and Denmark. In sawn materials, these countries produced 27 percent of Europe's and 7 percent of the world's supply. They produce one-fifth of the world's total supply of woodpulp, one-third of the cellulose and one-eleventh of the paper. Their exports amounted to 84 percent of the total woodpulp exports of all nations, 71 percent of the cellulose, and 24 percent of the paper.

Alaska's forest industries will be one of the foundation stones of the much-needed industrial development of the Territory, providing a new and vital role for Alaska in the framework of world economy.

AGRICULTURE

> *"Plants stand still until summer rains come."*
>
> *"Irrigations would have permitted me to have my lettuce ready for market 2 weeks earlier."*
>
> *"Lack of water in spring is a limiting factor on pasture."*
>
> *"Insufficient moisture to bring up plants resulted in a failure of my carrot crop."*
>
> *"Would like to irrigate my potatoes."*

Some of Alaska's agricultural lands are as thirsty for water as Alaska's economy is hungry for increased agricultural production. The above quotations are but a few of the expressions made by Alaskan farmers to interviewers conducting a survey in 1948 for the Department of the Interior-Department of Agriculture Committee on Group Settlement in Alaska. Analysis of Alaska's food imports indicates that there is a need and a potential market for a great increase in crop production in the Territory. The following paragraphs explain the pressing need for irrigation, fertilizers, clearing, rural electrification, improved cropping practices, and better seed selection as well as development of new varieties.

Increased Production Through Irrigation

Attainment of increased economic agricultural production on present acreage of Alaska farms is possible through employment of irrigation. The early summer months of May and June, when hours of sunshine are at a maximum, are relatively dry periods in most farming areas. Farmers have repeatedly stated that lack of sufficient moisture during these months has definitely retarded plant growth.

The Territorial Commissioner of Agriculture, G. W. Gasser, reports that while "low precipitation of early summer is not usually detrimental to crop growth in Matanuska Valley, the region has experienced droughts of some severity. In the Tanana Valley, dry weather in late spring and early summer sometimes checks plant growth to such an extent as to cause low yields of cereal crops."

For the Bureau of Reclamation Eklutna (Alaska) Project Report dated October 1948 the Agricultural Experiment Station in Alaska wrote: "Where sufficient water is available for irrigation there is no doubt that crop irrigation will be both possible and profitable. During the dry season in May, June and early July there is always a shortage of precipitation, and the percentage of soil moisture falls to a level so low that crops develop very slowly.

Homestead near Moose Creek showing the hard labor required to clear the land.

"During this period, additions of irrigation water would undoubtedly permit normal growth of plants and increase crop yields. This increase can be conservatively estimated at from 15 to 25 percent, and for market vegetables much more."

Use of water on home gardens has been a common practice in Matanuska and Tanana Valleys. Several commercial gardeners have had experience with irrigation of truck crops. In 1946, one operator irrigated portions of his potato field, the other part was at too high an elevation for application of available water. The irrigated portion yielded 7 tons per acre. The part not irrigated was not worth harvesting.

The above operator stated his belief that where water is available, the increased yield of vegetable crops would pay for a sprinkler system in 1 year under present market conditions. Immature lettuce was sprinkled for 3 nights in September 1948 in an attempt to prevent frost damage. The temperature dropped to 20° F., a coat of ice covered the field but the lettuce remained undamaged and matured during the 2 weeks of warm weather which followed the frost.

Experience to date indicates that irrigation not only increases yields but also extends the growing and marketing season. Those who have used irrigation plan to maintain or increase its use.

Although there is little doubt that irrigation will increase, there is a scarcity of available information concerning the economic feasibility of constructing irrigation systems and its effect on competitive relationship among crop and livestock enterprises in Alaska. Additional information is required regarding the specific effect of irrigation on yields of various crops; the effect of water and soil temperature on the plants' response to irrigation; suitability of glacial water for irrigation; the effect of various methods of application as well as the quantity of water applied on growth of various crops; sources of water supply and the cost of obtaining and supplying water under actual farming conditions in Alaska.

Fertilizers Essential for Economic Production

It is agreed among agriculturists that fertilizers are essential for economic production of crops in Alaska. Their use is expected to increase but much specific information regarding kinds and amounts required is still lacking.

A group of scientists from the Department of Agriculture who made exploratory investigations in 1946 reported: "Most soils in Alaska require fertilizers from

Ultimate reward: farm typical of most in Matanuska Valley.

the start for optimum production. Most farmers, including practically all those growing vegetables and potatoes, now use commercal fertilizers containing phosphate, potash and nitrogen, but only the vaguest notions are available as to the proper ratios and amounts of such fertilizers for the various soils and crops. Low yields suggest there are now great wastes of labor and materials from using inadequate amounts of fertilizers or the wrong mixtures. Use of lime should be investigated, especially in the Matanuska Valley. It is likely that some of the minor elements are necessary for optimum production.

"Particular emphasis needs to be given to studies of the use of nitrogen, because either a deficiency or an excess has an extreme effect on both yield and quality of crops."

A 5-5-10 fertilizer is the most common mixture now used in the Territory. Imports of fertilizer in 1947 totaled about 1,000,000 pounds, an average of almost 100 pounds per acre of cropland harvested. Probably less than half the acreage received fertilizer, most of it being used on potatoes and vegetables which ordinarily receive applications of 500 pounds or more per acre.

Agricultural authorities have recommended a greater use of fertilizer. With rotations which include grass-legume hay, where livestock are kept and the manure used on the land, the following applications were recently suggested: for grain, 200 pounds of 3-12-5; for

potatoes, 600 pounds of 5-10-10 and for hay and pasture, 400 pounds of 5-10-10.

Development farms have proved an effective means of obtaining information regarding irrigation, fertilizer, and crop adaptability on reclamation projects in the United States. These farms are usually operated under lease by practical farmers. The lease contracts provide for the operator's cooperation in conducting specified trials and tests under general supervision of the sponsoring agency.

Part of the farm is set aside for detailed experiments relating to irrigation, crop varieties, fertilizers, rotations, and other factors. These experiments are conducted by competent scientists in various fields and usually involve cooperation among a number of Federal and State agencies. The development farm thus provides both detailed experimental data including practical tests under actual farming conditions. There are many reasons why such farms should be developed in Alaska as it would prove an effective means of assisting in the solution of farm development problems. The need in Alaska is even greater than in the States.

Gap Between Supply and Demand

Food production in Alaska is a matter of great importance to the armed forces. Immediately following the Pearl Harbor attack, Alaska was so vulnerable that men and war supplies were rushed to her defense. Matanuska Valley farmers by almost superhuman efforts were able to furnish much of the necessary food supply in those critical days thus freeing additional shipping space for defense materials. Before any similar emergency again arises, additional agricultural lands should be brought under cultivation and production increased by irrigation wherever needed.

The recent widening of the gap between supply and demand was caused by greatly increased demand rather than by failure to make any increase in agricultural production. The gap may be reduced but not closed entirely by improved practices. Additional crop acreage is required. Developments in communication, transportation, mining, industry, and commerce would bring still greater local demands for products which could be economically produced on Alaska farms.

A portion of the recent increase in demand has been due to the influx of population resulting from the large amount of defense construction and facilities related thereto. This program will probably continue for a few years and will continue to provide a vast market for agricultural products. Should there be a sudden cessation of defense activities, however, it is still not unreasonable to assume that the demand would stay at a high level. The recent impetus which has been given in part by defense activities to housing, transportation, and power facilities, will help in combination with the rich natural resources of the Territory to assure continued growth of population and demand for agricultural production.

Increasing the acreage of cropland is, however, time-consuming and requires investment of considerable capital. In their natural state most of the better agricultural lands are covered with timber. Once the land has been cleared it often takes a year or two to bring it to full productive capacity.

The magnitude of the total investment which is necessary before the first crop can be harvested has been discussed previously. For example, the initial investment in a potato farm for essential improvements, machinery, a normal complement of livestock, land clearing, plus seed potatoes, fertilizer, and labor, might exceed $18,000.

The first year might bring a tragic crop failure. One year out of three, insufficient moisture could turn a potential profit into a real loss. In the Western States, activities of the Bureau of Reclamation remove some of the speculative elements from farming. On Reclamation projects farmers are no longer at the mercy of droughts. Likewise, irrigation of Alaskan farms could do much to insure crop production. It is not presupposed that all the methods used in the Western States would be strictly applicable to Alaskan conditions, but there is no reason to doubt that experience gained during almost half a century of work in those Western States can aid materially in the solution of the problems peculiar to Alaskan agriculture.

Present limited production of needed foods which can be produced in Alaska are recounted throughout this report. The United States Department of Agriculture, in chapter VII, notes that the rapid increase in civilian and army personnel has created a shortage of dairy products and that it is doubtful if the production of fluid milk will reach the saturation point for this population for many years. Because of this, very little butter, cottage cheese, or buttermilk are produced. The Department further points out that few sheep and cattle have been produced and that expansion is possible; that hogs have been produced in all the agricultural areas of Alaska for many years and that increased pork production is possible; and that poultry husbandry has been slow in developing but that it can be an economic enterprise.

Well-supported organized efforts are necessary to achieve the substantial agricultural development needed to supply existing demands for foodstuffs in Alaska. Some indication as to quantities required can be obtained from examining the import figures for 1947.

Chopping and storing ensilage for winter feeding of cattle on Alaska farm.

Typical high yield of Arctic seedling potatoes.

Quantities of specified agricultural imports from United States to Alaska, 1947, and an estimate of acreages required to produce these products in the Territory is listed in table 31 on page 105.

Imports listed in the above statistics do not include supplies brought in for military forces. They do not include flour, canned goods, or other foods which might be produced in Alaska.

In terms of live weight, these imports represent 17,992,000 pounds of cattle, hogs, and poultry. Production of cattle would require 8,100 dairy cows and 12,500 beef cows. Including the necessary complement of male and youngstock, the total number would be approximately 40,000 head. Pork products would require litters from 3,500 sows and gilts. Production of eggs and poultry would require 175,900 laying hens, plus the raising of about 480,000 chicks annually. It would require more than 50,000 acres of cropland to produce feed for dairy stock, including an additional 50,000 for beef cattle. Grain for hogs would take 18,000 and for poultry 12,000 acres. Potatoes and fresh vegetables would require about 1,000 acres. The combined acreage to produce products equivalent to these imports would be around 135,000—10 times the present crop acreage.

Competitive Position of Alaska Farmers

Opinions differ regarding the quantities of food imports that could be replaced through local production. Many foods, which Alaskans want, cannot be produced in the Territory by ordinary farming methods. However, only a few of the vegetables would be in this class. Livestock and poultry are now being produced. Plant facilities for processing meat into many of its imported forms are still lacking.

TABLE 31.—*Agricultural imports (1947) and estimate of acreage required to produce products in Alaska*

Product	Quantity imported (1000 pounds)	Live-weight equivalent of imports (1000 pounds)	Live-stock needed [1] (number)	Needed [2] (acres)
Milk, evaporated, unsweetened	7,167	--------	2,000	14,000
Butter	1,500	--------	6,100	39,650
Beef and veal, fresh and frozen	6,262	11,272	[3] 12,500	[4] 50,000
Pork, fresh or frozen	307	--------	--------	--------
Ham and shoulder, cured	1,184	--------	--------	--------
Bacon	1,114	--------	--------	--------
Sausage, not canned	738	--------	--------	--------
Animal oils and fats, edible	739	--------	--------	--------
Total hog products	4,082	5,300	3,500	18,000
Eggs in shell (1,000 dozen)	1,759	--------	175,900	11,430
Poultry	945	1,420	[5] 43,000	430
Potatoes	6,237	--------	--------	600
Other fresh vegetables	5,580	--------	--------	400
Total	------	17,992	--------	134,510

[1] Milk cows, beef cows, brood sows, laying hens, and broilers. Youngstock are not included in these numbers but the usual complements of youngstock were taken into account in computing livestock yields and feed requirements.
[2] Estimates of crop acres in Alaska needed to produce the equivalents of imported products. They are based on crop yields slightly higher than Matanuska Valley farmers' estimates of usual yields and appreciably higher than yields reported for 1947. These higher yields were used because improved practices, including increased use of fertilizer and irrigation, are expected to become more common in the future than they have been in the past.
[3] To produce beef in addition to veal and beef from dairy herds.
[4] Assuming 40 percent of feed from range.
[5] Broilers to produce meat in addition to that from farm poultry flocks.

Approximately 30 percent of Alaska's population reside in Southeastern Alaska. The majority of food imports from Canada enter this region. In 1946, these included 44,000 pounds of beef, 5,000 pounds of poultry, and 4,000 pounds of other animal products; 145,000 dozen fresh eggs, 715 pounds of butter, and 87 pounds cheese; 28,000 pounds of flour, 344,000 pounds of potatoes, and 191,000 pounds of other fresh vegetables. Food imports from Canada vary largely from year to year being subject to many influences, including maritime labor strikes. Because this region is more accessible from British Columbia and Seattle it appears that it will be some time before it would be supplied from farming areas in the interior of Alaska.

In view of this inability, at least for the present, of Alaskan farmers to compete with farmers from the States and Canada for markets in Southeastern Alaska, the acreage figure derived in table 32 on this page should be revised to exclude imports to that area. Accordingly, the table following includes quantities of specified agricultural imports from the United States to Alaska (excluding estimated imports to Southeastern Alaska) for the year 1947, and an estimate of the acreage required to produce these products in the Territory. As in the previous table, the imports listed do not include supplies brought in for military forces, nor do they include flour, canned goods, or other food products which might be produced in Alaska.

Ten-weeks growth of white clover from seed near Fairbanks.

TABLE 32.—*Agricultural imports (1947), excluding imports to Southeastern Alaska, and estimated acreage required to produce products in Alaska*

Product	Quantity imported (1000 pounds)	Live-weight equivalent of imports (1000 pounds)	Live stock needed [1] (number)	Needed [2] (acres)
Milk, evaporated, unsweetened	4,660	--------	1,300	9,100
Butter	980	--------	4,000	25,800
Beef and veal, fresh or frozen	4,070	7,330	[3] 8,000	[4] 32,500
Pork, fresh or frozen	200	--------	--------	--------
Ham and shoulder, cured	770	--------	--------	--------
Bacon	720	--------	--------	--------
Sausage, not canned	480	--------	--------	--------
Animal oils and fats, edible	480	--------	--------	--------
Total hog products	2,650	3,450	2,300	11,700
Eggs in shell (1,000 dozen)	1,140	--------	114,000	7,400
Poultry	610	920	[5] 28,000	280
Potatoes	4,050	--------	--------	390
Fresh vegetables	3,630	--------	--------	260
Total	------	11,700	--------	87,430

Footnotes shown in table 31 are applicable to this table also.

Swedish-style hay-curing near Palmer. Modern equipment is expected to supplant this method.

It is believed that the figure of 87,000 acres derived in the preceding table is a reasonable estimate, for reconnaissance purposes and subject to detailed studies of physical and economic feasibility, of the needed acreage of new agricultural land in the Territory for which a market is now available.

The Alaskan farmer's ability to compete successfully with farmers in the United States and Canada is influenced by both economic and physical factors. Economic difficulties associated with a slightly developed Territory are of major importance. Solutions to high development and production costs must be found, and the extent of the market for the agricultural production of the Territory must be determined. Rail, highway, and water transportation facilities must be greatly extended and improved before major agricultural developments become feasible in many localities. Problems relating to soil, crops, and livestock must be studied. The need for low-cost electric power, for land clearing, and for irrigation and drainage, when and if they are needed, must be met.

Expansion of dairying is being retarded by lack of sufficient cleared land in Matanuska and Tanana Valleys. Egg production depends largely on imported feed. The principal deterrents to increased potato and vegetable production appear to be production problems coupled with inadequate grading, storage, and marketing facilities, rather than lack of cropland.

This reconnaissance report does not attempt to present a solution for all the problems which are facing and will face the farmer in Alaska. Instead it tries to indicate the need for increased agricultural production, to mention some of the obstacles in the way of making that increase, and to stress the importance of a thorough study of all factors in the development of a sound agricultural program for the Territory.

Current information concerning agricultural development permits three broad generalizations: (1) there is a market in the Territory for the production of approximately 87,000 acres of new agricultural land, this estimate being subject to detailed studies of economic feasibility; (2) there are hundreds of thousands of acres of uncleared or undrained land of which the soil, topography, and climate may be as suitable for agricultural production as land now being farmed; (3) agricultural growth should be geared to developments in industry, commerce, and national defense, with respect to both its location and magnitude.

Estimates of Potential Agricultural Acreage Differ

Estimates differ regarding the total amount of land suitable for tillage and pasture. Dr. C. C. Georgeson, the first director of Alaska Experiment Stations, made an early estimate of 41,600,000 acres that could be tilled, plus an additional 22,400,000 acres for pasture land. In an article entitled "What of Alaska," W. A. Rockie, of the Soil Conservation Service, estimated that 2,870,000 acres were available for crops and 4,228,000 for grass and range. A group of scientists from the Department of Agriculture who visited Alaska in 1947 estimated "there is probably not more than about 1,000,000 acres of suitable farm land, though much more might be developed if the need for local production should become critical." The group reported that summer range and pasture were extensive.

Despite lack of knowledge of Alaska's land, a considerable amount of information has been compiled since Dr. Georgeson made his first estimates. The University of Alaska has made field examinations of a number of areas. Detailed examination has been made of 10 areas—2 by the Soil Conservation Service and 8 by the Bureau of Land Management. These 10 areas covered 1,206,142 acres. Examinations showed 27 percent of the acreage physically suitable for production of general crops—small grains, hardy vegetables, and forage crops—35 percent suitable principally for grazing and 38 percent unsuited for agricultural use.

Difference in estimates of the amount of land suitable for farming may be explained, at least in part, by differences in the view of various estimators regarding the overall possibilities for economic development of Alaska and the degree to which the present situation, as contrasted with assumed future conditions, influenced their judgments. It would appear the group of agricultural scientists in arriving at an estimate of about 1,000,000 acres gave considerable weight to the present extent of economic development since they reported that "much more might be developed if the need for local production should become critical."

Commissioner of Alaska Department of Agriculture, G. W. Gasser, who has been actively engaged in agricultural research and administration in Alaska for many years maintains that conditions which presently prevent extensive development of agriculture in Alaska are

University of Alaska campus at Fairbanks.

economic, not agricultural. His estimate of agricultural possibilities assumes that economic obstacles will eventually be surmounted. He includes in his appraisal a total of approximately 17 million acres physically and climatically suitable for crops or for grassland but points out that the exact extent of potential agricultural lands is not known. There are marked differences in soil, temperature, and precipitation in various parts of Alaska. This recent estimate of potential agricultural lands is as follows:

TABLE 33.—*Potential agricultural areas*

Areas	Acres
Aleutian Islands	(area unknown)
Kodiak Island	451,840
Kenai Peninsula	5,882,880
Matanuska Valley	195,600
Susitna Valley	96,000
Copper River Basin	3,392,000
Tanana Valley	4,000,000
Dunbar	64,000
Forty-Mile	1,667,500
Yukon Valley	457,000
Koyukuk Valley	64,000
Kuskokwim Valley	450,000
Healy-Lignite	143,360
Yakutat	1,280
Gustavus (Strawberry Point)	40,000
Haines	2,000
Unalakleet	1,000
Total	16,908,460

Location of Agricultural Areas

Agricultural lands are for the most part situated along the river valleys. They are shown in yellow on the accompanying map, adapted from a similar one appearing in Circular No. 1 of the Alaska Agricultural Experiment Station reissued and revised June 15, 1937. The yellow portions of the map broadly indicate agricultural areas. The extent of the yellow area, however, does not necessarily indicate its importance as a future farming area as the percentage of land suitable for agriculture differs greatly from place to place. Paucity of detailed information precludes definite delineation of potential agricultural lands.

Usefulness of Data From Other Arctic Countries

Detailed information regarding agricultural developments under comparable soil and climatic conditions in the Scandinavian countries and in Finland, where economic development is more mature and pressure of population on land resources greater, might be helpful in estimating probable limits for agricultural development in Alaska.

Such information is also helpful in other ways. Data concerning agricultural advances in Russian Siberia might serve similar purposes. According to an article entitled "Fruit, Grain Flourish in Soviet Arctic," appearing in the September 22, 1948, issue of the U. S. S. R. Information Bulletin released by the Soviet Embassy, the Soviets have registered outstanding gains in development of Arctic agriculture.

A variety of winter wheat has been developed, the report states, which gives yields in excess of 30 bushels per acre. A strain of early-ripening potatoes developed above the Arctic Circle was found to produce two harvests per year when planted farther south. Experiments in fruits and berries resulted in producing 208 new varieties, which give greater yields, more frost resistant and superior flavor. Just below the Arctic Circle, the report stated, 40,000 acres of orchards have been planted. In the city of Gorno-Altaisk, 2,000 gardens provide much of the vegetable needs of the population.

There has not been sufficient time to obtain an adequate analysis and comparison of the climatic and economic conditions in northern Europe and Siberia with Alaska conditions. Such comparisons should be included in subsequent investigations relating to agricultural potentials in specific localities in Alaska.

Some dangers of working on the simple assumption that developments in northern Europe eventually will be duplicated in Alaska are pointed out in the report of the Alaska Resources Committee in the publication "Regional Planning Part VII—Alaska, its Resources and Development."

This report, on pages 15 and 16, states: "The assumption is frequently made that because millions of people live happily and thrive in Scandinavian countries, which are said to have no more favorable climate and less abundant store of natural resources, Alaska can support a similarly dense population. But the case is quite different. Not only are soil and climatic conditions different but what is perhaps of more immediate importance, the economic and social setting are so radically dissimilar that European experience would seem to have little application to the Alaska situation." After developing specific points in more detail the authors conclude, "Differences in population, living conditions, proximity to markets, soils, and climatic conditions in Alaska and Scandinavian countries are highly significant."

It is true that differences between Alaska and Scandinavian countries are highly significant and should not be overlooked in taking advantage of experience in these countries. However, it does not necessarily follow that American methods and ingenuity will be less effective

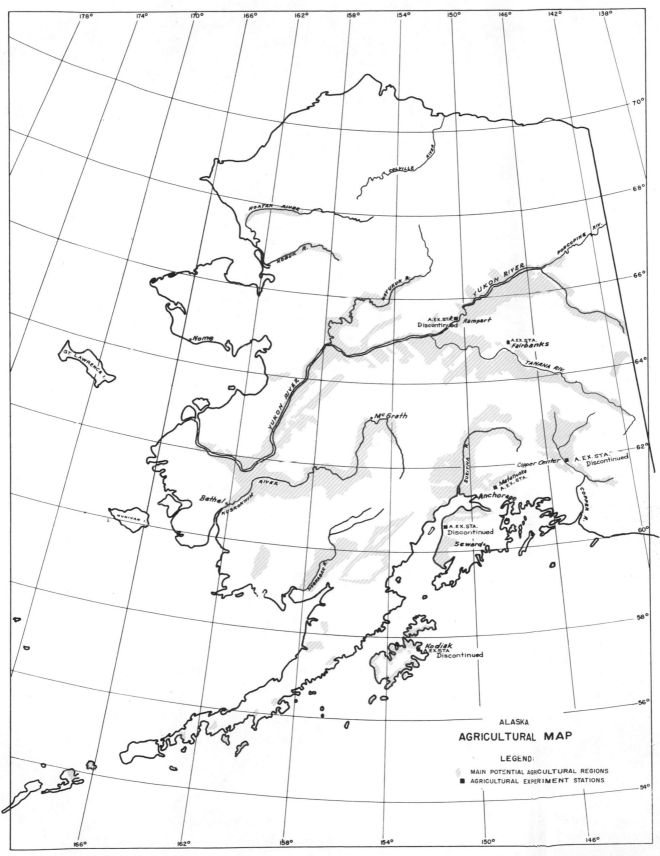

ALASKA

AGRICULTURAL MAP

LEGEND:

▨ MAIN POTENTIAL AGRICULTURAL REGIONS
■ AGRICULTURAL EXPERIMENT STATIONS

Hundreds of thousands of reindeer could thrive on the 200,000 square miles of Alaska tundra, considered unsuitable for other purposes.

northern and interior Alaska for reindeer meat. Through proper sales promotion a substantial export market could be established for reindeer meat as a specialty product.

Climate of Agricultural Districts

The June 1, 1948, revision of Circular Number 1, "Information for Prospective Settlers in Alaska" by the Alaska Department of Agriculture, contains a number of charts which are reproduced in this report.

The first shows the growing season and normal mean temperature curves for spring, summer and fall months (plate A). The second shows the growing season and precipitation at various points in Alaska (plate B).

The fourth chart presents precipitation, growing season and temperature data for a number of stations in the southcentral region and shows areas of agricultural land in lower Matanuska and Susitna Valleys and on the Kenai Peninsula (plate D).

The fifth chart presents precipitation, growing season, and temperature data for a number of stations in the middle part of the Tanana Valley and shows areas of agricultural land in the interior area centered at Fairbanks.

MANUFACTURE, COMMERCE AND TRADE

In the now-dawning age of the Pacific, Alaska is destined to play an increasingly important role as a manufacturing, commercial, and trading entity. It is nearer the vast Asiatic markets than are any of the States. It is on the main line of the new trans-world aviation routes. It has room. Its population could be increased 50-fold and still give Alaska a smaller population density than all but 7 of the 48 States.

Although Alaska has produced goods valued at almost $3,000,000,000 during its 81-year history as a Territory of the United States, development of its natural wealth is still only in its infancy. Many resources have been subjected to almost no use at all. Orderly development will permit Alaska to produce more billions of dollars worth of products from the mines under the ground, the forests on the ground, and the fisheries in the seas.

Alaska offers opportunity for immediate large-scale development requiring millions of dollars of capital, and equally good opportunity for immediate small-scale development requiring only a few thousands of dollars. These opportunities are discussed at greater length and detail in chapters dealing with development possibilities of the respective basic resources.

Southeastern Alaska forests are suitable for estab-

in subjugating Arctic lands to agricultural use than those of other countries.

The United States takes a second place to none in the effective economic use of land on the "dry" margin of land development. There is no reason why it should be less effective on the "cold" margin. Our Nation has repeatedly demonstrated that intelligent use of capital by highly skilled labor and management can more than offset the alleged advantages of an abundant and cheap labor supply. A minor example of this is occurring in Matanuska Valley where the laborious "old country" method of curing hay on stakes driven into the ground is being supplanted by machine methods requiring less labor.

Possibilities for Export

Although any Alaska agricultural program will be extremely limited in its ability to compete successfully in export of foodstuffs and will to a large extent be centered on food products for home consumption, opportunity does exist for export of other than domestic crops. For instance, a $2,000,000 annual industry has been developed in the State of Washington by gathering, processing and shipping of wild huckleberry branches. Common sword fronds are also gathered, sent to florists throughout the United States for use in wreaths, sprays, and other floral pieces.

Infinite varieties of lichens, mosses, sedges, edible berry-producing shrubs, willows and dwarfed birches, horsetails, tall grasses, and others, all of which may have some potential export value, are found in Alaska. Aircraft now fly flowers to Alaska. They can as well carry decorative materials, native flowers, and small fruits to southern markets. A limited quantity of Alaska wild flower seeds have already been exported to the States.

The peat industry is also open for development. Alaska has enormous deposits of peat scattered around thousands of small lakes and bogs. A general survey of Alaska peat moss, made by A. D. Dachanowski Stokes, specialist for the Department of Agriculture, reported the presence of sphagnum peat moss deposits of the same type and quality as now imported to the United States from Sweden and other European countries, amounting to about 100,000 tons annually.

Alaska peat moss could be dried, pressed, and packed into bales for export. Development of this industry is feasible if special commodity freight rates were established to fill empty southbound railway cars and ships. Alaska peat would then be in a more favorable position to compete with the Canadian and Pacific Coast States product.

Investigations made in 1946 by M. T. Zarotschentzeff, internationally known food expert and originator of the "Z" quick-freezing process used in Europe and South America, reported closer cooperation could be attained between the agricultural and fisheries industry. He elaborated a formula for fish chowder to be packed in salmon canneries, pointing out it would provide a marked advancement to both industries. The salmon canning industry has actually recorded little progress, its methods and processing being the same as 50 years ago. The fish chowder formula consisted of 50 percent salmon, 20 percent potatoes, 10 percent cabbage, 3 percent peas, 4 percent onions and 5 percent fish stock, plus salt, pepper, citric acid and bay leaf. Food value would be 1,000 calories per can.

When conducting the investigation there was considerable demand from international food organizations for fish and vegetable chowder for export to European and Asiatic countries. It was estimated these exports could amount to 10,000,000 cans. This would require about 2,000 tons of potatoes and vegetables—much more than Alaska was capable of producing at that time.

Development of Reindeer Industry

The Bureau of Biological Survey, in 1934, estimated there were 350,000 square miles of grazing land in Alaska, of which 200,000 square miles were particularly suited for reindeer. The carrying capacity of such an area was reported to be approximately 4,000,000 reindeer, the annual surplus of which would yield 1,000,000 hides and 150,000,000 pounds of meat.

Since then, a decline in numbers rather than the anticipated expansion of the reindeer industry has occurred. The Reindeer Act of 1937 limited ownership of reindeer to natives only. Reindeer formerly owned by whites were taken over by the Federal Government, to be administered by the Alaska Native Service. Reindeer associations were organized in various Eskimo villages. Community ownership resulted in a lack of interest in the herds in many villages. Reindeer were considered by many natives as an immediate source of food, with little or no thought being given to building up herds for local marketing and export.

Unused and underutilized grazing lands of Alaska are potential sources of income. Some grazing lands are expected to be used by cattle and sheep but large areas in the north are likely to find their best utilization by reindeer.

It is entirely possible that veterans trained in animal husbandry and familiar with cattle raising would be interested in reindeer production, contributing materially to the profitable development of the industry.

In many areas, reindeer are needed now for food and clothing. There is considerable demand throughout

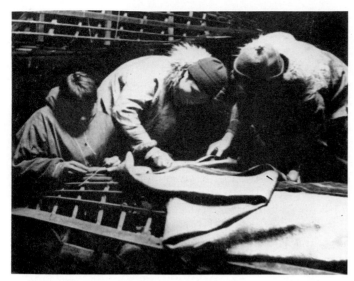

Eskimos and Aleuts are instinctive boat builders.

lishment of paper and pulp mills, plywood plants, furniture and toy factories, shingle and lumber mills. The interior forests are ideal furniture and specialty manufacture for local and export trade. In 1947, Alaska imported $1,075,493 in lumber and $599,967 in furniture. Total timber product imports amounted to more than $6,000,000, while exports were only $700,000.

Alaska's vast and varied mineral deposits are open for prospecting and development. New mineral deposits will be found, new uses will be found for old deposits, and improved technology will make it possible to work many properties now idle. From Alaska's non-metallics, it is possible to manufacture building materials, fertilizers, and other chemicals—all critically needed in the Territory today.

Although the fisheries sustain Alaska's leading industry, it is still far from the complete stage of its development. Many types of fish are not taken by the fishermen today, and many parts of the fish that are caught are still not utilized. It was not until the 1930's that it was found that halibut livers were rich in oil. This relatively single discovery has resulted in millions being paid the fisherman for bringing in a product that had formerly been thrown back into the sea as waste. New discoveries of utilizing fish-waste, development of by-products and new methods of preparation and marketing will further advance the industry.

The tourist industry is capable of tremendous growth in Alaska. Only a comparative handful of tourists now visit the Territory. Establishment of hotels, cabins, and lodges; the building and operation of boats for charter and the manufacture of curios and novelties present another manufacturing opportunity of no small magnitude.

As Alaska's resources are developed, opportunities

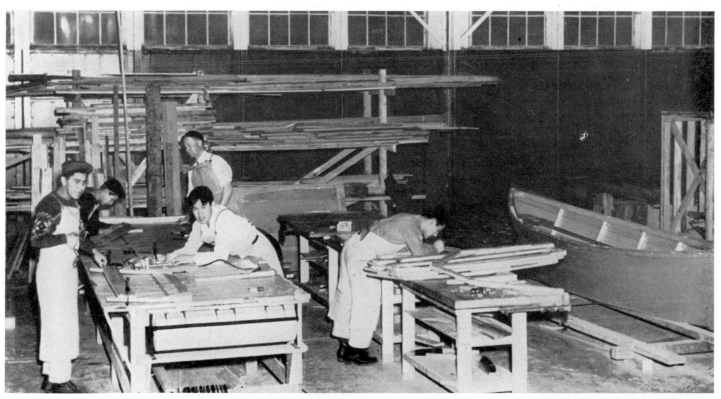

Instinctive boat-building skill of Eskimos and Aleuts can become the basis for the establishment of small commercial enterprises.

would be created in the trades, services, and professions. One additional payroll creates need for another store, another doctor, another teaching staff, another bus route, et cetera.

Nothing about the economy and business of Alaska is static and unchanging. The development of one industry will bring about a change in another. Many of the features about Alaska's economy that might appear disappointing today would vanish with even minor development. For instance: existing high freight rates are not to be taken as a discouraging feature for prospective manufacturing industries because the offering of substantial southbound cargoes, now almost entirely lacking except during the fishing season, would either make it profitable for present lines to reduce rates or for new lines to start.

Not the least among Alaskan possibilities is the one which would involve new business in and for Alaska by transfer of some wholesaler and jobber or distributor functions from the States into Alaska itself. Some products from the Eastern or Middle Western States could be brought to Alaska much more cheaply by way of the Canadian National Railways to Prince Rupert, British Columbia, thence by barge or other type of vessel to Southeastern Alaska towns or to the interior by trans-shipment to motor carriers at Haines. This practice, however, has been prevented by two things: (1) lack of volume on some items, and (2) the fact that exclusive distribution rights for Alaska are tightly held by brokers in the States.

As Alaska grows, its commerce with the States obviously will increase. However, it is not desirable that they extend to the things which build up the States at the expense of Alaska: such as the present system which now gives Seattle a cut out of every Alaska dollar. Wholesale and distributing facilities for an expanding Alaska should be feasible in all the larger communities and such important terminal cities as Haines and Valdez.

One of the present major obstacles facing development of industry in Alaska is high production costs. An abundance of low-cost electrical energy would be the greatest contributing factor toward lowering production costs. Establishment of new industries and development of its natural wealth to make Alaska a self-sufficient, self-supporting geographic area would result in a marked reduction in living costs, another obstacle. Finally, as has been previously pointed out, new industries will have an advantageous effect in lowering present high freight rates.

Opportunities for establishment of new manufacturing industries are many and varied. A complete picture of the many Alaskan manufacturing opportunities can be seen by examining the following lists of imports from the United States, which, as in preceding lists, do not include goods brought in for the Armed Forces. After examination of each item, the question appears: "Why should Alaska import that item (be it canned meat, butter, paper, or building materials)? Why shouldn't Alaska itself manufacture or produce it?" This reconnaissance report does not attempt to answer these questions. For a few items there appears to be no reason why the product could not be manufactured or produced in Alaska. For others, it is obvious that production in the Territory is impossible. For all items, however, thorough and detailed studies of the physical and economic feasibility of local production would be necessary to arrive at a satisfactory answer to the above questions. They are asked here in order to provoke some thought regarding the possibilities.

The shipment of goods from the United States (mostly through Seattle) to Alaska in 1947 are reported as follows by the Foreign Trade Division of the Bureau of the Census:

TABLE 34.—*Shipments from the United States to Alaska*

Commodity description	Unit of quantity	Net quantity	Value (dollars)
Animals and animal products, edible:			
Beef and veal, fresh or frozen	Pound	6, 262, 268	2, 960, 961
Pork, fresh or frozen	Pound	307, 377	693, 091
Hams and shoulders, cured	Pound	1, 183, 966	763, 092
Bacon	Pound	1, 113, 434	752, 863
Mutton and lamb			149, 965
Sausage not canned	Pound	738, 105	324, 948
Canned meats	Pound	1, 180, 737	551, 715
Poultry and game, fresh	Pound	944, 583	563, 205
Other meats and sausage casing	Pound	397, 310	165, 912
Animal oils and fats, edible	Pound	738, 504	235, 453
Milk, evaporated, unsweetened	Pound	7, 166, 852	949, 875
Butter, natural oil, and spreads	Pound	1, 500, 264	1, 178, 961
Cheese	Pound	431, 033	212, 273
Other dairy products			304, 002
Fish and fish products	Pound	598, 470	342, 315
Eggs in the shell	Dozen	1, 758, 785	1, 163, 558
Animals and products, edible [1]		76	85, 384
Total			11, 397, 573

[1] Not elsewhere specified.

TABLE 34.—*Shipments from the United States to Alaska*—Continued

Commodity description	Unit of quantity	Net quantity	Value (dollars)
Animals and animal products, inedible:			
Boots, shoes, and other footwear			923, 184
Other leather and manufactures			284, 152
Furs and manufactures			842, 309
Animals and products, inedible [1]			132, 057
Total			2, 181, 702
Vegetable food products and beverages:			
Wheat flour	Hundredweight	81, 383	601, 021
Biscuits and crackers	Pound	1, 082, 266	244, 869
Cereal foods	Pound	598, 878	74, 776
Grain and preparations [1]			272, 446
Fodders and feeds			382, 280
Potatoes, white			274, 334
Other fresh vegetables			542, 286
Canned vegetables and juices	Pound	5, 918, 031	831, 565
Vegetables and preparations [1]			498, 162
Fresh fruits			629, 254
Canned fruits	Pound	4, 300, 872	727, 080
Dried fruits and preparations [1]			274, 567
Vegetable oils and fats, edible	Pound	922, 867	339, 889
Coffee	Pound	1, 781, 947	762, 776
Sugar, refined	Pound	5, 827, 176	526, 514
Confections and chewing gum			762, 422
Malt liquors	Gallon	1, 496, 136	1, 895, 534
Whisky	Proof gallons	394, 708	6, 317, 768
Distilled liquors [1]	Proof gallons	27, 068	397, 916
Wines	Gallon	72, 933	261, 682
Beverages and fruit juices [1]			203, 276
Vegetable food products [1]			318, 959
Total			17, 139, 376
Vegetable products, inedible except fibers and wood:			
Rubber boots and shoes	Pair	133, 778	496, 381
Rubber belting hose and packing	Pound	151, 777	139, 454
Cigars and cheroots	Thousand	3, 056	190, 452
Cigarettes	Thousand	273, 733	1, 782, 971
Smoking tobacco	Pound	110, 580	89, 559
Vegetable products, inedible [1]			885, 564
Total			3, 584, 381
Textiles:			
Work clothing, men's [1]	Dozen	10, 001	259, 174
Cotton wearing apparel [1]		6	874, 042
Cotton manufactures [1]			1, 426, 616
Flax, hemp, and ramite manufactures [1]			440, 334
Manila cordage			375, 148
Jute, yarn, fiber cordage [1]	Pound	724, 157	221, 632
Vegetable fiber, straw grass			188, 468
Wool knit wearing apparel			322, 552
Wool outer apparel, men's and boys'	Number	39, 867	436, 841
Wool clothing, women's and children's			385, 011
Wool or mohair manufactures [1]			583, 825
Silk manufactures			33, 238
Textiles and manufactures [1]			1, 534, 485
Total			7, 081, 366
Wood and paper:			
Boards, scantlings, Douglas fir	Thousand board feet	13, 795	1, 075, 493
Cooperage			134, 938
Doors, sash and blinds	Number	51, 004	293, 112
Wood furniture			599, 967
Wood and manufactures [1]			2, 514, 274
Cork manufactures	Pound	622, 468	150, 560
Wallboard paper, pulp, and fiber	Square foot	4, 377, 850	285, 392
Boxes and cartons	Pound	8, 620, 682	541, 896
Paper and paper products [1]			1, 082, 338
Total			6, 677, 970
Nonmetallic minerals:			
Coal	Short ton	6, 860	112, 272
Gasoline	Barrel	782, 657	4, 868, 290
Gas, oil, distillate, fuel oil	Barrel	1, 502, 384	4, 856, 956
Residual fuel oil	Barrel	212, 049	321, 795
Lubricating oil, red and pale	Barrel	31, 853	679, 448
Lubricating oil [1]	Gallon	432, 918	286, 867
Other petroleum products			751, 102
Hydraulic cement	Barrel	53, 424	140, 051
Glass and glass products			405, 588
Clay and clay products			247, 941

[1] Not elsewhere specified.

TABLE 34.—*Shipments from the United States to Alaska*—Continued

Commodity description	Unit of quantity	Net quantity	Value (dollars)
Nonmetallic minerals—Continued			
Salt			104, 919
Mineral products, nonmetallic [1]			375, 586
Total			13, 150, 815
Metals and manufactures except machinery and vehicles:			
Iron and steel bars and rods			142, 754
Tin plate and taggers tin		120	500
Structural iron and steel			398, 897
Welded pipe and fittings			141, 450
Tubular products and fittings [1]			477, 661
Wire, uncoated, galvanized, barbed			342, 764
Wire and manufactures [1]	Pound	4, 566, 609	606, 252
Nails and bolts, except railroad			181, 400
Castings and forgings			111, 486
Tin cans, finished, unfinished	Pound	40, 334, 833	4, 714, 584
Safes, vaults, metal furniture and fixtures			295, 868
Stoves and parts, except electric			711, 325
Tools			294, 939
Hardware			1, 382, 059
Iron and steel manufactures [1]			1, 771, 273
Copper and manufactures			309, 538
Brass and bronze and manufactures			224, 737
Metals, ores and manufactures [1]			571, 275
Total			12, 678, 762
Machinery and vehicles:			
Batteries			281, 420
Electrical appliances and parts			1, 460, 017
Radio apparatus			1, 233, 568
Electrical apparatus and parts [1]			2, 426, 044
Steam engines, boilers and parts			335, 289
Internal combustion engines and parts			1, 013, 400
Construction, conveyance and road machinery			1, 011, 706
Mining and quarrying machinery			457, 415
Pumping equipment, except parts			301, 138
Metal-working machinery and parts			454, 077
Cannery machinery			817, 975
Industrial machinery and parts [1]			2, 430, 540
Office appliances and machines			408, 753
Tractors	Number	152	504, 382
Agricultural machinery and implements			873, 286
Motor trucks, busses, chassis	Number	915	1, 914, 744
Passenger cars and chassis	Number	1, 332	1, 860, 095
Automobile parts and accessories			944, 356
Aircraft parts and accessories			1, 911, 969
Internal combustion marine engines	Number	2, 479	720, 500
Vehicles and parts [1]			1, 334, 333
Total			22, 695, 008
Chemicals and related products:			
Coal tar products, except medicinals			12, 463
Medicinal pharmaceutical preparations			469, 239
Industrial chemicals and specialties			713, 210
Ready mixed paints, stains, enamels	Gallon	124, 409	428, 834
Paints, pigments, varnish [1]			319, 905
Fertilizers and materials			29, 262
Dynamite	Pound	952, 010	139, 231
Other explosives, fuses, etc			62, 011
Soap	Pound	1, 502, 654	324, 701
Toilet preparations			318, 521
Total			2, 817, 377
Miscellaneous:			
Motion picture films	Linear foot	23, 924, 952	527, 237
Photo and projection goods [1]			686, 126
Scientific professional instruments and apparatus			268, 295
Musical instruments and parts			461, 816
Toys, athletic and sporting goods			479, 268
Firearms, ammunition, pyrotechnics			440, 774
Books and printed matter [1]			648, 573
Household and personal effects			4, 315, 349
Merchandise, value less than $50			7, 157, 298
All other articles			2, 420, 213
Total			17, 404, 949
Total shipments			116, 819, 779
Total merchandise			116, 809, 279
Total gold and silver			10, 500

[1] Not elsewhere specified.

TABLE 35.—*Shipments from Alaska to the United States*

Commodity description	Unit of quantity	Net quantity	Value (dollars)
Total shipments			129, 527, 479
Total merchandise			123, 640, 885
Total gold and silver			5, 886, 594
Foreign merchandise			733
United States products returned			6, 524, 705
Alaskan products			117, 115, 447
Merchandise:			
Live animals	Number	46	2, 540
Halibut, fresh or frozen	Pound	25, 035, 722	6, 369, 640
Salmon, fresh or frozen	Pound	15, 107, 754	3, 841, 396
Other fish, fresh or frozen	Pound	3, 923, 123	544, 535
Salmon, canned	Pound	216, 715, 861	86, 528, 133
Cod, cured or preserved	Pound	30, 373	6, 177
Herring, cured or preserved	Pound	2, 195, 522	284, 578
Salmon, cured or preserved	Pound	5, 397, 909	2, 139, 167
Clams	Pound	437, 794	212, 349
Crabs	Pound	501, 863	414, 931
Shrimp	Pound	398, 537	370, 960
Fish meal	Ton	15, 018	2, 228, 679
Fish oil	Gallon	4, 468, 945	3, 664, 374
Other fish and fish products			1, 504, 681
Furs and skins:			
Beavers	Number	26, 395	834, 021
Black and silver fox	Number	3, 922	119, 205
Blue fox	Number	2, 275	59, 758
Red fox	Number	3, 303	32, 085
White fox	Number	2, 332	41, 946
Seal skins (including hair seal)	Number	61, 895	3, 561, 413
Marten	Number	15, 071	586, 017
Mink	Number	55, 584	1, 291, 400
Muskrat	Number	195, 818	333, 987
Otter	Number	2, 903	82, 312
Other	Number	13, 233	80, 277
Fur manufactures			61, 408
Fur seal oil	Gallon	34, 000	37, 749
Fur seal meal	Ton	300	40, 448
Wood, timber and lumber	Thousand board feet	9, 609	744, 011
Platinum ore	Ounce	11, 534	658, 286
Other ores and metals (except gold and silver)			108, 078
Trophies, specimens, curios, etc			48, 283
Pictures and paintings	Number	22	2, 500
All other articles			280, 123
Gold and silver:			
Gold ore and base bullion	Troy ounce	88, 865	3, 015, 452
Gold bullion, refined	Troy ounce	81, 144	2, 869, 075
Silver ore and base bullion	Troy ounce	10	7
Silver coin			2, 060

LABOR FORCE

Because of its small population, Alaska does not have a large surplus labor force. It does, however, have numerous men and women available for work in or near the various large communities. Many of those who work in the fisheries or other seasonable occupations are available to work in new industries at other times of the year.

That industry can muster an adequate labor force for new industries should go without question. The thousands of inquiries received annually by the Alaska Development Board from workers in the States show that many want to come to Alaska to live—and they will do so if and when there is work for them. That appeal—the appeal of the frontier—is the best guarantee of a good labor force that any industrialist can ask.

Alaska natives, both Indians and Eskimos, are an important labor force which cannot be overlooked in the Territory's future industrial picture. Both races have already demonstrated their ability to fit into the economic, social, and political patterns of the respective areas.

In Southeastern Alaska, the Indian plays a prominent role in the fishing and logging industries as well as in the trades and professions. At Metlakatla and Klawock, fish canneries are operated under native management with a complete native labor force. The natives have proved to be excellent machinists, electricians, sawyers, plumbers, carpenters, vessel operators, and proficient at other skilled occupations. In the professions, they have attained considerable recognition as attorneys, physicians, legislators, et cetera. Native girls have found their place as clerks, stenographers, teachers, and nurses.

The Eskimos have become actively associated with mining, longshore, lighterage, and construction work as well as many other trades. Many are employed as "cat-skinners," truck drivers, carpenters, dredge men, machinists, and are proficient at other skilled occupations. The majority of employers praise their ability and aptitude. It appears certain that with proper education and training, the Eskimos could become a most valuable asset in development of the region.

Like the Indians, the Eskimos have elected members of their own race to represent them in Alaska's Territorial Legislature.

The Alaska Native Service has directed their educational programs toward training both Indians and Eskimos in trades common to Alaska.

UTILITIES

Fortunately, nature was kind, for every corner of Alaska is within easy power transmission range of hydroelectric sites. Many of these sites are not at all unusual, but interspersed among them are "power giants"—not one but several—any one of which is as large or larger than anything yet developed on the North American Continent.

There will be sufficient low-cost power for future generations of "button pushers"—more than 50,000,000,000 kilowatt-hours annually. As a comparison, this is equivalent to the average amount of power used in the States last year by 30,000,000 people.

Once constructed, these "power giants" could pump more electricity into Anchorage, Fairbanks, or Juneau, than is now available to any city in the world regardless of its size.

In a power-hungry world such a potential is certain to motivate mass migration of industries and people. The knowledge that such power possibilities exist is a dynamic force to hasten their development for the industrialization of Alaska.

There will be no spectacular and overnight development of Alaska's power resources. Development will be slow in the next few years, with demands for power gaining in momentum with time. Several medium-size dams should be constructed immediately to supply pent-up demand for power. Several more should be constructed soon to supply power demands assured in the near future. However, by the end of the next 10 years talk should turn to the early construction of the "power giants." Plans should be finished and ready for the go-ahead signal.

Domestic and Commercial Requirements

The average day is lower in temperature in Alaska than for most of the United States. This would result

Indian totem at Kaasan.

in higher consumption in an all-electric Alaskan home. Space heating in homes and commercial establishments with low-cost hydroelectric energy is a distinct possibility. It is also reasonable to assume that greater use will be made of deep-freeze units since the typical Alaskan family accumulates greater amounts of food-stuffs resulting from hunting, fishing, trapping, and purchases in large quantities because of transportation difficulties. Taking these and many other factors into consideration it is known that the typical Alaskan consumer would have greater need for electric energy than a similar customer in the United States.

It is estimated that energy requirements for an all-electric home would range from about 15,000 kilowatt-hours a year in Southeastern Alaska to 20,000 kilowatt-hours for interior Alaska. Annual energy consumption in an average home today, where low-cost hydroelectric power is available, approximates 4,300 kilowatt-hours. It is estimated that energy usage by 1958 will approach 7,500 kilowatt-hours annually in the future Alaskan home.

Commercial establishments throughout Alaska are large users of electricity. Air conditioning units for purification, freshening and humidity control in commercial establishments are now used and will be more generally adopted in future years.

Owing to the long hours of darkness throughout winter months, energy consumption is considerably higher than for a comparable enterprise in the States. Even during summer months when twilight is present or through the midnight hours electric consumption in stores and shops, particularly for display purpose, is a major load on most utility systems.

Agricultural Use

As previously discussed, farm development in the Territory has been slow. The more salient factors mentioned as contributing to this situation have been (1) excessive cost of clearing lands, (2) lack of sufficient funds to purchase necessary farm implements, (3) deficiency of an adequate power supply for general farm use, (4) the need for irrigation or drainage of some lands, (5) the lack of roads and transportation facilities to transport products to market, and (6) the strength of competition from Stateside producers.

The Rural Electrification Administration is pursuing

Native carvers at work on a 55-foot totem. Their skills would be highly adaptable to specialty furniture making.

Southeastern Indians readily acquire mechanical and manual skills at Edgecumbe School in Sitka.

an aggressive construction program for bringing electric service to the rural Alaskan areas. The areas where rural electrification is being most widely extended are Anchorage, Palmer, Fairbanks, Juneau, and Homer. In interior Alaska, where wells for water supply penetrate the permafrost areas, difficulty has been encountered in keeping the water from freezing. Wherever electric service is available, electrically heated cable wrapped around well piping solves this problem, thereby assuring a source of water at all times.

In the opinion of Alaskan farmers, irrigation water would increase crop production. In some localities irrigation water could be pumped from underground wells or from surface streams.

An adequate source of power in the agricultural areas at rates which would be conducive to greater use, would increase consumption to 10,000 kilowatt-hours annually on the average farm.

Large areas of potentially productive land may require drainage. Recent experiments, both in the laboratory and field by the Corps of Engineers, disclosed the feasibility of accomplishing soil stabilization through the electroosmosis method. This method may have possibilities in its application to drainage problems in Alaska.

Industrial Use

The need for a Territorial source of petroleum and petroleum products is of vital importance to the security and economic development of Alaska. With this objective, research has been instigated by the Corps of Engineers in collaboration with the Bureau of Mines and Bureau of Reclamation for a coal hydrogenation plant with an output capacity of between 10,000 and 30,000 barrels per day. Power requirements for the ultimate plant output will aggregate about 200,000 kilowatts of installed capacity. The major source of energy could most economically be derived from water-power resources contiguous to the industrial site. The energy requirements for this plant are included in the 10-year projected forecast of load requirements for the rail-belt area and curve entitled "Estimated Future Power Requirements—Railbelt Area."

Most building supplies for Alaska, except locally produced lumber, are shipped in from the outside. Most public buildings and larger commercial establishments are of framed stucco construction or reinforced concrete.

Concrete varies in cost from $35 to $80 per ton depending on the geographic location of its use and quantity purchased. In the vicinity of McKinley National Park, near the Alaska Railroad, a large high-grade limestone deposit lies dormant. Coal, gypsum, and

Southeastern Indians working on an automobile motor at the Edgecumbe School in Sitka.

other necessary ingredients are nearby. Investigations are now under way which in all probability would lead to erection of a 350,000-ton-per-year cement plant. It is estimated 10 million kilowatt-hours annually would be needed for this operation.

In Southeastern Alaska limestone has been mined and shipped to the northwest aluminum industries of Washington for processing bauxite.

In estimating future power requirements, consideration is also given to the likelihood of successful development of petroleum fields in the northernmost part of the Arctic region. Once the field is proven it is assumed a pipeline would eventually extend from the oil fields to Fairbanks where a modern refinery would be constructed and operated.

Additional power loads can be expected from the mining industry. Production of the following minerals are included in the overall estimate of power requirements: barite, zinc, antimony, pitchblende, chromite, copper, lead, platinum, mercury, graphite, and asbestos.

Military Requirements

Military construction in Alaska is of outstanding importance. Alaska should develop and manufacture the materials that go into these bulwarks. This would lower governmental cost while simultaneously building up the economy of the Territory.

The present extensive construction program of the armed services is expected to accelerate during the next few years before it declines and then levels off. Most of the military installations will be permanently manned; this factor has been taken into consideration in estimating the energy requirements 10 and 20 years hence.

Load Forecast

Forecasts of energy requirements are shown graphically for the four largest cities in Alaska—Anchorage (which includes Palmer), Fairbanks, Juneau, and Ketchikan. Wherever possible estimated energy re-

Youths learning to operate lathes at the Edgecumbe School in Sitka.

quirements were broken down and allocated between domestic-commercial loads, industrial and military establishments.

In the Anchorage-Palmer area forecasts were limited to a 10-year period (1948–58) since it was not deemed feasible to predict a full 20-year period as was done for the other three cities. The reason for this departure is occasioned by the mushroom-rate of growth which has been experienced, and is expected to continue, in the Anchorage area. Postal authorities in Anchorage admit they are unable to ascertain the population of Anchorage but hazard a guess of 35,000 inhabitants for the metropolitan area.

Forecasts of future loads in the year 1958 for each class of consumer in the entire Territory follows:

TABLE 36.—*Estimated future load summary*

Class of consumer	Estimated total load—1958 (kilowatt hours)
Domestic and commercial	350, 000, 000
Farm	41, 000, 000
Mining	145, 000, 000
Pulp mills	402, 000, 000
Other industrials including transportation	[1] 1, 342, 000, 000
Military	78, 000, 000
Total consumption	2, 358, 000, 000
Transmission and distribution losses	230, 000, 000
Total load requirements	2, 588, 000, 000

Maximum demand; 360,000 kilowatts.

[1] Includes power requirements from outside sources for coal hydrogenation plant, but does not include requirements that will be supplied by power generated in the hydrogenation process.

This summary discloses that the bulk of the energy requirements will be supplied to high-load-factor consumers. Pulp mills and coal hydrogenation plants operate almost continuously with load factors ranging between 90 and 95 percent. With such large load-factor customers it will be possible to supply power and energy at very low rates. The weighted average load factor for all classes of customers is about 75 percent.

TRANSPORTATION

Orderly economic development of Alaska depends to a large degree on efficient low-cost shipping and other transport mediums. However, present high costs are not to be considered an insurmountable development obstacle since establishment of new industries would provide badly-needed cargo for southbound ships, which now return to Puget Sound ports with holds almost empty. New industries would mean construction of new harbors, new roads, airports, and railway spurs or branch lines. As in the previous chapter, air, land, and water transportation are discussed individually.

Air Transportation

Although aviation has been developed to a high level in Alaska, there is still room for further expansion. In addition to the single, two- or four-engine airplanes which now service the Territory, helicopters are destined to play an important role. This type of aircraft would be ideal for flying prospectors into formerly inaccessible areas; for engineering, geological, and agricultural surveys; for transporting sportsmen to remote hunting and fishing areas.

Population gains in interior Alaska would increase air traffic between the Territory and the United States, resulting in establishment of new scheduled air lines. Competition in this area has developed a high-grade of service and efficiency among airlines operating between the interior and the States. In Southeastern Alaska, there appears to be opportunity for immediate establishment of additional airlines to link that area with Pacific Coast States. Although one-third of the Territory's population is concentrated in this region, only one scheduled carrier now renders service to "outside" points.

Because of its geographical position, Alaska is fast becoming the aerial crossroad of the world. One airline is now utilizing the great circle route to the Orient on scheduled flights. Four other airlines have made applications to operate planes on this route. The great circle air route from San Francisco to Japan by way of the Aleutian Islands is about 1,700 miles shorter than the old route by way of the Hawaiian Islands. Huge international airports are now under construction at Anchorage and Fairbanks.

The contemplated growth of traffic between the United States and Asia via Alaska, and between the United States and Alaska can be seen by examining the following estimates prepared by Northwest Airlines for the period 1947 to 1957. These figures gain significance when it is noted that the 1947 and 1948 expectations were realized.

TABLE 37.—*Estimated Northwest Airlines passenger traffic*

Year	Local	Through	Total
1947	25, 000	5, 000	30, 000
1948	35, 000	20, 000	55, 000
1949	46, 000	60, 000	106, 000
1950	60, 000	120, 000	180, 000
1951	75, 000	160, 000	235, 000
1952	93, 000	150, 000	243, 000
1953	111, 000	170, 000	281, 000
1954	132, 000	180, 000	312, 000
1955	150, 000	190, 000	340, 000
1956	170. 000	195, 000	365, 000
1957	185, 000	200, 000	385, 000

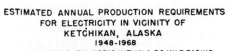

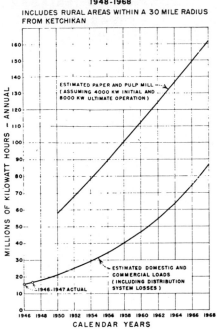

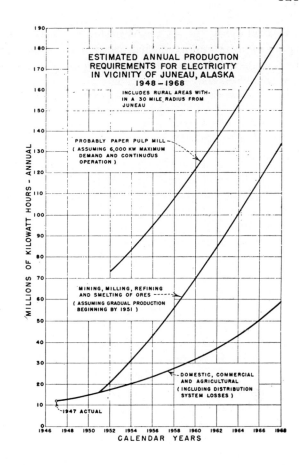

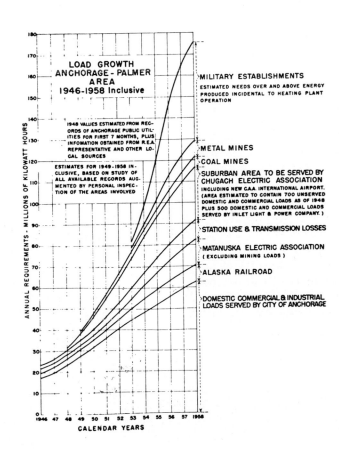

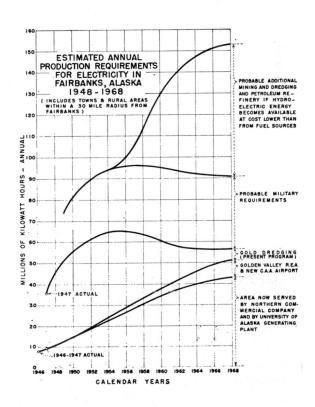

In preparing the above estimate, Northwest Airlines' traffic experts reported that during their peak month they expected to handle 48,200 passengers; the peak day 1,920 and the peak hour, 320.

Land Transportation

When the Alaska Highway was under construction, the building of a military railroad to connect the Canadian rail system with the Alaska Railroad was considered by the War Department and a route survey made. This survey took advantage of a remarkable natural land feature, the Rocky Mountain trench, which lies just west of the main chain of the Rockies. This route provided easy gradients and a straight alignment with few natural obstructions, from a junction with the Canadian National Railways at Prince George, British Columbia. Because of the improvement in the strategic and tactical situation in the North Pacific following the naval action at Midway, the project was abandoned.

The establishment of substantial means of land transport to Alaska of greater capacity and reliability than can be provided by highway or air appears inevitable. In this connection, there are two points that may not be generally appreciated:

(1) Permanent hard-surfaced highways are more costly to construct and maintain than a railway line, particularly through remote and rugged terrain. The establishment and maintenance of crews with their equipment for the upkeep of a long and remote highway system require an extensive and widely dispersed organization, difficult to establish and costly to house, service and maintain. The maintenance of a railway is inherent in its operation, and patrol of the 7- to 10-mile sections is carried out daily by section crews.

(2) Moreover, such a railway is not only of prime importance as a defense measure but also in the interest of development of Alaska, particularly in its effect in controlling freight costs as well as providing better access to areas rich in natural wealth. A railway to Alaska would not have to depend wholly on Alaska-consigned freight for its north and southbound hauls since the railway would have a beneficial effect on development of the rich Peace River area in British Columbia, and other potentially rich regions in the northern part of that province and the Yukon Territory. Studies made by the Canadian Government reveal this region is capable of supporting as many as 6,000,000 persons.

Industrial development in interior Alaska would result in expansion of the Alaska Railroad by construction of spur lines to mining, agricultural, and manufacturing sites. At the present time the Alaska Rail-

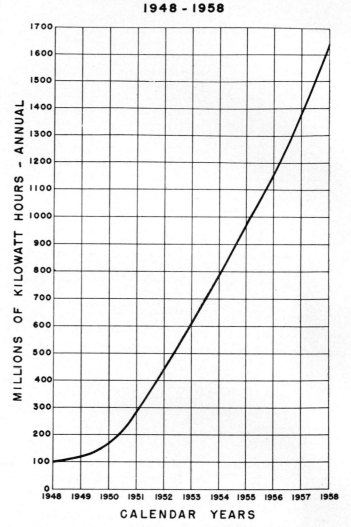

ESTIMATED FUTURE POWER REQUIREMENTS
RAIL BELT AREA
(SEWARD TO FAIRBANKS)
1948 - 1958

road is engaged in a rehabilitation program costing millions of dollars.

Likewise, the Alaska highway system will branch into new areas as they are opened for development. Construction of a highway to link Alaska with Pacific Coast States would also follow. This highway would permit construction of lateral roads to Southeastern Alaska communities. Since Ketchikan, Wrangell, Petersburg, and new cities which would spring up with full utilization of forest, mineral, and recreational resources are or would be located on islands, car ferries could link these communities with coast laterals.

Water Transportation

Beset by maritime labor difficulties as well as numerous operating and traffic problems, there appears to be no immediate solution to make present shipping opera-

Air-conscious Alaskans fly in all weather, with wheels, skis, flying boats, or amphibians, depending on conditions.

tions more efficient and profitable. An extensive survey of the Alaska shipping industry is now being made by the Department of Interior since current high transportation costs on vital necessities not only work a hardship on many Alaskans, but also have a detrimental effect on the general economy of the Territory.

The Alaska Development Board, which has studied Alaska's shipping problems, reports there appears to be opportunity for establishment of a fast steamer service operating on regular schedules from Seattle, carrying passengers, express, perishables, and mail to major ports with subsidiary lines serving minor ports with smaller or slower boats. The combination freight and passenger boats now operating to Alaska under the American flag have been unable to maintain regular schedules because of the uncertainties of cargo handling. A reliable schedule would insure getting passengers back to Seattle in time to take up their train and hotel reservations and would be a big selling point in promoting tourist trade.

More exclusive cargo carriers are needed to care for an expanding Alaska, the Board reports. One of the great difficulties met in previous years by American operators has been the almost complete lack of outbound cargo, as compared with demands for north-

bound cargo space. Alaska imports almost all its foodstuffs, all its clothing, machinery, and other manufactures. Return cargo has been mostly canned salmon, almost all of which is shipped out in a few weeks. A pulp mill or two will ship several hundred tons daily to the markets of the world—and cargo carriers probably will be required to take pulp and paper directly to its destination, be it Sydney or Shanghai, Los Angeles or New York.

Barge service had a wartime test when thousands of tons of freight were taken from Prince Rupert through the sheltered Inside Passage to Skagway. This method of transportation might present a solution to the high costs besetting other forms of cargo carriers, at least for some types of freight.

Use of the port of Prince Rupert would have a most beneficial effect on transportation costs if Canadian vessels were permitted to carry freight from that port to Alaska. Present maritime laws of the United States contain a provision permitting transport of merchandise between points within the continental United States over through routes recognized by the Interstate Commerce Commission "when such routes are in part over Canadian rail lines and their own or other connecting water facilities." Alaska is, however, expressly

Alaska's rails meet the sea at Seward.

excluded from this provision. This means that goods shipped in bond to Prince Rupert from points in the United States can not be delivered from there to any Alaskan port in ships that are not of United States registry.

This legislation has thus denied Alaska the use of Canadian steamship lines to take advantage of favorable transportation costs afforded by existing rail connection between the United States and Prince Rupert, only 90 miles from the nearest Alaska port. Established United States lines, based in Seattle, have not chosen to develop the use of this lower-cost routing.

The transportation cost advantage lies in the fact that rail rates from Middle West and Eastern States are the same via Canadian rail lines to Prince Rupert as they are to the United States Pacific coast ports. Steamship rates from Prince Rupert (640 miles north of Seattle) to Alaskan ports reflect the saving in ocean haul.

The magnitude of this differential is indicated in a study showing comparative rates for 88 principal commodities normally shipped to Alaska from Seattle. Of the 88 items, 85 show a differential in favor of Prince Rupert; 81 items ranging from 15 to 254 percent, only 4 less than 15 percent.

There is perhaps no part of the world where two nations have more closely identical problems, conditions, and objectives than the United States and Canada have in their lands in the northwestern portion of the continent. The development of these lands, necessary in the broad national interests of the two countries, depends substantially, if not primarily, on transportation, and some move looking to cooperative action in this direction appears to be needed.

RECREATION

In his book *Alaska Now* Mr. Herbert H. Hilscher writes that "The ubiquitous American traveler will be Alaska's greatest gold mine in the years ahead. . . Alaska is already on America's 'tour circuit,' and soon tours of every description will be flooding the Territory. Tours will bring the family to the Aleutians to show the children where Daddy licked the Japs. Camera tours will reproduce in color the mountains and waterfalls of Alaska. The ladies of the American Botanical Study Club will see the beauties of nature in Mt. McKinley Park, at Point Hope and at Mt. Katamai. There will be artist tours to paint the glories of Eskimoland, historical tours to study the haunts of Baranof and general tours of the whole Territory.

"Alaskans will do their share of griping about the influx of the 'traveling cheechakos.' But, like the people of the State of Maine who reap $100,000,000 from travelers every year, Alaskans will secretly be happy to share the Territory's natural beauty, its romantic lure and its hospitality. . ."

There is, definitely, opportunity for great expansion in the recreational industries of Alaska. The Alaska Development Board reports that surveys have shown that millions of Americans would like to visit Alaska. If transportation were available, they would come north

Whittier, port of entry on the Kenai Peninsula, linked by the Alaska Railroad with Fairbanks.

by the hundreds of thousands, the Board states. Present transportation facilities—steamers, airplanes, and buses—are able to handle only a minute portion of the potential tourist traffic.

Alaska's recreational facilities require great expansion. Alaska is a recreational paradise. Its distinctive scenery will still be wild and beautiful and unsullied even after new industry helps to increase the population. It offers northern lights, colorful native crafts, and exciting history. Its hot springs can become famed spas. There is room in Alaska for much new industry, millions of permanent residents, and still room for tourists, hunters, and fishermen.

Presently, thousands of tourists come north every year. Most of them make the 10-day round trip to Southeastern Alaska, getting off their boats in each port for only an hour or two. Other thousands come on combination pleasure-business trips and thus manage to see more of Alaska by stopping off at various points.

In the future, the tourist is expected to come north as a stop-over visitor. He will want to hunt, fish, venture farther afield with his camera.

In order to accommodate this trade, many lodges must be built in attractive outlying spots all over Alaska. Construction of roads to some of the more remote areas, scenic drives around islands of South-

eastern Alaska will be necessary. Small boat charter services; retail stores to sell curios, Alaska clothing, pictures and photographic services; filling stations and overnight cabins on the Alaska Highway; guides to fishing and hunting areas; pilots for small boats cruising Alaska waters; guided airplane trips and similar services are also needed.

In connection with establishment of pulp and paper mills in Tongass National Forest, the Forest Service states all timber management plans will be carefully coordinated with plans for the preservation of scenic and recreational resources.

One of the great values of Alaska's recreational resources, which must not be overlooked, is their use by resident Alaskans, who are among the world's most ardent hunters and fishermen. As the population of the Territory grows there will be increased demands for adequate recreational facilities.

Ultimately, the value of Alaska's recreational resources will exceed the Territory's present largest industry—the canned salmon pack. To both residents and tourists the value of this resource, measured in terms of health and pleasure, will be incalculable. Therefore, care should be taken in choosing the location of industrial development sites to preserve potential scenic and recreational areas.

World-record brown bear killed at Cold Bay, May 28, 1948.

THE NEXT CENTURY

Projecting almost into the Eastern Hemisphere, Alaska can play a major role in the economic and social advancement of backward Asia. Few persons are aware of the position Alaska occupies on the globe. Nome, the most northerly and westerly city in Alaska, is more than 500 miles west of the Hawaiian Islands; less than 200 miles from Siberia. At the Bering Straits, Asia is only 56 miles from North America. Ketchikan, the most southerly city in Alaska, is 600 miles nearer the Orient than any of the Western States' ports. Comparative distances, in ocean-going nautical miles follow:

TABLE 38.—*Comparative distances in ocean-going nautical miles*

To—	From Ketchikan	From San Francisco	Differential
Hong Kong	5, 335	6, 041	706
Shanghai	4, 770	5, 491	721
Singapore	6, 600	7, 330	730
Vladivostok	4, 000	4, 650	650

Alaska is strategically and economically located at the crossroads of the Pacific. Trade relations with east Asia, whether by sea or air, will be linked with development of Alaska because it is the vital area through which goods can best flow from the factories of America to the markets of the Orient. A chain of war-constructed airports have established an air path from the heart of America to cities of Soviet Russia, the Orient, and India.

On the Great Circle route to the Orient, ships might dock at Alaska ports between Ketchikan and Seward to load cargoes of manufactures processed from the Territory's fisheries, wildlife, forest, and mineral resources. On return voyages to the United States, cargoes of Asiatic materials could be unloaded at these ports, where tremendous potentials of low-cost power are available, for further processing and manufacturing while in transit.

Undoubtedly there would be a great demand for Alaska-manufactured products within the United States as mineral and forest reserves and other resources become further depleted and the Nation's population pushes steadily on toward the 200,000,000 mark. Substantial increases in Alaska's population would justify development of a wide variety of manufacturing industries. In the case of manufactured metallic and nonmetallic products, availability of adequate transportation facilities, proximity to export markets, low-cost raw materials and low-cost fuel and power would make it economically feasible to locate industries at or near ore deposits.

Extraction of magnesium from dolomite, or sea water might be undertaken in Alaska. Importation of bauxite from Pacific islands such as Palau, which are nearer Alaska than the continental United States, would permit production of aluminum in the Territory. From thermal and electrolytic reduction plants magnesium and aluminum ingots would go to alloying plants, rolling mills, and light metal foundries for manufacture into sheeting, tubing, bars, foil, wire, forgings, and other products too numerous to mention in this report.

Eventual introduction of the iron and steel industry cannot be discounted in Alaska's future industrial picture. Electric furnaces, rolling mills, foundries, and subsequent manufacturing processes would permit Alaska to enter export markets with iron and steel wares.

The same production pattern applies to the nonferrous group of metals such as copper, lead, zinc, and others—all critically needed throughout the world. Shortages of these materials in the United States are emphasized in United States import figures. Imports of ferrous and nonferrous minerals increased from $128,775,000 in 1931 to $518,086,000 in 1945.

The importance of nonmetallics for building materials was stressed elsewhere in this report. The Territory has unlimited quantities of limestone—one of the most widely-used materials in the nonmetallic field. Crushed limestone could be diverted to the following Alaska markets: metallurgical, for use in iron blast furnaces, steel furnaces and nonferrous metal smelters; chemical, for use in sulphite pulp mills and sugar refining plants; agricultural, for fertilizer and building materials, for dimension stone, stucco, and road materials. The uses for refined lime have still a wider scope.

The ceramic industry offers opportunity for manufacture of common building brick, hollow tile, drain tile and sewer pipe as well as refractory brick, ornamental and floor tile. It also includes porcelain insulators and a wide variety of pottery products.

The chain of potential industries among the nonmetallics follows through the glass, abrasives, insulating, enamel, industrial chemicals and by-product industrial gas. Coal, one of Alaska's greatest resources—110,000,000,000 tons—would permit not only export to Asiatic and other markets, but also establishment of a wide variety of chemical and manufacturing plants related to coal tars and byproducts. Imports of these materials to the United States increased from $167,409,000 in 1931 to $481,629,000 in 1945.

Alaska's forest products would find a ready market. At current prices, the total production of six pulp and paper mills, the maximum that can be established in Southeastern Alaska, is valued at $143,000,000—about one-third of the value of United States imports of these products during 1945.

Proposed multi-use dam at Ramparts on the Yukon.

When Alaska matures, agriculture will assume an important role. No nation is sufficient unto itself from a standpoint of agricultural production. For example, the United States imports the products of 50,000,000 acres of foreign soil and in turn exports surpluses of other products. Likewise, Alaska can never hope to be entirely self-sufficient in food production. Climatic conditions would preclude the production of many desired foodstuffs. However, full development of Alaska's agricultural potentialities will play an important part in sustaining several million persons.

In contemplating full utilization of Alaska's resources, the adjoining northwestern regions of Canada—the Yukon Territory and northern British Columbia—should be taken into consideration. A recent Dominion Government survey shows this area is capable of supporting as many as 6,000,000 persons. Like Alaska, it, too, is rich in natural wealth. It is possible that a large portion of its mineral resources could be shipped to tidewater Alaskan plants for smelting, processing, manufacturing or marketing. Moreover, this Canadian

Salmon derby participants and their catch—part of Alaska's allure for a tourist business expected to reach $100,000,000 annually.

A dam at Wood Canyon on Copper River with a dam at Ramparts, would produce more firm power than Hoover and Coulee combined.

region would provide a nearby market for Alaska products.

As the northern region of the North American continent experiences development during the next century, it appears imperative the two nations cooperate to the utmost in exploring the economic possibilities of this vast region for full utilization of its natural wealth, the defense of its shores and skies, and the welfare of the millions who will settle it—the men and women who will ultimately add to the greatness of both the United States and Canada.

Using
The Water

"Water resources of Alaska are virtually untouched, yet represent one of the unused forces retarding the development of agriculture, timber, minerals, and other resources of the Territory. . . .

"The total potential firm energy production of the hydro power sites discussed in this report is 47 billion kilowatt-hours annually. . . .

"This amount of electric energy is equivalent to one-fifth of all sales by all electric utilities in the United States—[in 1947]."

Fairbanks, the "golden heart of Alaska," is subject to recurring flood damage.

CHAPTER V

Using the Water

Water resources of Alaska are virtually untouched, yet represent one of the unused forces retarding the development of agriculture, timber, minerals, and other resources of the Territory. Many of the streams require multiple-use of the waters for optimum development, including irrigation, power, navigation, flood control, fish migration, placer mining operations, and municipal and industrial water supplies. Drainage would be required in many potential agricultural areas.

ADEQUACY OF BASIC SOURCE MATERIAL

Reconaissance studies of the potential developments are based on interpretations of a few known basic data. Utilization of past experience and mature judgment, gained from investigations in other areas under similar conditions, have made it possible to extend these few data in order to determine roughly the potentialities of Alaska's water resources.

Although a considerable portion of Alaska has been topographically mapped, it is mostly on a 200-foot contour interval, too great for detailed studies.

Enough geologic data are available to make some reasonable estimate of foundation conditions.

Water supply studies were based on inadequate data on precipitation and stream runoff and on relatively small-scale topographic maps from which to estimate dam heights and reservoir capacities. The studies are strictly of a reconaissance nature and the results should be interpreted with that fact in mind.

Water supply studies were made more difficult by the lack of adequate data on stream flow, except in Southeastern Alaska, where the records give fair coverage, both in distribution and length of record. Records for the remainder of the Territory include the following: (1) streams on Seward Peninsula for from 1 to 5 years during the period 1906–10; (2) streams in the Yukon-Tanana region for from 1 to 6 years during the period 1907–12; and (3) streams in Southcentral Alaska for the years 1913. None of these data include records of runoff during the winter season; in general, however, the measured flow included from 50 to 75 percent of annual runoff. Records were taken on the Seward Peninsula and in the Yukon-Tanana region primarily as an aid for development of the placer mining industry, and most of them were of no use for this study. An expanded stream-gaging program has recently been started by the Geological Survey; however, no records are yet available.

Precipitation stations cover the lower elevations of the Territory fairly completely. There are very few records of precipitation at altitudes greater than 1,000 feet. The available records do not, therefore, indicate accurately the average precipitation over entire drainage areas. The average annual runoff per square mile of drainage area was estimated for the various streams by studying the records of stream flow and precipitation, tempered by knowledge of topography and direction of prevailing winds.

Storage requirements for complete stream regulation were estimated as a percentage of the average annual runoff. Factors considered for storage requirements were the amount of runoff, estimated annual variation in runoff, and the area of glaciers in the drainage basin. The receding glaciers of Alaska cause a larger runoff from some streams than might otherwise be expected. This recession may stop or even reverse and should not be counted on as a source of additional water supply until more data are available. Glacial melt, however, by maintaining the stream flow during periods of hot, dry weather, can reduce the amount of storage capacity required for adequate stream regulation.

SPECIAL ENGINEERING PROBLEMS

Most design and construction problems of Alaska that differ from those in the United States are different in degree rather than in type. The design for most structures would differ very little from those in the higher elevations of the West.

Permafrost, or permanently frozen ground, is unique to the northern latitudes, and presents a problem where the condition exists. In general, it occurs where the average annual temperature is less than 30° F. This includes the area which lies north of a line running from Kuskokwim Bay eastward, then northeast to the north side of the Talkeetna Mountains, north of Anchorage, then bends toward Chitina Valley, between the Wrangell and Chugach Mountains. Fundamental research in permafrost has been undertaken by the Geological Survey and the Army. Some of these studies will prove valuable in the designing of structures on permafrost. The results of earlier and present research in other countries are also available.

Most of the larger streams head in glaciers. Particularly in the past the silt load carried by the streams has been tremendous. Some of the reservoir sites will present a silt problem; however, most have adequate dead-storage volume to give a long life to the projects. In general, the glaciers of Alaska are receding, which may or may not be reflected in the silt load. The program of the Geological Survey includes silt studies in the streams of Alaska.

The design of most structures in Alaska should allow for eathquake possibilities. Consideration must also be given to the possibilities of rock and snow slides that may be initiated by earth tremors thereby causing structural failure. Earthquakes records in the Territory are incomplete. However, instrumental records are now being taken in Sitka and Fairbanks. Approximately 100 shocks of moderate to severe intensity have been recorded since the severe Yakutat earthquake of 1899. The epicenter for most shocks is unknown, but it is usually near the southern coast line. Many of the shocks are related to the volcanism in the Aleutian Chain, but it is there that data are most fragmentary. The interior has experienced some strong tremors, notably in Fairbanks in 1937.

IRRIGATION

Except on the southeast coast, precipitation in agricultural areas of Alaska is relatively light during early spring. Seeds sometimes do not germinate because of insufficient moisture. Plant growth frequently is retarded resulting in lower yields and inferior quality. Applications of water on commercial fields of potatoes and truck crops in the vicinity of Anchorage and Fairbanks have brought amazing results. Irrigation of other crops such as hay, grain, and pasture would increase yields of these crops appreciably.

A large portion of the potential agricultural areas shown by the Alaska Department of Agriculture lie in climatic regions classed by that department as semiarid. It is in these areas that use of water for irrigation becomes an important factor toward raising the crop yield and average dollar income per acre. In general, the average precipitation is less than 15 inches annually.

Killing frosts last in most agricultural areas until about June 1 and reoccur within 100 to 115 days. Early in the season water is required and again it is needed 2 or 3 weeks prior to the end of the growing season to hasten maturity. Crops are ofttimes a complete failure if water is not available.

The economic feasibility of extensive irrigation in Alaska has not been conclusively demonstrated, the amount of water required has not been determined nor can the extent of the potential benefits be ascertained until studies now under way by several Governmental agencies have been concluded. The greatest economic returns probably will come from irrigation of intensive crops such as vegetables and potatoes produced near major markets, but it may prove profitable to irrigate other crops where water can be applied at low cost. A great deal of study is necessary concerning the response of plants to irrigation in Alaska. The effect of the temperature and quality of water on the growth of different crops, the effect of irrigation on soil temperature, the amount of water which gives the optimum growth, and the best method of water application under various conditions are some of the things that need investigation. Bureau of Reclamation development farms have proved an effective means of obtaining information on irrigation in the States. Similar farms should be established in Alaska.

There are two major areas in which irrigation might be desirable now: Matanuska Valley and Tanana Valley. In the Kuskokwim Valley the ultimate need for irrigation should be determined by further studies.

Water could be diverted from the north side of the Matanuska River about 12 miles above Palmer and be conveyed by gravity to farms in the Matanuska Valley. A 175-foot dam at this location would, in conjunction with upstream regulation, make possible the production of 90,000,000 kilowatt-hours of firm energy each year. The raise in water surface behind this dam would facilitate a gravity diversion to supply some of the farms northeast of Palmer, the farms along the Alaska Railroad, and the farm land southeast of Palmer to the Matanuska River. This irrigation supply would come out of unregulated spills and would not reduce the potential output of firm energy. Gravity diversion from the Little Susitna River to other areas in the valley could also be made.

It might also be possible to irrigate with ground water pumped from the more pervious areas of Matanuska Valley or from the many lakes in the vicinity. The wells which have been drilled in the vicinity indicate that the areas of possible ground-water pumping may be isolated and scattered. Irrigation has been practiced to a limited extent in the area, with good results on vegetable crops. Further investigation is necessary to determine the economic feasibility of gravity or pumping irrigation in the Matanuska Valley.

Irrigation is probably needed as much in the Tanana Valley as in any part of Alaska. Two commercial truck growers have irrigated land near Fairbanks during recent years. The supply for the major portion of the land in the vicinity of Fairbanks would probably come from the Chena River. Further investigation will be required to determine the means of getting this water to the land and also the source of supply and plan of development for other agricultural areas in the valley.

There is little commercial agriculture in the Kuskokwim Valley at present. Ultimately the economy of Alaska will require extensive agricultural developments here. The climate is somewhat comparable to that of the Tanana Valley except that the annual precipitation is slightly greater. Irrigation probably would increase the yield of crops in this valley. Extensive investigations would be required to determine the desirability of irrigation in this area and the feasibility of possible plans of development.

At present there is a substantial amount of irrigation of gardens in Anchorage which are served by the city water system. There are a number of small holdings south of the main portion of the city where some irrigation is done. With the growth of Anchorage, irrigation in this manner will place too large a demand on the city system. Furthermore, with this expansion will come an increased demand for irrigation water for homesites. It will therefore be desirable to investigate means of supplying these areas with irrigation water, preferably under pressure. Still farther south of Anchorage is an area, which, if drained, should provide an extensive development of good agricultural land. This area would also be in need of irrigation water. The supply for these areas will probably come from one or more of the small creeks draining from the Chugach Mountains into Knik Arm and Turnagain Arm.

DRAINAGE

There are many poorly drained areas not only in the broad river valleys of Alaska but also on higher lands. Little or no study, however, has been given to possibilities of reclaiming lands for agricultural use by drainage. This is a field for investigation.

There is an area of several square miles along the Alaska Railroad south of the Matanuska station which might be reclaimed by drainage. There are areas on the low coastal plateau of the Kenai Peninsula which might be drained and developed for agricultural uses. Numerous situations comparable to those probably occur in other parts of Alaska where soil and climate are suitable for farming.

South of Anchorage along the Potter Road in the vicinity of Fish Creek and Campbell Creek is an area of low-lying land which appears to be capable of good crop production if it were drained. Drainage might be accomplished without too much difficulty, and this area should be investigated as a possible gardening area to supply the population center of Anchorage.

Drainage investigations should cover agricultural and engineering aspects. Chemical and physical characteristics of the soil, its suitability for various crops when drained, local frost conditions, tillage costs, and fertilizer requirements are some of the agricultural aspects to be studied. Engineering features include a study of the ground-water table, comparison of drainage by gravity and by pumping based on topography, soil profiles, and power costs, and an analysis of total drainage costs.

A potential new field for use of electric power for drainage is now a subject of research both as to its basic scientific aspects and its practical applications. This use is based on the fact that, under certain conditions of a mass composed of soil and water, an externally applied electromotive force will produce a movement of the liquid with respect to the solid, a reaction known as electrosmosis. Practical applications of this process have been used in construction problems at LaGuardia Field in New York and Europe, and the extension of its use to drainage of land for agricultural purposes may be only a matter of time.

FLOOD CONTROL

Damage and inconveniences caused by floods now constitute a major problem at some Alaskan towns. This will eventually be true at an increasing number of places as the Territory develops and grows in population. Regardless of the damage, danger, and inconvenience associated with floods, villages situated on river flood plains will continue to become the cities of a mature economy because of the greater advantages of their location.

Fairbanks is a typical example of a town affected by floods. The second largest city in Alaska, it is located on both sides of Chena Slough of the Tanana River. The town is only a few feet above the normal water surface and is inundated by spring floods with distressing regularity. The high water is caused by flood flows of the Chena River, which discharges into Chena Slough 9 miles above town. Investigations should be conducted for a dam site on the Chena River which might serve the multiple purposes of flood control, irrigation, power, and municipal and industrial water supply.

Other towns which now have flood control problems are McGrath, on the Kuskokwim River, and Juneau, which is bisected by Gold Creek. McGrath, a small village located near the mouth of the Takotna River, is inundated frequently by high flows of the Kuskokwim which sometimes force residents to seek refuge on higher ground. Floods on Gold Creek are now largely controlled by channel improvements; however, occasional high flows still cause a small amount of damage. Upstream storage regulation on both these streams would be helpful in controlling destructive and costly floods.

Other towns as yet unfounded or now only small villages will eventually face similar problems. As new highways are planned and built, careful thought must be given to their location and protection, that they are not made useless by recurring flood damage. The Alaska Railroad is often menaced by floods on the Nenana River. In many cases, the least expensive protection for all these developments will undoubtedly be obtained by multiple-purpose storage regulation.

NAVIGATION

Settlement of Alaska began along the coast, then moved inland along navigable rivers. Trappers, traders, and prospectors were the first to go inland and their crude boats sufficed for transportation until the interior was sufficiently settled for steamboats to be profitable. Today, more than 3,000 miles of inland water transportation routes are operated by several companies and the Government. Along these rivers are sufficient timbers, minerals, and potential agricultural lands to make river transportation a matter of continuing importance regardless of the advent of highways, railroads, and airlines. Movement of grains, lumber, ore, machinery, and petroleum products may ultimately require a greatly expanded water transportation system.

Present navigation of rivers is hazardous in many stretches. Navigation through the 200-mile-long Yukon Flats, for example, is difficult because of the ever changing channels, some being newly cut by floods, others being abandoned and slowly filling with silt. In places the river is 18 miles wide across its numerous channels and intervening islands. Navigation charts are useless, and pilots operate solely by experience gained over a period of years. Upstream movement of freight and passengers on the Yukon from Alaska into Canada is limited because traffic is slowed by the rapid river current.

Many rivers are rendered nonnavigable at present by rapids or shoals. Large areas of the interior could maintain a movement of river freight if dams and locks were placed on some rivers at strategic places. Similarly, storage of flood flows and release during the low-water period would be of great value to navigation on some rivers such as the Kuskokwim and the lower Yukon.

Multiple-purpose river-control systems should be planned to aid in the navigation of Alaska's inland waterways.

MUNICIPAL AND INDUSTRIAL WATER SUPPLIES

Provision of domestic water supplies for larger towns and cities will be of increasing importance. In the past, small creeks and underground supplies have furnished sufficient water for towns, but these sources may not be adequate to supply the growing population centers of the future. Furthermore, as the country becomes more developed, stream pollution will undoubtedly increase and may eventually require some sort of control. Expanded facilities for storage and purification may soon become problems to be faced by those responsible for municipal water systems.

Water supplies for mining purposes have long presented difficult problems. In some localities it has been necessary to hoist pay gravel to the surface in winter and store it in dumps for washing early in the summer at the time of high flows. Some mining companies have gone to great expense in the construction of ditches to provide water for thawing frozen ground and water and head for "hydraulicking." A specific project of this type is the Salmon Lake development discussed under power sites in the Seward Peninsula region. In this project water used first to generate power would be diverted to thaw frozen ground prior to dredging operations.

With the advent of new industrial plants to the Territory, furnishing water supplies for the operation of these plants will be necessary. In many industries an adequate supply of water for processing and plant operation is quite as essential as is an adequate supply of low-cost power. Industries of this type which may soon be established in Alaska are pulp plants in southeastern Alaska and the synthetic fuels plant at Healy.

These domestic and industrial uses should be coordinated with other possible uses in planning multiple-purpose projects in the Territory.

POWER

The inventory of potential hydroelectric power development following is of necessity very incomplete. Many potential sites are not included because of lack of adequate maps and opportunity for field inspection. Some sites are probably yet unknown. This inventory, however, is sufficiently complete to indicate the magnitude of the undeveloped water power resources of Alaska.

Secondary power has not been estimated, but it may be of considerable quantity at some sites. The estimates of firm generation are conservative. Only those sites having a computed installed capacity of more than 5,000 kilowatts are included. The total potential firm energy production of the hydropower sites discussed in this report is 47 billion kilowatt-hours annually. The total potential firm energy production of all hydropower sites in the Territory is estimated to exceed 50 billion kilowatt-hours annually. This amount of electric power is equivalent to one-fifth of all sales by all electric utilities in the United States last year.

In addition to the water power resources of flowing streams, there are other natural sources of potential power development. The large tidal range at some locations and the constricting topography of numerous inlets suggest further study for development of tidal power. Volcanic areas may be favorable for transformation of heat energy into electrical energy. Consistently strong winds may be another local source of low-cost energy.

In the following discussion of water-power resources, the Territory was divided into six regions, some of which were further subdivided into areas or major river

basins. The descriptions begin with the Ketchikan area in the southeastern region and continue northward and westward to the Arctic region.

TABLE 39.—*Summary of potential hydroelectric power development by regions and areas*

Region and area	Installed capacity (kilowatts)	Annual firm production (kilowatt-hours)
Ketchikan area	133, 000	730, 000, 000
Wrangell area	218, 000	1, 250, 000, 000
Sitka area	58, 000	320, 000, 000
Angoon area	37, 000	210, 000, 000
Juneau area	1, 775, 000	9, 760, 000, 000
Subtotal: Southeastern region	2, 221, 000	12, 270, 000, 000
Gulf of Alaska area	1, 744, 000	9, 780, 000, 000
Cook Inlet area	1, 519, 000	8, 660, 000, 000
Subtotal: South central region	3, 263, 000	18, 440, 000, 000
Kuskokwim River basin	850, 000	4, 800, 000, 000
Upper Yukon River area	44, 000	250, 000, 000
Yukon Flats area	1, 500, 000	8, 800, 000, 000
Tanana River basin	156, 000	890, 000, 000
Subtotal: Yukon – Kuskokwim Region.	2, 550, 000	14, 740, 000, 000
Seward Peninsula Region	35, 000	200, 000, 000
Artic region	225, 000	1, 280, 000, 000
Total	8, 294, 000	46, 930, 000, 000

TABLE 40.—*Summary of estimated regulated streamflow*

No.	Region, area, and power plant	Drainage area (square miles)	Average precipitation (inches)	Average annual runoff		
				Unit af/ square mile	Total 1000 af	Regulated 1000 af
	Southeastern region:					
	Ketchikan area					
1	Davis River	(1)			670	500
2	Wilson River	65		9200	597	328
3	Punchbowl Creek (lower)	} 17		8100	{ 111	Same
	Punchbowl Creek (middle)				27	Same
4	Granite Creek (middle)	} 10. 5		11800	{ 54. 6	47
	Granite Creek (lower)				69. 2	61. 5
5	Manzanita-Ella—Fish:					
	Mirror Lake	22. 8		10600	221	171
	January Lake	2. 6		9800	25. 5	24. 0
	Manzanita Lake No. 1	66. 9		3700	245	Same
	Manzanita Lake No. 2	72. 6		4500	326	694
	Ella Creek	15. 9		9300	148	0
6	Grace Creek	28. 3		10300	290	288
7	Orchard Creek	59		7100	417	373
8	Swan Lake	35. 4		9600	340	320
9	Reynolds Creek	} 5. 8		10500	{ 42	Same
	Powerhouse No. 1				27	Same
	Powerhouse No. 2 (Summit Lake, Lake Josephine)				12	Same
	Wrangell area					
10	Tyee Creek	14. 2		9200	130	Same
11	Harding River	91		8800	801	655
12	Stikine River	19800		430	8450	Same
13	Cascade Creek (plan B)	17. 3		10800	186	151
14	Scenery Creek:					
	Scenery Lake	18		8700	157	Same
	South Fork	3. 6		8600	31	Same

See footnote at end of table.

TABLE 40.—*Summary of estimated regulated streamflow*—Continued

No.	Region, area, and power plant	Drainage area (square miles)	Average precipitation (inches)	Average annual runoff		
				Unit af/ square mile	Total 1000 af	Regulated 1000 af
	Southeastern region—Continued					
	Sitka area					
15	Maksoutof River	27. 1		10700	291	Same
16	Brentwood Creek	6. 6		14900	98	Same
17	Blue Lake	37. 5		9500	354	274
18	Takatz Creek	11. 2		16500	185	Same
	Angoon area					
19	Hasselborg River (plan No. 2)	73. 9		6900	510	488
20	Thayer Creek	53. 2		5800	306	288
21	Kathleen Creek	31. 4		5500	171	153
	Juneau area					
22	Sweetheart Falls Creek:					
	Sweetheart Lake	26		9200	239	Same
	Upper Lake	3. 5		9200	32	Same
23	Tease Creek	11. 4		9600	109	73
24	Speel River	182		9000	1645	1165
25	Crater Creek (independent unit)	11. 9		11800	141	135
26	Long River	33. 2		9500	324	Same
27	Dorothy Creek	10. 3		7600	78	Same
28	Carlson Creek	22. 3		10400	232	160
29	Antler River	5. 5		6000	33	33
30	Endicott River No. 1	17		6600	113	109
	Endicott River No. 2	75		7800	582	197
31	Taiya River No. 1					5760
32	Taiya River No. 2					5760
	Southcentral region:					
	Gulf of Alaska area					
33	Chitina River	6190	14. 95	[2] 1200	7430	5800
34	Nizima River	1420	14. 95	[2] 1200	1700	1450
35	Copper River No. 1	23500	14. 95	[2] 1200	28200	25700
36	Copper River No. 2	24400	14. 95	[2] 1200	29300	25700
37	Resurrection River	204		1600	326	Same
	Cook Inlet area					
38	Kenai Lake	602	19. 41	1600	964	Same
39	Eklutna Creek		15. 00			
40	Caribou Creek No. 1	333	13. 00	[2] 1000	333	280
41	Caribou Creek No. 2		13. 00			280
42	Matanuska River No. 1	993	13. 00	[2] 1000	993	840
43	Rush Lake	107	13. 00	[2] 1000	107	80
44	Matanuska River No. 2	1880	13. 00	[2] 1000	1880	1330
45	Susitna River No. 1	4270	33. 48	[2] 1800	7700	Same
46	Susitna River No. 2	5390	33. 48	[2] 1800	9700	Same
47	Susitna River No. 3	5930	33. 48	[2] 1800	10700	Same
48	Talkeetna River No. 1	750	33. 48	[2] 1800	1350	1150
49	Talkeetna River No. 2	864	33. 48	[2] 1800	1550	1350
50	Talkeetna River No. 3	1260	33. 48	[2] 1800	2270	1980
51	Sheep River	372	33. 48	[2] 1800	670	570
52	Chakachatna River	1140	33. 48	[2] 1800	2050	Same
	Yukon-Kuskokwim region:					
	Kuskokwim River Basin					
53	Kuskokwim River	30800	15. 69	[2] 1000	30800	Same
	Upper Yukon River area					
54	Fortymile River	5600	13. 0	[3] 300	1680	Same
	Yukon Flat area					
55	Rampart	195000	14. 0	[3] 400	72000	Same
	Tanana River Basin					
56	Chisana River No. 1	628	24. 0	[3] 650	408	Same
57	Chisana River No. 2					418

See footnotes at end of table.

TABLE 40.—*Summary of estimated regulated streamflow*—Continued

No.	Region, area, and power plant	Drainage area (square miles)	Average precipitation (inches)	Average daily runoff		
				Unit af/ square mile	Total 1000 af	Regulated 1000 af
	Yukon-Nuskokwim region—Continued					
	Tanana River Basin—Continued					
58	Nabesna River	1700	24.0	[3] 650	1100	1548
59	Nenana River No. 1	678	24.0	[3] 650	440	440
60	Nenana River No. 2				440	440
61	Nenana River No. 3	1253	24.0	[3] 650	812	507
62	Nenana River No. 4	1843	24.0	[3] 650	1200	1113
	Seward Peninsula region:					
63	Fish River	1060	24.0	[3] 650	690	Same
64	Salmon Lake					300
65	Tuksuk	4120		[3] 600	2470	Same
	Arctic region:					
66	Kobuk River	787	24.0	[3] 650	1246	1135
67	Noatak River No. 1	6290	10.0	[3] 250	1570	Same
68	Noatak River No. 2	7050	10.0	[3] 250	1760	Same
69	Noatak River No. 3	8320	10.0	[3] 250	2080	Same
70	Noatak River No. 4	8500	10.0	[3] 250	2120	Same
71	Noatak River No. 5	12450	10.0	[3] 250	3110	Same
72	Colville River	9940	6.0	150	1913	1850

[1] Unsurveyed.
[2] Finally reduced to these figures to be more conservative.
[3] Reduced by 50 percent factor for conservatism.

Information obtained for numbers 1 to 11 and 13-30 from Federal Power Commission and Forest Service Report "Water Powers, Southeast Alaska" except unit runoff per square mile, which was computed from drainage area and average runoff reported.

Information obtained for numbers 31 and 32 from report on "The Potential Hydroelectric Power of Southeast Alaska and the Yukon Territory" by McClellan and Puls, January 1948.

Available References:—

In general reference information was exceedingly meager. For a few small areas covering the Seward Peninsula; Yukon-Tanana Region; South Central Region; Yukon at Eagle and Southeastern Alaska, United States Geological Survey Water Supply Papers were reviewed.

Some topographic information was derived by use of available aeronautical charts also recent quadrangle sheets prepared by the Department of the Army, covering, not in its entirety, but a large number of the potential power sites contained in these investigations.

Runoff estimates were made at power sites investigated by the Bureau of Reclamation for the most part through use of a relationship of precipitation to runoff developed from known data. Precipitation records were used to indicate unit square runoff which was applied to drainage areas obtained from best available maps. Runoff thus extrapolated was further reduced by 50 percent or more for conservatism. The above tabulation lists runoff used in estimating power potentialities. Runoff tabulated for sites reported on by the Federal Power Commission and Forest Service in their report entitled "Water Power, Southeast Alaska", 1947, was taken from that report and was derived by methods discussed in that report.

SOUTHEASTERN REGION

Most of the individual streams considered in the southeastern region are relatively small and are scattered over islands as well as the mainland. Rather than treat them singly they have been arbitrarily grouped according to their geographic relation to the nearest center of population. Such grouping allows for a better conception of the possibilities of establishment of power networks.

The Federal Power Commission and the Forest Service compiled valuable data on more than 200 power sites in Southeastern Alaska. This information was published in 1947 as a joint report entitled "Water Power, Southeast Alaska." From this report were selected 29 of the larger projects which appear most feasible for inclusion in this inventory. Many of the sites have been visited in the field. Minor adjustments in the estimated data were made as thought necessary. Additional sites on the mainland are also discussed, some of which involve international agreements with Canada.

Most of the potential projects are entirely within the Tongass National Forest, which is increasing in national importance as a source of timber products, particularly pulp for paper, and fabrics. Most of the existing hydroelectric plants in Alaska are situated in Southeastern Alaska, but all are small units. Some of the power sites have been privately licensed but only a few are being actively investigated. The grouping of the basins and their respective power sites include the Ketchikan, Wrangell, Sitka, Angoon, and Juneau areas.

Ketchikan Area

The largest streams in the Ketchikan Area are the Salmon, Chickamin, and Unuk rivers. The Salmon River flows from Canada into the head of the Portland Canal. The Chickamin River and Leduc River, its most important tributary, head in Alaska near the International Boundary. The Unuk River drainage also extends into Canada and includes the Blue River as its chief tributary. This report does not include power possibilities on the streams because of insufficient data on runoff and storage possibilities. Nine power sites are considered, four on the mainland, four on Revillagigedo Island on which Ketchikan is located, and one on Prince of Wales Island. In addition, potential tidal power in a narrow inlet of Southeastern Alaska is briefly discussed.

Davis River Site

Davis River discharges into Portland Canal 13 miles southwest of the village of Hyder. The stream is 15 miles long, but no lakes have been reported in the basin. In a canyon 2,000 feet upstream from its mouth a concrete dam 440 feet high, with a 1,200-foot crest length would create a reservoir with a storage capacity of 180,000 acre-feet. The water would be conveyed to a plant at sea level, where more than 160,000,000 kilowatt-hours of firm energy could be produced each year.

TABLE 41.—*Potential hydroelectric power plants*

No.	Region, area, and power plant	Installed capacity (kilowatts)	Annual firm production (kilowatt hours)
	Southeastern region:		
	Ketchikan area:		
1	Davis River	29, 000	160, 000, 000
2	Wilson River	9, 000	50, 000, 000
3	Punchbowl Creek	13, 000	70, 000, 000
4	Granite Creek	9, 000	50, 000, 000
5	Manzanita-Ella-Fish Creeks	27, 000	150, 000, 000
6	Grace Creek	16, 000	90, 000, 000
7	Orchard Creek	9, 000	50, 000, 000
8	Swan Lake	12, 000	60, 000, 000
9	Reynolds Creek	9, 000	50, 000, 000
	Wrangell area:		
10	Tyee Creek	23, 000	130, 000, 000
11	Harding River	20, 000	110, 000, 000
12	Stikine River	120, 000	700, 000, 000
13	Cascade Creek	30, 000	170, 000, 000
14	Scenery Creek	25, 000	140, 000, 000
	Sitka area:		
15	Maksoutof River	24, 000	130, 000, 000
16	Brentwood Creek	7, 000	40, 000, 000
17	Blue Lake	11, 000	60, 000, 000
18	Takatz Creek	16, 000	90, 000, 000
	Angoon area:		
19	Hasselborg River	16, 000	90, 000, 000
20	Thayer Creek	12, 000	70, 000, 000
21	Kathleen Creek	9, 000	50, 000, 000

TABLE 41.—*Potential hydroelectric power plants—* Continued

No.	Region, area, and power plant	Installed capacity (kilowatts)	Annual firm production (kilowatt hours)
	Southeastern region—Con.		
	Juneau area:		
22	Sweetheart Falls Creek	22, 000	120, 000, 000
23	Tease Creek	10, 000	50, 000, 000
24	Speel River	37, 000	210, 000, 000
25	Crater Creek	17, 000	100, 000, 000
26	Long River	33, 000	180, 000, 000
27	Dorothy Creek	26, 000	140, 000, 000
28	Carlson Creek	9, 000	50, 000, 000
29	Antler River	8, 000	40, 000, 000
30	Endicott River	13, 000	70, 000, 000
31	Taiya River No. 1	800, 000	4, 400, 000, 000
32	Taiya River No. 2	800, 000	4, 400, 000, 000
	South central region:		
	Gulf of Alaska area:		
33	Chitina River	140, 000	770, 000, 000
34	Nizina River	44, 000	250, 000, 000
35	Copper River No. 1	1, 200, 000	6, 700, 000, 000
36	Copper River No. 2	350, 000	2, 000, 000, 000
37	Resurrection River	10, 000	60, 000, 000
	Cook Inlet area:		
38	Kenai Lake	25, 000	140, 000, 000
39	Eklutna Creek	30, 000	100, 000, 000
40	Caribou Creek No. 1	7, 000	40, 000, 000
41	Caribou Creek No. 2	10, 000	60, 000, 000
42	Matanuska River No. 1	18, 000	100, 000, 000
43	Rush Lake	7, 000	40, 000, 000
44	Matanuska River No. 2	15, 000	90, 000, 000
45	Susitna River No. 1	350, 000	2, 000, 000, 000
46	Susitna River No. 2	350, 000	2, 000, 000, 000
47	Susitna River No. 3	450, 000	2, 600, 000, 000
48	Talkeetna River No. 1	25, 000	140, 000, 000
49	Talkeetna River No. 2	35, 000	200, 000, 000
50	Talkeetna River No. 3	35, 000	200, 000, 000
51	Sheep River	12, 000	70, 000, 000
52	Chakachatna River	150, 000	880, 000, 000
	Yukon-Kuskokwim region:		
	Kuskokwim River basin:		
53	Kuskokwim River	850, 000	4, 800, 000, 000
	Upper Yukon River area:		
54	Fortymile River	44, 000	250, 000, 000
	Yukon Flats area:		
55	Rampart	1, 500, 000	8, 800, 000, 000
	Tanana River basin:		
56	Chisana River No. 1	7, 000	40, 000, 000
57	Chisana River No. 2	35, 000	200, 000, 000
58	Nabesna River	21, 000	120, 000, 000
59	Nenana River No. 1	10, 000	60, 000, 000
60	Nenana River No. 2	12, 000	70, 000, 000
61	Nenana River No. 3	14, 000	80, 000, 000
62	Nenana River No. 4	57, 000	320, 000, 000
	Seward Peninsula region:		
63	Fish River	7, 000	40, 000, 000
64	Salmon Lake	7, 000	40, 000, 000
65	Tuksuk	21, 000	120, 000, 000
	Arctic region:		
66	Kobuk River	19, 000	110, 000, 000
67	Noatak River No. 1	22, 000	120, 000, 000
68	Noatak River No. 2	23, 000	130, 000, 000
69	Noatak River No. 3	40, 000	230, 000, 000
70	Noatak River No. 4	28, 000	160, 000, 000
71	Noatak River No. 5	26, 000	150, 000, 000
72	Colville River	67, 000	380, 000, 000
	Total	8, 294, 000	46, 930, 000, 000

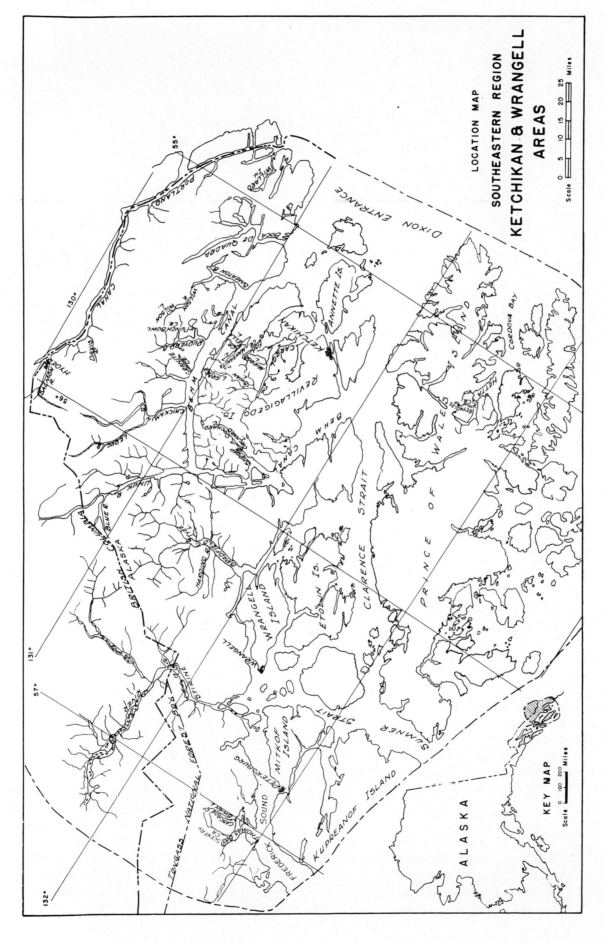

LOCATION MAP

SOUTHEASTERN REGION

KETCHIKAN & WRANGELL
AREAS

Scale

KEY MAP

Scale

Willard Inlet, near International boundary. Constricted alternating tidal currents may be a potential power source.

Wilson River Site

Wilson Lake, at elevation 280, discharges into Wilson River, which then flows 4.7 miles to Smeaton Bay of Behm Canal east of Ketchikan. A 100-foot dam with a 570-foot crest length would create 100,000 acre-feet of storage space, partially regulating the runoff. A power plant 1.1 miles downstream from the dam would have an average annual firm production in excess of 50,-000,000 kilowatt-hours.

Punchbowl Creek Site

The outlet of Lower Punchbowl Lake discharges into Punchbowl Creek, which flows 0.7 mile to Rudyerd Bay of Behm Canal. This lake is at elevation 586. Two chains of lakes are tributary to the lower lake. One of the upper lakes could be tapped by a tunnel 2,000 feet long to a power plant at the lower lake. The runoff into Lower Punchbowl Lake could be regulated by a 40-foot dam and conveyed through a 3,500-foot penstock to tidewater. The active storage capacity would be 80,000 acre-feet. The combined firm output of the two plants would be at least 70,000,000 kilowatt-hours annually.

Granite Creek Site

Granite Lower Lake drains into Granite Creek, which flows 2 miles to Behm Canal 37 air miles northeast of Ketchikan. This lake, the lowest of four lakes in the

basin, is at elevation 825. The next higher lake could be tapped by a tunnel which would convey the water to a power plant at the lower lake. A concrete dam 60 feet high with a 300-foot crest would provide additional storage space at the lower lake, from which water would be conveyed 10,500 feet to a power plant at tidewater. The total storage capacity in the basin would be 40,000 acre-feet. These two plants could generate at least 50,000,000 kilowatt-hours of firm energy every year.

Manzanita-Ella-Fish Creeks Site

Manzanita Creek flows into the Behm Canal on the east side of Revillagigedo Island. The watershed contains Manzanita Lake at elevation 232 and the smaller January Lake at 650 feet. The adjoining basins of Ella Creek and Fish Creek contain Ella Lake at 248 feet and Mirror Lake at 377 feet, respectively. The lakes and creeks are so situated that four separate power houses are suggested, subject to further study. January Lake, with only a low diversion dam, could be tapped by a tunnel and the water conveyed 2,900 feet to a power plant at Manzanita Lake. A 13-foot dam at the outlet of Mirror Lake, combined with some improvements in the saddle leading to Ella Lake, would permit storage of 30,000 acre-feet and diversion of water from Fish Creek to a power plant at Ella Lake. A 65-foot dam at Ella Lake would impound 120,000 acre-feet of storage, and a 6,100-foot tunnel would divert the regulated runoff to Manzanita Lake. A dam 80 **feet high,**

Upstream view of damsite on Stikine River, potential source of power for timber products industries.

with a crest length of 190 feet, would provide 110,000 acre-feet storage at Manzanita Lake. The water would be conveyed 2,600 feet to a power house at the 135-foot elevation. Another dam on Manzanita Creek would divert the water to a fourth plant 0.4 of a mile above the mouth of the creek. The combined annual output of all four plants would exceed 150,000,000 kilowatt-hours of firm energy.

Grace Creek Site

Lake Grace, at elevation 425 feet, drains into Grace Creek, which flows 2.5 miles to Behm Canal northeast of Ketchikan. One-half mile downstream from the lake outlet a concrete dam 70 feet high with a crest length of 180 feet would create a storage capacity of 120,000 acre-feet, providing partial regulation. The water would be conveyed from the dam 5,000 feet downstream to a power plant which would generate more than 90,-000,000 kilowatt-hours of firm energy annually.

Orchard Creek Site

The outlet of Orchard Lake, at elevation 134, drains into Orchard Creek, which flows only 0.3 mile to Shrimp Bay, near the north end of Revillagigedo Island. Topographic conditions at the outlet limit the economic height of the dam to 60 feet, with a crest length of 420 feet. Such a dam would create a storage capacity of 100,000 acre-feet which would partially regulate the runoff. The water would be conveyed to tidewater by 1,100 feet of tunnel and a 400-foot penstock. The firm energy output at this site would be at least 50,000,000 kilowatt-hours per year.

Swan Lake Site

Swan Lake, at elevation 220, drains into Falls Creek, which then flows 1.3 miles to the upper end of Carroll Inlet. A storage capacity of 110,000 acre-feet, created by a concrete dam 0.8 mile downstream from the outlet, would partially regulate the run-off. This dam would be 127 feet high, with a 330-foot-long crest. From the dam, the water would be conveyed 3,000 feet to tidewater, where a power plant would produce annually more than 60,000,000 kilowatt-hours of firm energy.

Upstream view of Chickamin River, another potential source of power for timber products industries.

Reynolds Creek Site

On the southwest side of Prince of Wales Island, Reynolds Creek discharges into Hetta Inlet of Cordova Bay. The creek drains a number of high lakes, the lowest being Lake Mellen at elevation 870. One power plant would be located upstream from Lake Mellen and would use water from Summit Lake and from Lake Josephine, which lies in an adjoining watershed. A second plant would be located at tidewater near the mouth of Reynolds Creek, water being conveyed thereto from Lake Mellen by a 4,000-foot conduit. A total of 30,000 acre-feet of storage space would be provided at the three lakes by drawdown tunnels at Summit Lake and Lake Josephine and by a 40-foot dam below Lake Mellen. The combined firm energy output of both plants would be more than 50,000,000 kilowatt-hours annually.

Willard Inlet Site

Willard Inlet is one of the many narrow inlets of Southeastern Alaska that exhibit swift tidal currents susceptible of power development. The inlet is situated at the extreme southeastern end of Alaska near the mouth of Portland Inlet. Willard Inlet is 13 miles long and averages three-fourths of a mile in width. It is constricted in rock to less than 500 feet near the mouth, at which point the water depth is about 50 feet. One 12-hour period of observations in the constriction indicated maximum surface current velocities exceeding 30 feet per second and an average velocity for incoming and outgoing tides at the surface in mid-channel of more than 20 feet per second. Both slack water periods were less than 10 minutes in duration, lagging 1 to 2 hours behind the tide changes in the open water. No estimates have been made of the power potential in the tidal inlets, but it should exceed the possible output at many of the sites in southeastern Alaska.

Wrangell Area

Wrangell, often called the "Gateway to the Stikine," is on Wrangell Island, which is separated from the mainland by a narrow channel. The five stream basins discussed in this report are on the mainland.

Tyee Creek Site

The outlet of Tyee Lake drains into Tyee Creek, which flows 2 miles to Bradfield Canal. A concrete dam 60 feet high with a 260-foot crest length would raise the lake to elevation 1,390. A drawdown tunnel

would be located to leave 70,000 acre-feet of storage capacity and would convey the water 6,400 feet to a power plant at tidewater. The firm generation would exceed 130,000,000 kilowatt-hours each year.

Harding River Site

The Harding River enters Bradfield Canal 35 air miles southeast of Wrangell. Fall Lake, at an elevation of 182 feet, has an area of only 170 acres. A 190-foot concrete dam, with a 280-foot crest length would create 170,000 acre-feet of storage capacity, which would only partially regulate the runoff. The water would be conveyed to Bradfield Canal, a distance of 20,000 feet, where a power plant would produce annually at least 110,000,000 kilowatt-hours of firm energy.

Stikine River Site

No detailed studies have been made of the Stikine River for power development. More than 95 percent of the 20,000 square miles of drainage area is in Canada, where two relatively small sites have been reported in a recent potential resource study by the Dominion Government. The stream is navigable for its 20-mile length in Alaska and an additional 100 miles in Canada. Although there are no outstanding dam sites on the stream in Alaska, there is one point 10 miles upstream from the mouth which warrants further study. The valley there is broad but is well confined by rock abutments, and a dam at this site would back the water well up into Canada. It is estimated that more than 700,-000,000 kilowatt-hours of firm energy could be generated at this site each year. It is believed that navigation could be benefited, but that fish migration and the reservoir silting may be difficult problems. An international agreement with Canada would be necessary prior to investigation and construction of this project.

Cascade Creek Site

Cascade Creek enters Thomas Bay of Frederick Sound 40 air miles northwest of Wrangell. There are two lakes in the watershed: Falls Lake and Swan Lake, the latter at an elevation of 1,487 feet. Of several possible plans for development the best involves use of Swan Lake only. (This lake should not be confused with Swan Lake near Ketchikan.) A concrete dam, 100 feet high with a 280-foot crest length, combined with a drawdown tunnel to tap the lake, would create a storage capacity of 120,000 acre-feet. The water would be conveyed by a 14,500-foot tunnel and 300-foot penstock to the mouth of the creek. A power plant at this site would have an annual firm output in excess of 170,000,000 kilowatt-hours. The same power plant building could be used in conjunction with a smaller development on nearby Delta Creek if desired.

Scenery Creek Site

Scenery Creek also discharges into Thomas Bay. Of the several lakes in the basin, Scenery Lake at elevation 1080 is the one considered here for power development. The lake could be raised either by a long, low dam at the outlet or by a 95-foot-high dam with short crest length, 200 feet downstream. Tapping the lake with a drawdown tunnel would provide 140,000 acre-feet of storage space, sufficient to regulate the runoff at Scenery Lake and also a diversion from the South Fork of Scenery Creek. The water would be conveyed by an 18,000-foot tunnel to a power plant at tidewater, where 140,000,000 kilowatt-hours of firm energy counld be produced each year.

Sitka Area

There are numerous sites on Baranof Island, but only four are considered here. Sitka, the center of population of the area, is on the west side of the island.

Maksoutof River Site

The Maksoutof River drains into Sandy Bay on the west side of the south end of Baranof Island. The river drains an extensive lake system; the lowest lake is Maksoutof Lake at elevation 575. With an 80-foot dam at Khvostof Lake and a 70-foot dam at the outlet of Maksoutof Lake, the resulting storage of 160,000 acre-feet would completely regulate the runoff. A 3,100-foot tunnel would convey the water to the mouth of the river. The annual firm generation at this site would exceed 130,000,000 kilowatt-hours.

Brentwood Creek Site

The outlet of Brentwood Lower Lake discharges into Brentwood Creek, which flows one-half mile to Patterson Bay in Chatham Strait 39 miles southeast of Sitka. The lower lake is at elevation 610, and Brentwood Upper Lake is 1.2 miles upstream. A 30-foot-high dam at the outlet of each lake would provide 30,000 acre-feet of storage space, which would partially regulate the flow. A drawdown tunnel at each lake would be required for this amount of storage. The water would be conveyed from the lower lake to a power house at Pat-

terson Bay, a distance of 2,800 feet. The firm energy production would be more than 40,000,000 kilowatt-hours each year. A smaller development, utilizing Parry Lake in an adjoining drainage basin, could make use of the same plant.

Blue Lake Site

Medvetcha River, also known locally as Sawmill Creek, drains Blue Lake at an elevation of 210 feet and then flows 1.7 miles to Silver Bay near Sitka. A concrete dam 160 feet high with a 160-foot crest length would impound 90,000 acre-feet of storage, partially regulating the runoff. The water would be conveyed 6,600 feet downstream to a power plant at tidewater, where at least 60,000,000 kilowatt-hours of firm energy could be produced annually. This site has recently been considered by private interests in connection with a proposed pulp mill near the mouth of the stream.

Takatz Creek Site

The outlet of Takatz Lake, at elevation 927, discharges into Takatz Creek and flows 2 miles to Takatz Bay in Chatham Strait, directly across Baranof Island from Sitka. At a site 400 feet downstream from the outlet, a dam 75 feet high with a crest 420 feet long would create a reservoir of 80,000 acre-feet capacity. The lake would be tapped by a drawdown tunnel, and the water would be conveyed 4,800 feet to a power plant at Takatz Bay. The firm output of the plant would exceed 90,000,000 kilowatt-hours annually.

Angoon Area

Of eight sites previously studied on Admiralty Island, three are of sufficient capacity to warrant attention here. Angoon is a centrally located village on the west side of the island on Chatham Strait.

Hasselborg River Site

The drainage area of Hasselborg River is characterized by six large lakes and many small ones. Hasselborg Lake, at elevation 247, has an area of 3,500 acres and is the largest and lowest of the lakes. It discharges into Hasselborg River, which flows into a tidal slough in Kootznahoo Inlet, near Angoon. The north end of the lake is 4 miles from tidewater at Windfall Harbor on the east side of the island. Further study would be necessary to determine the most feasible development. However, the best plan seems to include (1) diverting Guerin Lake into Hasselborg Lake, (2)

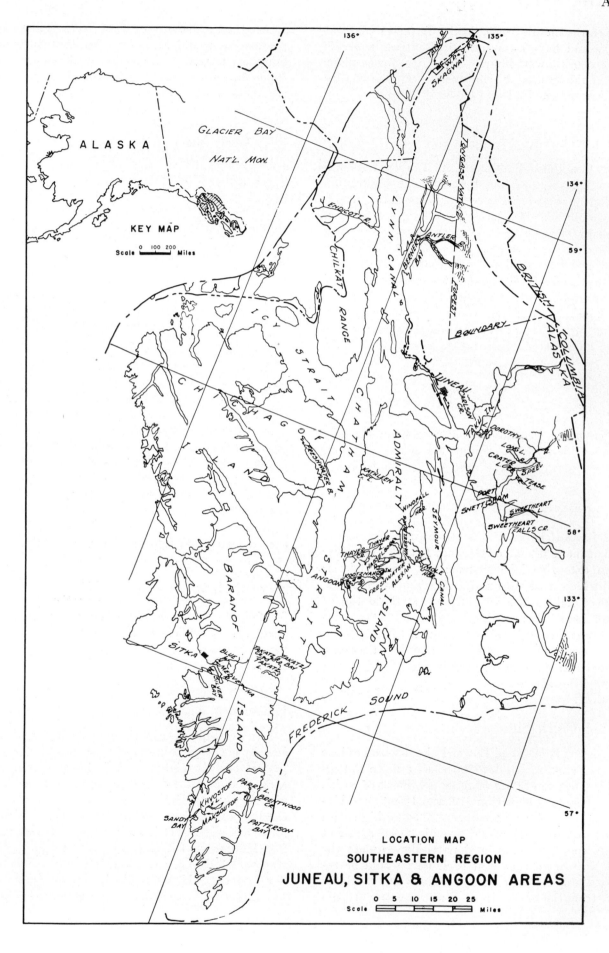

KEY MAP

Scale 0 100 200 Miles

LOCATION MAP

SOUTHEASTERN REGION

JUNEAU, SITKA & ANGOON AREAS

Scale 0 5 10 15 20 25 Miles

Sweetheart Lake in Southeastern Alaska is an important source of water for potential production of hydroelectric energy.

raising Hasselborg Lake with a 48-foot-high dam to give a storage capacity of 190,000 acre-feet, which would partially regulate the runoff, (3) connecting Hasselborg Lake with Alexander Lake by a 3,000-foot tunnel, and (4) conveying the water through 6,500 feet of tunnel and 3,300 feet of conduit from Alexander Lake to a power house at Mole Harbor on Seymour Canal. The annual production at this site would be more than 90,000,000 kilowatt-hours of firm energy.

Thayer Creek Site

The outlet of Thayer Lake, at elevation 375, discharges into Thayer Creek, which flows six miles eastward to Chatham Strait. The lake has an area of 3,155 acres, with an arm extending within 1.85 miles of Freshwater Lake, at an elevation of 5 feet. Freshwater Lake drains into a slough off Kootznahoo Inlet. A drawdown tunnel tapping Thayer Lake would allow storage of 130,000 acre-feet, partially regulating the runoff. By conveying the water 11,000 feet to a power plant at Freshwater Lake, more than 70,000,000 kilowatt-hours of firm energy could be produced each year.

Kathleen Creek Site

Lake Kathleen at elevation 460 discharges into Kathleen Creek, which flows 1½ miles westward to

Blue Lake in Southeastern Alaska, another source of water for potential production of hydroelectric energy.

Aerial view of Lake Dorothy near Juneau, a potential source of power for Southeastern Alaska.

Chatham Strait, 29 miles north of Angoon. A 20-foot dam, limited to this height by a low saddle, combined with a drawdown tunnel to provide 40,000 acre-feet of storage, would partially regulate the runoff. A conduit 8,000 feet long would convey the water to a power plant located 0.8 of a mile north of the mouth of Kathleen Creek. The annual firm energy output would exceed 50,000,000 kilowatt-hours.

Juneau Area

All the sites in the Juneau Area are on the mainland. Nine of them are on streams or lakes which drain areas lying entirely within Alaska. The other two sites would be developed by transmountain diversion of water from the Lewes River drainage basin in Canada to the Taiya River in Alaska. All the power plants would be within possible, though sometimes difficult, transmission line access to Juneau.

Sweetheart Falls Creek Site

After draining Sweetheart Upper Lake and Sweetheart Lake, the creek flows into the south arm of Port Snettisham 36 miles southeast of Juneau. A 10-foot dam and a 2,700-foot drawdown tunnel at the upper

lake would provide 20,000 acre-feet of storage space. The tunnel would convey the water to a powerhouse near the head of Sweetheart Lake. The level of shallow Sweetheart Lake could be raised to elevation 615 by a 90-foot-high dam with a 200-foot crest, impounding 120,000 acre-feet of water. With 9,500 feet of tunnel and 1,200 feet of penstock, the water could be conveyed to a power plant at sea level which would generate least 120,000,000 kilowatt-hours of firm energy each year.

Tease Creek Site

Tease Creek drains Tease Lake at elevation 1,006, only 0.8 of a mile from tidewater at Port Snettisham. A dam 80 feet high with a crest length of 550 feet and a tunnel tapping the lake would allow storage of 20,000 acre-feet, partially regulating the runoff. The tunnel and penstock to a power plant at sea level would total 4,400 feet in length. The annual output of firm energy would exceed 50,000,000 kilowatt-hours.

Speel River Site

The Speel River discharges into tidewater at the head of Speel Inlet of Port Snettisham. The lower 7 miles is a deltaic fill; for the next 1½ miles the valley is narrow, then broadens again and splits into its upper tributaries. One-half mile downstream from the mouth of Long River a 160-foot dam would have a crest length of 460 feet, with rock abutments and a foundation of alluvium believed to be shallow. The dam would impound 390,000 acre-feet, only partially regulating the runoff. The water would be conveyed by 5,500 feet of tunnel and penstock from Second Lake, on a small tributary of Long River below Long Lake, to a power plant at the mouth of Speel River. The annual firm generation at this site would be more than 210,000,000 kilowatt-hours. Potential silting in the reservoir should be studied.

Crater Creek Site

Crater Lake discharges into Crater Creek at an elevation of 1,013 feet. Crater Creek is 1 mile of continuous rapids to its confluence with Speel River, near the mouth of the latter. A concrete dam at the outlet of the lake, 55 feet high with a 310-foot crest length, would permit regulation of 90,000 acre-feet, if the lake were tapped by a tunnel. This storage would only partially regulate the runoff. The conduit and penstock would be 4,500 feet long to the mouth of Speel River. A power plant at this location would produce in excess of 100,000,000 kilowatt-hours of firm energy each year. With a longer conduit, it would be possible to use the Speel River power plant if the projects were developed jointly.

Long River Site

Four lakes drain into Long River, a tributary to Speel River 8 miles above its mouth. Long Lake is the largest of these with an area of 1,345 acres at 807 feet elevation. Complete regulation of the runoff could be provided by constructing a dam and by tapping the lake with a tunnel to provide 220,000 acre-feet of storage capacity. A concrete dam 50 feet high with a 430-foot crest length could be constructed near the outlet, using a rock island for part of the support. The tunnel and a penstock would convey the water 8,800 feet to a power plant at Speel River that could be used jointly with the Speel River development. The potential energy production of the Long Lake development is more than 180,000,000 kilowatt-hours annually.

Dorothy Creek Site

Lake Dorothy, at an elevation of 2,415 feet, is the highest and largest of three lakes in the Dorothy Creek basin, which drains into Taku Inlet 14 air miles south-

east of Juneau. By constructing a 15-foot dam with a 200-foot crest length at the lake outlet and by tapping the lake with a drawdown tunnel, 100,000 acre-feet of active storage capacity could be obtained. The tunnel would be 8,000 feet long, intercepting the slope above Taku Inlet to the west, where a mile-long penstock would carry the water to a power plant at sea level. The annual output of this plant would be at least 140,000,000 kilowatt-hours of firm energy.

Carlson Creek Site

The mouth of Carlson Creek is at Taku Inlet directly east of Juneau. There is no large lake in the basin, but a dam in a narrow section of the valley could be constructed 185 feet high with a crest length of 1,220 feet. With a normal water surface elevation of 440 feet, the capacity would be 50,000 acre-feet partially regulating the runoff. The water would be conveyed to a power plant at sea level by a 6,800-foot tunnel and 200-foot penstock. The firm generation at this site would exceed 50,000,000 kilowatt-hours annually.

Aerial view of Great Falls on Baranoff Island, another potential source of power for Southeastern Alaska.

Antler River Site

On the east side of Lynn Canal, Antler Lake discharges into a small stream which flows 0.9 of a mile to the South Fork of Antler River, then 7 miles to Berners Bay, 40 miles northwest of Juneau. Available data are insufficient to determine the ultimate output; however, with 20,000 acre-feet of storage space available at an elevation of 2,000 feet, the annual production would be more than 40,000,000 kilowatt-hours of firm energy.

Endicott River Site

Directly across Lynn Canal from Berners Bay is the Endicott River which drains eastward from the Chilkat Range, an extension of the St. Elias Range. No lakes exist along the stream, but a large flat valley at the head of a 9½-mile canyon could be flooded by a concrete dam 50 feet high with a 540-foot crest length, impounding 50,000 acre-feet and partially regulating the run-off. The waters would be conveyed 18,000 feet downstream to a power plant at the surface of a second reservoir. The structure forming this reservoir would be a concrete dam 250 feet high with a 250-foot crest length. There would be no active storage at this site, but the runoff would include a small diversion from Second South Fork Creek. The waters from the lower dam would be conveyed 2,000 feet to a power plant at elevation 90. The combined output of both plants would be at least 70,000,000 kilowatt-hours of firm energy each year.

Taiya River Sites

Taiya River discharges into the north end of Lynn Canal 10 miles north of Skagway. A power development involving transmountain diversion of water from the Lewes River drainage basin in Canada to the Taiya River has been studied. Lewes River is the principal upstream branch of the Yukon River. Upper Lewes River, which heads in northern British Columbia, is characterized by large lakes in the upper basin, notably the Atlin Lake group, Atlin Lake itself extending for at least 70 miles. A large volume of water flowing at a low gradient allows seasonal travel by river boats on the Yukon River, and upstream on the Lewes River as far as Whitehorse. Miles Canyon, on Lewes River 4 miles upstream from Whitehorse, is a rock canyon suitable for only a low-head power development. There is now a small dam 10 miles above this site which is used to control releases of water for navigation. The mean annual runoff of Lewes River at Whitehorse has been estimated at more than 6,500,000 acre-feet.

A small dam at Miles Canyon damsite in Yukon Territory near White Horse, would create a multilake reservoir having 500 square miles of surface area.

Two plans for optimum development of the water resources of the Lewes River have been suggested by previous Bureau of Reclamation studies. An international agreement would be a necessary prerequisite for serious consideration. Both plans involve diversion of water from Lake Lindeman, a small lake just south of Lake Bennett, by a tunnel through the Coast Range to the Taiya River in Alaska. Both plans suggest two power plants, each under 1,000 feet of head. The diversion tunnel would be in two sections, 11 and 4 miles long, respectively. Lake Lindeman would be interconnected with other lakes in the basin to obtain a storage area of more than 300,000 acres. The most economical plan for developing the estimated storage requirement of approximately 6,000,000 acre-feet can be determined only after extensive investigations.

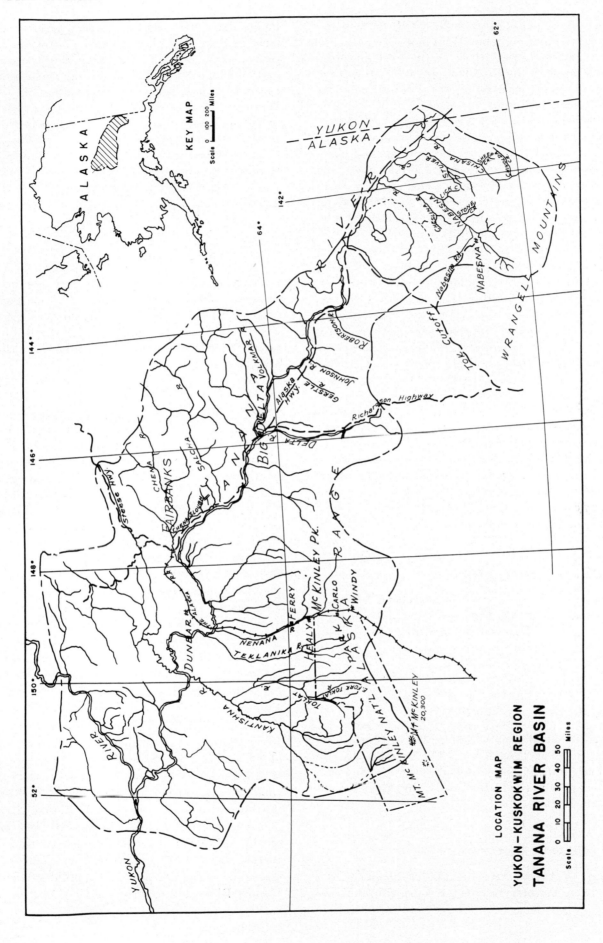

KEY MAP

Scale 0 100 200 Miles

LOCATION MAP

YUKON–KUSKOKWIM REGION
TANANA RIVER BASIN

Scale 0 10 20 30 40 50 Miles

Plan A is designed to allow sufficient water to maintain normal navigation below Whitehorse. It consists of (1) a dam on Lewes River at the head of Miles Canyon, (2) a small hydroelectric plant at Miles Canyon, with an operating head of 20 to 30 feet, or at the base of Whitehorse Rapids downstream at a total head of 75 to 85 feet, to furnish low-cost power to Whitehorse and vicinity, (3) a small concrete gravity dam at the outlet of Atlin Lake, (4) improvement of channels between Lake Lindeman and Lake Bennett and between Lake Bennett and Tagish Lake, and (5) diversion of 2,300,000 acre-feet per year to the Taiya River power plants to produce more than 3,500,000,000 kilowatt-hours of firm power annually.

Plan B is designed to subordinate normal navigational use of the water to power generation. The construction features are (1) a higher dam on Lewes River, (2) a power plant near Miles Canyon as in Plan A, (3) a small dam at outlet of Atlin Lake as in Plan A, (4) larger-scale channel improvements between lakes than in Plan A, (5) a regulating dam across the channel between Tagish Lake and Lake Bennett at Carcross, or relocation of 27 miles of the White Pass and Yukon Railroad along the shore of Lake Bennett, (6) extension of the railroad from Whitehorse to the mouth of the Teslin River, or navigation locks and dams to provide slack-water navigation, (7) increased capacity of the diversion tunnels to the Taiya River power plants, and (8) increase in capacity of the two power plants to generate more than 8,800,000,000 kilowatt-hours of firm energy each year. Plan B is shown in the summary tables and on the maps in this report.

Whiting, Taku, Chilkoot, Chilkat, and Alsek Rivers

The above rivers are streams in the Juneau Area that have relatively large drainage areas, but have not yet been investigated. No good storage sites are apparent on the streams, but future investigations may disclose feasible potential power developments.

SOUTH CENTRAL REGION

The South-central Region includes the Gulf of Alaska Area and the Cook Inlet Area. The region is rich in potential mineral, agricultural, and power development, being rivaled in the latter only by the Yukon-Kuskokwim Region.

Gulf of Alaska Area

The Gulf of Alaska Area includes the drainage into the gulf from Yakutat Bay to the south end of Kenai Peninsula. The coastline is very irregular, particularly in Prince William Sound. There are also many rocky islands and offshore bars along the coast. The basin includes portions of several snow and glacier-covered mountain ranges, including the Chugach, Wrangell, and Alaska. Economic activity is centered in fishing, canning, and water transportation on the coasts, and mining in the interior. The principal towns in the area are Cordova, Valdez, and Seward, all on the coast. The basins of Copper River, Power Creek, Duck River, and Resurrection River are discussed in the following pages.

Copper River Basin

The Copper River basin has received considerable prominence because of its copper ores and the railroad, now abandoned, that once carried the ore from the Kennecott Mines to Cordova. It sounds fantastic to hear that copper "nuggets" weighing more than 3 tons have been found.

The basin, embracing an area of more than 25,000 square miles, is characterized by a variety of picturesque features. The basin is bounded on the east by the St. Elias Range and the Wrangell Mountains, on the north by the Alaska Range and the Mentasta Mountains, on the northwest by the poorly defined divide on the Copper River Plateau, and on the south and southwest by the Chugach Mountains, through which the river cuts to reach the Gulf of Alaska. Copper River heads in the north slope of the snow and ice-covered Wrangell Mountains, makes a sweeping semicircular arc westward, then southward and southeastward around the foothills of the mountains, and then takes a general southerly course to the gulf. The total length of the main stem is about 300 miles. The valley of the Chitina River, 100 miles long, forms a partial continuation of the arc around the Wrangell Mountains, beginning at its point of confluence with the Copper. The geological evidence suggests that, during the Ice Age, tremendous glaciers from the Chitina Valley area moved northwestward, receiving contributions from the adjoining mountains, crossed the Copper River Plateau area and thence westward at a high level along the Susitna River Valley. There were smaller spillways, however, through the Matanuska Valley, possibly one to Valdez, and a smaller one southward along the lower course of the present Copper River. The melting of the glacier left in its wake a large portion of the sedimentary accumulation that makes up the surface of the Copper River Plateau and the terraces along the major streams. The middle section of the Copper River and most of the Chitina River have cut

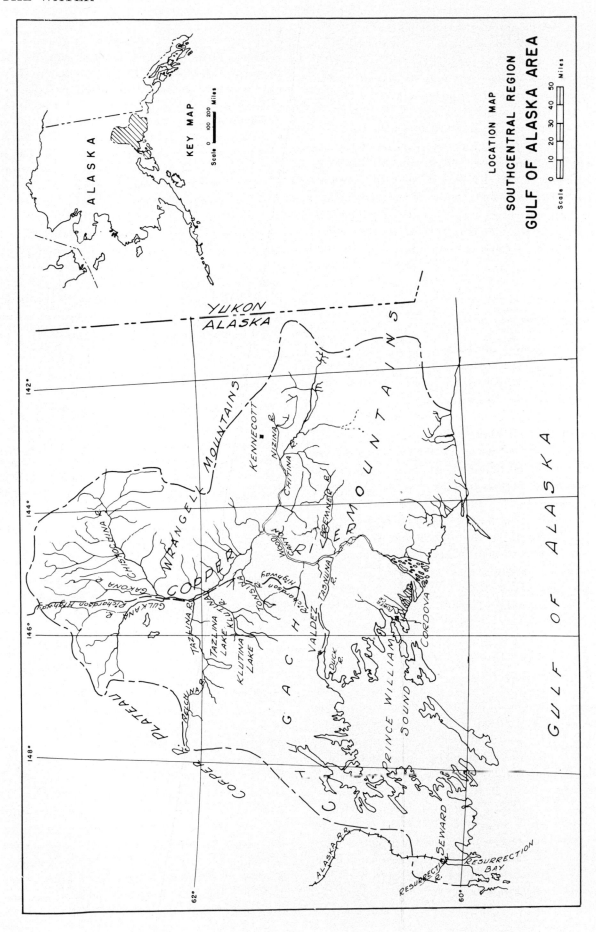

KEY MAP

Scale 0 100 200 Miles

ALASKA

LOCATION MAP

SOUTHCENTRAL REGION
GULF OF ALASKA AREA

Scale 0 10 20 30 40 50 Miles

YUKON
ALASKA

142°

144°

146°

148°

62°

60°

WRANGELL MOUNTAINS

CHITINA R.

KENNECOTT

NIZINA R.

COPPER RIVER MOUNTAINS

CHISTOCHINA R.

GAKONA R.

Richardson Highway

GULKANA R.

GAKONA

TAZLINA R.

TAZLINA LAKE

KLUTINA R.

KLUTINA LAKE

TONSINA R.

Richardson Highway

WOODY

KLAWASI

VALDEZ

BREMNER R.

TASNUNA R.

CHUGACH MOUNTAINS

DUCK R.

PRINCE WILLIAM SOUND

CORDOVA

COPPER R.

ALASKA R.R.

SEWARD

RESURRECTION R.

RESURRECTION BAY

GULF OF ALASKA

PLATEAU

deeply into the sedimentary accumulation that averages 10 miles in width. At its confluence with the Chitina the Copper River leaves the broad valley to travel southward through a rock-walled canyon to its graphic delta. In the lower course three large glaciers enter the valley, partially obstructing the flow.

The principal tributaries, in addition to the Chitina, are Christochina, Gakona, Gulkana, Tazlina, Klutina, Tonsina, Tasnuna, and Bremner Rivers, all heading in ice fields. The Nizina River is a short but important tributary of the Chitina. Sites considered in this report include storage sites on the Tazlina and Klutina, and power sites on the Chitina, Nizina, and the main stem of the Copper. There are no major towns in the basin.

Tazlina River Storage Site

Tazlina River heads in Tazlina Lake, nearly 20 miles long and two miles wide, located in the west central portion of the Copper River basin. It is served chiefly by Tazlina and Nelchina Glaciers. The lake has an area of 40,000 acres at elevation 1,785. By constructing an earthfill dam 60 feet high with a 300-foot crest length at the outlet, 1,600,000 acre-feet of active storage could be obtained. This storage would only partially regulate the runoff at the site. A higher dam would have a much longer crest. There is a possibility of developing head downstream for power production on this stream, but that is not considered here. The only function of the site would be to store water for the two power plants on the main stem. This site is within the permafrost belt, a fact which must be considered in evaluating the site in advance stages of the basin study.

Klutina River Storage Site

The Klutina River basin lies just south of that of the Tazlina, to which it is similar. Klutina Lake, glacier-fed, is 17 miles long and 2 miles wide, with an area of 29,000 acres at elevation 1,790. The valley at the outlet is broad, but the stream becomes incised into the alluvial terrace of the Copper River valley as it proceeds downstream. An earthfill dam near the outlet, 60 feet high with a crest length of 4,000 feet, would impound 1,000,000 acre-feet, which would completely regulate the flow at the lake. The downstream canyon of the Klutina is of questionable geologic nature for a high dam for production of power.

Chitina River Site

About 45 miles from the confluence of the Chitina River and the Copper River, the Nizina River enters the Chitina from the northeast in a narrow, rock-walled canyon with glacial sediments on the upper slopes. Seven miles upstream from the mouth of the Nizina, the Chitina narrows partly because it cuts through some rock at low level. An earthfill dam 325 feet high with a 4,000-foot crest would create an active storage capacity of 2,500,000 acre-feet. This would only partially regulate the runoff of the stream. The exact elevation and character of the sediments in the terrace above the river would determine the reservoir level. A power plant at this site would produce annually more than 770,000,000 kilowatt-hours of firm energy. The site is near the division zone between permafrost and non-permafrost areas. Silting of the reservoir might be a problem, but the 400,000 acre-feet of dead storage should be adequate for silt deposition.

Nizina River Site

The Nizina River is relatively short but drains a number of large glaciers. The large Kennecott copper mines are in the basin. Before entering the Chitina River, the stream becomes incised into terrace sediments and then into a rock canyon. A dam in the canyon, 425 feet high with a 2,500-foot crest length, would impound 1,400,000 acre-feet of active storage, providing only partial regulation of the runoff. A power plant at this site would have an annual firm generation of at least 250,000,000 kilowatt-hours. Future field studies may indicate the practicability of combining the reservoirs of the Chitina and Nizina to produce power at a single plant at the Nizina site.

Copper River Site No. 1 (Wood Canyon Site)

Three miles below the mouth of the Chitina, the Copper River enters Wood Canyon, the narrowest portion of its lower course. For a distance of several miles the river occupies the entire valley floor between partly metamorphosed rocks extending high above stream level. A concrete dam 3 miles below the head of the canyon, constructed to a height of 700 feet above bedrock in the foundation, would raise the water surface 575 feet and would have a crest length of 1,500 feet. The reservoir of 14,000,000 acre-feet active capacity would extend to the tailwater of the Nizina site. This amount of active storage would completely regulate the inflow below the four upstream reservoir sites. A power plant at the Wood Canyon site would produce more than 6,700,000,000 kilowatt-hours of firm energy each year.

Copper River Site No. 2

Just upstream from the mouth of the Tasnuna River, the valley of the Copper is broad at the base, but is confined by rock walls. The valley bottom, filled with alluvium, is about one-half mile wide, but because of the large regulated flow, consideration should be given to power development at this site. An earth dam 175 feet high with a 3,000-foot crest and a supplementary dike and spillway 100 feet high and 1,000 feet long would back the water to Site No. 1, providing only dead storage for the creation of power head. The annual firm output of a power plant at this site would be at least 2,000,000,000 kilowatt-hours.

Power Creek Basin

Power Creek enters Eyak Lake at its northeastern end, about 5 miles east of Cordova. Eyak Lake, in turn, drains south to the Gulf of Alaska. The creek heads in ice fields of the Chugach Range but flows only 5 miles southwesterly to Eyak Lake. The valley is one-fourth to one-half mile wide near the upper part of the basin, but 3 miles above Eyak Lake it narrows abruptly to pass through a bedrock canyon around a projecting ridge. The canyon at this point is favorable for a dam 100 or more feet high. There is some question, however, concerning the water-tightness of the ridge, which consists, at least in part, of very pervious glacial moraine. If the moraine is continuous across the ridge at any point below reservoir level, too much water may be lost. It would be necessary to explore it thoroughly before constructing a dam. Considering that the pervious condition may not be extensive or beyond correction, a dam 100 feet high with a crest length of 200 feet could be constructed, but data are unavailable to determine the storage. An 800-foot tunnel through the rock section of the ridge and a 5,000-foot conduit would develop more than 350 feet of head. A power plant at this site would produce enough power for the immediate needs of Cordova and vicinity.

Duck River Basin

Duck River enters Galena Bay of Valdez Arm of Prince William Sound about 17 airline miles southwest of Valdez and about 6 miles northeast of the Ellamar Mining District. The river has not been investigated, but early work by the Geological Survey suggests the potential power resources of the basin. The stream, 2 miles long, has its source in Silver Lake at elevation 250. Silver Lake, between 3 and 5 miles long, could be raised at least 30 feet by a concrete dam with a short crest. Enough power to serve local needs could be produced by tapping the lake and conveying the water 1½ miles to a power plant at sea level.

Resurrection River Basin

Resurrection River drains into Resurrection Bay near Seward. The river is in a broad glacial valley with a constriction 9 miles above the mouth. An earth dam 235 feet high with a 2,000-foot crest length would create a reservoir with an active capacity of 320,000 acre-feet. A tunnel would convey the water 5 miles downstream to a penstock and power plant, where the annual firm output would be more than 60,000,000 kilowatt-hours. There is some question, however, of the feasibility of the dam site for either an earthfill or concrete structure. Geologic conditions suggest deep, pervious overburden in the valley floor.

Cook Inlet Area

The Cook Inlet Area is the hub of Alaska, geographically, industrially, as a transportation center, and for accelerated development in agriculture and miscellaneous enterprises. The growth of the area is a healthy one, for it is not dependent on a single industry nor on unstable resource development. Yet many of the resources are virtually untouched, a major one being the water resources. Agriculture, coal and metal mining, lumbering, fishing, and transportation have combined to serve as a nucleus for a stable economy. Lack of power and other water resource development has thus far prevented an even more impressive "chain reaction" that would not only expand the existing developments, but would attract new manufacturing industries to the area.

The basin embraces a roughly elliptical area of about 35,000 square miles trending north-northeast by south-southwest and almost entirely enclosed by high mountain ranges. The inlet is 150 miles long and about 30 miles wide, terminating in Knik Arm and Turnagain Arm near Anchorage. The western and northern boundaries of the basin are the Aleutian Range and the Alaska Range with many peaks over 10,000 feet in elevation, all dwarfed by Mount McKinley near the north end of the area. There are passes to the Yukon-Kuskokwim Plateau, however, that are below 3,000

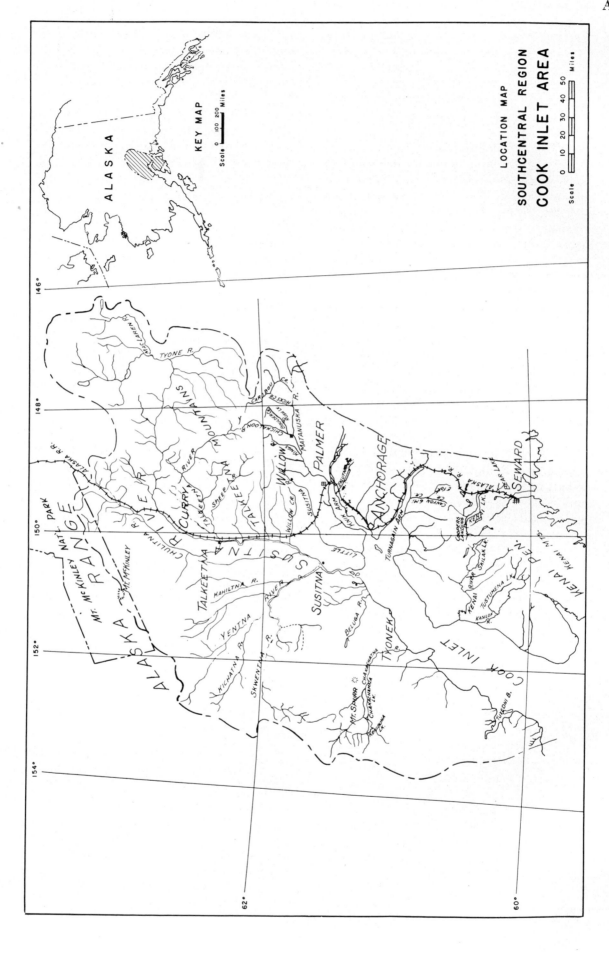

KEY MAP

Scale 0 100 200 Miles

LOCATION MAP

SOUTHCENTRAL REGION

COOK INLET AREA

Scale 0 10 20 30 40 50 Miles

feet in elevation, notably Broad Pass at 2,400 feet used by the Alaska Railroad. The drainage divide with the Copper River Basin to the east is on the Copper River Plateau near 3,000 feet in elevation. The divide on the southeast is the crest line of that portion of the rugged Chugach Range from Copper River to the end of the Kenai Peninsula.

Many major and minor streams originate in glaciers on the slopes of the mountains. The glaciers are remnants of the Ice Age when all of the mountains were capped by ice masses that moved down to coalesce in the basin area and to move southwestward to the sea. It was this mass ice movement that shaped the existing lowland topography by erosion of preexisting valleys and deposition of drift in its wake. The general topography has been little modified since the Ice Age. The broad lower Susitna River Valley, the Knik Arm area, the lowlands near Tyonek, and the west side of Kenai Peninsula are all glacially built terraces that are existing or potential farming areas. A typical profile across a side of the basin would show a high, snow-topped mountain with glaciers in the upper valleys, steep slopes with deeply incised valleys often containing lakes, foothills that merge with high-level terraces, lower-level terraces, and a beach or stream floodplain.

The bedrock of the basin is of all geologic ages and includes sedimentary, metamorphic, and igneous rocks. The diverse geologic activity through all the geologic periods has resulted in formation of nonmetallic and metallic minerals in the basin that have not been thoroughly prospected. Lode and placer gold and coal have been exploited more than any other minerals, but chromite and tungsten have been produced, and copper, antimony, lead, and other minerals are known to be present.

The most important towns in the area are Anchorage, near the junction of Knik Arm and Turnagain Arm, and Palmer, in the Matanuska Valley farming area. For the discussion of potential water use, the Cook Inlet Area is divided into the following principal basins: Kasilof River, Kenai River, Sixmile Creek, Eklutna Creek, Matanuska River, Susitna River, Beluga River, and Chakachatna River.

Kasilof River Basin

Tustumena Lake, 25 miles long and 5 miles wide, is the outstanding feature of the Kasilof River Basin. The lake lies in the lowland between the Kenai Mountains, from which its inflow comes, and Cook Inlet. The river itself is only about 15 miles long. There are no apparent power developments within the basin. The importance of the basin lies chiefly in its agricultural possibilities and the fact that much of it is underlain

by coal-bearing sediments. A comprehensive study has not yet been made of the possible benefits of irrigation and drainage.

Kenai River Basin

The salient features of the Kenai River basin are the numerous lakes, largest of which are Kenai Lake and Skilak Lake. The main stream heads in Kenai Lake at elevation 435. The lake, 24 miles long and more than 1 mile wide, is served by many tributaries in the Kenai Mountains. Many of the tributaries, most of which head in glaciers, have lakes in their courses. From Kenai Lake the stream flows for 15 miles through an extension of the valley occupied by the lake, but filled with glacial sediments. The stream has cut a secondary valley into those sediments. Cooper Creek and Russian Creek, heading in lakes to the south, are the largest tributaries entering this section of the river. It then enters Skilak Lake, 16 miles long and 2½ miles wide, at elevation 150 feet, from which it meanders some 40 miles to Cook Inlet.

The Alaska Railroad passes through a large part of the basin near the eastern side, paralleled in part by a highway that is being extended from Seward to Anchorage. Both ends of Kenai Lake can be reached by road from Seward, and seasonal road travel is possible to the mouth of the river. A small amount of mining activity takes place in the basin, but not to full potentialities. Gold, antimony, and an unknown amount of other metallic minerals occur in the upper basin, and coal deposits underlie a large portion of the lower basin. Tourist trade has been of importance because of the scenery, accessibility, and variety of game. Farming in the lower basin is a prospect for development.

The basin offers numerous possibilities for small-power installations at relatively low construction cost. The only development considered is one using Kenai Lake for storage.

Kenai Lake Site

An earthfill dam 100 feet high with a crest length of 1,800 feet, near Coopers Landing at the outlet of Kenai Lake would back water over the delta being built into Kenai Lake at the southeast end by the braided mouth of Snow River. This would bring the lake waters closer to the divide with the Resurrection Bay drainage to the south, which may be further accomplished by a small amount of dredging in the Snow River. The divide area, made up principally of bedrock, would be pierced by a tunnel less than 4 miles long from Kenai Lake to Bear Lake, now at elevation 200. By means of a one-half-mile tunnel to Lost Creek, Bear Lake could be lowered at least 50 feet. A power plant at the north end of Bear Lake would produce more than 140,000,000 kilowatt-hours of firm energy each year. Control of Kenai Lake by the dam and tunnel would provide an active storage capacity of 1,000,000 acre-feet. The power plant would be within the boundaries of the Gulf of Alaska area. Conditions are favorable for tying this power production into networks to the north as well as to Seward and the nearby outlying villages and farms. Highway and railroad relocation would be involved in the plan given above.

Sixmile Creek Basin

Sixmile Creek, on Kenai Peninsula, drains northward from the Kenai Mountains to Turnagain Arm of Cook Inlet. Nine miles from its mouth the creek divides into the East Fork Sixmile Creek and Canyon Creek. Small glaciers and lakes occur at the heads of the minor tributaries. All of Canyon Creek and the main stem, and the lower part of East Fork, are in narrow rock canyons. Gold placer mining is taking place in the basin, and a road from Turnagain Arm to Seward and other Kenai points passes through the basin. Construction operations are underway to connect the road to Anchorage. Two damsites were investigated, but there is doubt about their practicability because of inadequate storage capacity.

Eklutna Creek Basin

Eklutna Creek enters Knik Arm from the Chugach Mountains 24 miles northeast of Anchorage. The principal feature of the basin is Eklutna Lake, which is at an elevation of 868 feet and is 7 miles long and 1 mile wide. The lake is in a steep-sided trough-like valley, 23 miles long, headed by a glacier and snow field. The City of Anchorage has constructed a low storage dam at the lake outlet, a downstream diversion dam, and a tunnel to a power plant which has an installed capacity of 2,000 kilowatts. The urgent need for power in the Anchorage vicinity resulted in a study of the possibilities of more complete regulation of the waters of upper Eklutna Creek. Preliminary work was done by the Geological Survey, and recent investigations have been completed by the Bureau of Reclamation. The contemplated improvements include (1) reconstruction of the existing storage dam and spillway to raise the normal lake surface 2 feet, (2) construction of a tunnel 4½ miles long to carry the water northward toward Knik Arm, and (3) construction of penstocks and a power plant on the south side of Knik Arm. The active reser-

voir capacity of 123,000 acre-feet would partially regulate the runoff. The annual firm generation would exceed 100,000,000 kilowatt-hours.

Matanuska River Basin

Matanuska River, about 65 miles long, heads in the Matanuska Glacier and flows into the east end of Knik Arm of Cook Inlet. The river and its floodplain form a valley within a valley, the higher-level valley being a broad, U-shaped, irregular trough carved by glaciers. The terrace thus formed is partially bedrock, and a much smaller portion is topped by unconsolidated fill and small lakes. The remainder of the basin consists of mountain slopes deeply etched by tributary streams.

The basin is best known for the pioneer agricultural colonies near the mouth. Coal resources are also important. Gold and tungsten are produced near the basin.

The largest town is Palmer, located in the agricultural area of the lower valley. Caribou Creek, Chickaloon River and Kings River are the principal tributaries. Four sites are considered for potential power production.

Caribou Creek Sites

Caribou Creek flows into Matanuska River at its head near Matanuska Glacier. A preliminary study of the stream suggests partial regulation of the runoff at a site 5 miles above the mouth, where a concrete dam 350 feet high would have a crest length of 1,000 feet. The runoff would be partially regulated by an active storage capacity of 170,000 acre-feet. A power plant at this site, designated Caribou Creek No. 1, would generate in excess of 40,000,000 kilowatt-hours of firm energy each year.

The tailwater could be diverted through a 5-mile tunnel to a second power plant, Caribou Creek No. 2, located just above the normal water surface of the reservoir at Matanuska River Site No. 1. The annual firm output of Caribou Creek No. 2 would be more than 60,000,000 kilowatt-hours.

Matanuska River Site No. 1

The higher of two power sites on the Matanuska River is located one-half mile downstream from Hicks Creek. The flood plain of the river, 400 feet wide, is confined by steep rock walls. Bedrock is at an unknown depth, probably too deep for consideration of a concrete dam. An earthfill dam constructed to a height of 400 feet above the river level would have a crest length of 1,200 feet and would impound 290,000 acre-feet of active storage. Firm energy generation at this site would exceed 100,000,000 kilowatt-hours annually. Silting of the reservoir would be a problem.

Rush Lake Site

By diverting the flow of Boulder Creek, a lower tributary of Chickaloon River, at a point 6 miles upstream from their confluence, it would be possible to utilize natural basins to the south for storage. From the point of diversion the water would be conveyed by a 6,500-foot canal and a 2,600-foot tunnel to Rush Lake at 2,400 feet elevation, thence by a 1,500-foot tunnel to the unnamed lakes to the south at elevation 1,900, and finally by a 6,000-foot tunnel and a penstock to a power plant at the Matanuska River elevation of 930 feet. A 25-foot-high dam at the outlet of Rush Lake and a 100-foot dam and 90-foot saddle dike on the lower lake combined with drawdown tunnels tapping each lake, would be necessary to provide 60,000 acre-feet of active storage space. The power plant would produce at least 40,000,000 kilowatt-hours of firm energy annually.

Matanuska River Site No. 2

Nine miles upstream from Palmer, the Matanuska River makes two sharp turns in passing through a relatively narrow rock canyon with nearly vertical walls 175 feet high. The floodplain extends from wall to wall, a width of 450 feet. The depth to bedrock is unknown, but if it is too great for a concrete dam, an earth dam could be constructed to raise the water 150 feet above the floodplain. The active storage capacity of 180,000 acre-feet would only partially regulate the inflow below the upstream reservoirs. The annual firm production of a power plant at this site would exceed 90,000,000 kilowatt-hours. Economic regulation of the runoff would require more storage than suggested above, particularly if a large amount of dead storage is required for silt deposition. There are some possibilities of additional upstream storage, but these have not been studied in sufficient detail.

Susitna River Basin

The Susitna River is the most strategically situated of all Alaska streams by virtue of its proximity to Anchorage and Fairbanks and the connecting railbelt. The basin occupies the northern half of the Cook Inlet Area and is bounded on the west and north by the Alaska Range, and on the east by the Copper River Plateau.

The river enters Cook Inlet 25 miles west of Anchorage. The main stream heads in a series of glacier-bearing peaks 90 miles south of Fairbanks and 200 miles northeast of Anchorage. The highest of the peaks is Mount Hayes at 13,940 feet. The course of the river for 50 miles is generally southward over a broad alluvial fan and plateau. It then turns sharply westward for 75 miles through a practically continuous canyon incised in a high-level broad valley and thence abruptly south for 125 miles in a broad lowland. The principal tributaries head in high mountain glaciers: the Maclaren River, heading in the Alaska Range; Tyone River from the Talkeetna Mountains; Chulitna River from the Alaska Range in Mount McKinley National Park; Talkeetna River from the Talkeetna Mountains; and the Yentna River system, from a large portion of the Alaska Range.

The economic activity is chiefly in the lower 120 miles of the basin along the Alaska Railroad. Placer gold, lode gold, tungsten, and construction materials are produced in the basin. Coal and other minerals are present, but have received little attention. However, the possibilities of power production and other uses of the Susitna River, including flood control, will vitally affect the economy of the entire railbelt from the Kenai Peninsula to Fairbanks. No large settlements are located within the basin itself.

A reconnaissance of the Susitna River basin suggested seven sites for potential power development: three on the main stem, three on the Talkeetna River, and one on Sheep River, a tributary of the Talkeetna. There is an excellent possibility of adding one or more low-head sites on the Susitna, downstream from Site No. 3 after up-stream regulation is substantially complete. The Yentna and Chulitna basins have not been explored, but maps indicate they warrant future study.

Susitna River Site No. 1

The highest site for a dam on the Susitna River is near the upstream end of the 75-mile canyon section 17 miles below the mouth of Tyone River. It would serve the double function of creating head for this site and impounding regulatory storage for this and downstream sites. The main dam would be in a steep-walled, rock canyon 100 feet wide at the bottom. A concrete dam 575 feet high with a crest length of 1,200 feet would create a reservoir with 9,000,000 acre-feet of active capacity. The left bank would require a supplementary concrete or earthfill saddle dike 225 feet high and 4,500 feet long. The bedrock is steeply dipping metamorphic rock believed capable of supporting the structures with low to moderate cost of grouting and stripping. The canyon is topographically favorable for a

Potential damsite on the Matanuska River.

gravity arch dam. A power plant at this site would generate more than 2,000,000,000 kilowatt-hours of firm energy each year.

Susitna River Site No. 2

Thirty-six miles downstream from Site No. 1 the valley bottom is less than 300 feet wide and rock slopes rise far above the river at 45° angles. Bedrock is believed to be at a reasonable depth below the floodplain. A concrete dam raising the water 425 feet would create a reservoir reaching to the tailwater of Site No. 1, and containing 1,000,000 acre-feet of active storage space. The annual output at this power plant would exceed 2,000,000,000 kilowatt-hours of firm energy.

Susitna River Site No. 3 (Devil Canyon Site)

The third site on the Susitna is 30 miles downstream from Site No. 2, near the mouth of the canyon section. In this reach of the 75-mile canyon, the river occupies the entire width of the valley bottom and creates rapids and low waterfalls over bedrock and shallow overburden. The rock walls rise on steep slopes, approaching vertical in places, to heights of 600 to 1,000 feet above the stream. The bedding of the partly metamorphosed rock is almost vertical and at nearly right angles to the direction of the canyon. The site is topographically favorable for a concrete gravity arch dam, but the

rock quality has not been investigated. A dam high enough to raise the water 525 feet would have a crest length of 1,000 feet and create backwater to Site No. 2. The active storage capacity would be 1,000,000 acre-feet. The firm energy production would be more than 2,600,000,000 kilowatt-hours annually.

Talkeetna River Site No. 1

Talkeetna River, which enters Susitna River 80 miles above its mouth, is geologically and hydrologically similar to the Upper Susitna. Site No. 1 which provides most of the storage regulation for the three Talkeetna sites, is located 40 miles above the mouth of the river. A concrete dam 325 feet high would have a crest length of 2,500 feet and would create an active storage capacity of 750,000 acre-feet, only partially regulating the flow. A power plant at the dam would generate in excess of 140,000,000 kilowatt-hours annually.

Talkeetna River Site No. 2

Twelve miles downstream from Site No. 1 the stream is in a narrow canyon adaptable for a concrete dam 325 feet high with a crest length of 900 feet. Such a dam would impound 220,000 acre-feet, regulating all the inflow below Site No. 1 and backing the water up to that site. The firm energy output would exceed 200,000,000 kilowatt-hours each year.

Talkeetna River Site No. 3

The stream flows through another narrow canyon 10 miles below Site No. 2, just below the mouth of Disappointment Creek. A concrete dam, high enough to raise the water 225 feet utilizing all the head below Site No. 2, would have a crest length of 500 feet. The active storage capacity would be 320,000 acre-feet, only partially regulating the incremental inflow. More than 200,000,000 kilowatt-hours of firm energy would be produced each year.

Sheep River Site

Sheep River enters the Talkeetna 6 miles downstream from Talkeetna Site No. 3. The river flows over a broad valley for most of its length but is constricted in a canyon 14 miles above its mouth. A concrete dam 325 feet high with a 1,500-foot crest length would provide 520,000 acre-feet of active storage, partially regulating the stream. A power plant at this site would have a firm generation of at least 70,000,000 kilowatt-hours annually.

Beluga River Basin

Only a small part of the Beluga River basin has been topographically mapped. A cursory reconnaissance in the basin disclosed that the stream, heading at large glaciers in high mountains, enlarges to a lake where it enters the lowland area, and thence passes through a low ridge before reaching Cook Inlet. A dam 22 miles above the mouth could back water into the lake area, but data are insufficient to estimate the potential energy that might be generated.

Chakachatna River Basin

The central feature of the Chakachatna River basin is Chakachamna Lake at elevation 1,170. The lake, 14 miles long and 2 miles wide, is deeply nestled among high mountains, the tallest of which is Mount Spurr, 11,050 feet high. Two glaciers reach the lake. One forms a barrier between Chakachamna Lake and 6-mile-long Kenibuna Lake, and the other partially blocks the outlet of Chakachamna Lake. The lake is fed by four other large glaciers and numerous small ones. From the lake, Chakachatna River flows around Barrier Glacier before entering a moderately broad terrace and rock-walled valley. After flowing 13 miles in this valley, the river enters the lowland, which it traverses an additional 25 miles to Cook Inlet. The rock on the north side of the deep valley section is composed largely of lavas from Mount Spurr, the northernmost volcano of the Aleutian group. The south bank is granitic, while the outcrops of the lowland are coal-bearing sedimentary rocks.

The best damsite below the ice barrier of the lake is 4 miles downstream where a dam 300 feet high with a 2,000-foot crest length would provide 2,100,000 acre-feet of active storage. The water would be conveyed from the dam through a 9-mile tunnel to a power plant in the valley, resulting in a firm output of more than 880,000,000 kilowatt-hours annually.

Cook Inlet Tidal Power

Cook Inlet has one of the highest tidal ranges in the world. Among the combination of factors that cause such large differences between high and low tides, at times exceeding 50 feet, are the configuration of the inlet and its bottom topography. This potentiality is worthy of future study.

Potential damsite on the Susitna River. This and other sites in the rail belt area have impressive power possibilities.

SOUTHWESTERN REGION

The Southwestern Region comprises the Aleutian Islands, the Alaska Peninsula, and the area which drains into Bristol Bay south and east of the Kuskokwim River basin. There is only a small amount of data on the major streams in the region. The following discussion indicates the lack of necessary information and suggests areas for future investigation. There are no major settlements within the region.

Basins Southwest of Egekik Basin

The Aleutian Islands and the southwestern end of the Alaska Peninsula are featured by small drainage basins and numerous volcanoes. Of the 39 volcanoes that have been active since 1760, all but 7 are situated west of the Egekik River basin. At least 19 others show evidence of activity in very recent geologic time. The important discovery of zinc on Unga Island of the Shumagin Group near the southwestern end of the Alaska Peninsula, and showings of zinc on Sedanka Island near Dutch Harbor in the Fox Island Group, offer encouragement for prospective industries. Like other mineral industries in Alaska, economic development of the resources would depend largely on availability of low-cost hydroelectric power. The paucity of water resources in the areas and the impracticability of power transmission from areas rich in potential hydropower suggest emphasis on the study of the potential energy of the superheated rock in the Aleutian Arc.

Egekik River Basin

The Egekik River is an unimportant feature of its basin. Becharof Lake, occupying a large portion of the basin, is about 40 miles long, extending southeastward to within 5 miles of the Pacific Ocean. The exact elevation of the lake is unknown, but it is probably too low for hydroelectric development. Hot springs on the shore of Becharof Lake, associated with Mount Peulik, an active volcano, offer some evidence of potential volcanic energy development in the area. Prospective use of the energy thus created would depend on the ultimate exploitation of the zinc resources of the district. The southwest end of the Alaska Peninsula has not been thoroughly prospected, but showings of iron, lead, copper, coal, and oil, as well as the zinc, have been noted.

Naknek River Basin

The Naknek River basin is similar to the Egekik basin. Naknek Lake, some 50 miles long, and evidences of volcanic action are the principal natural features. The lake and its arms are nestled among volcanic mountains on the east, but the west side is in a low coastal plain and is probably less than 50 feet above sea level. Most of the lake is within the boundaries of the Mount Katmai National Monument, established because of the natural wonders of the volcanic activity of the area. Of particular interest is the Valley of Ten Thousand Smokes, where countless jets of steam issue from a network of fissures or from domes or craters. The superheated steam is invisible where it first rushes out with a temperature of 1,200° F. It is believed that part of the steam is derived from vaporization of surface drainage, but the presence of some gases other than water vapor suggest that much of it may be of volcanic origin. Practically no seasonal change is noted in the behavior of the jets, but some unconfirmed reports indicate some general decline in activity in the past decade.

Exploitation of volcanic energy has been undertaken in Italy and it is possible that utilization of the subsurface energy of the Naknek and other southwestern Alaska areas, including the Aleutian Islands, may be feasible.

Except for the important fishing and canning industries on the coast, there are no important industries in the area at present. Even the number of tourists visiting the national monument is small.

Kvichak River Basin

The Kvichak River basin may best be identified by the two large lakes in the basin: Lake Clark with an area of 143 square miles, and Lake Iliamna, the largest in Alaska, with 1,226 square miles. The basin, 60 miles wide, extends northeastward from the northeast tip of Bristol Bay for a distance of 170 miles into the northwest slopes of the Aleutian Range. The streams entering Lake Clark are short, and most of them have high gradients. Some of the streams have glacial lakes along their courses. At least one of these, the Tanalian River, contains a lake favorably situated for power development. The lake is 14 miles long and is fed by melting glaciers. The site has not been investigated in the field, but it is reported to lie near elevation 560 or 345 feet above Lake Clark.

Lake Clark drains into Lake Iliamna by way of Newhalen River, with a drop of 165 feet in 23 miles. A low-head development may be possible here. Most of the streams entering Lake Iliamna are short creeks with high gradients draining from the north and east. Some of these streams contain high-level lakes. Pile Bay on the east end of the lake is separated from Cook Inlet by a low mountain ridge 12 miles wide. Field studies of the geology and hydrology of the area have

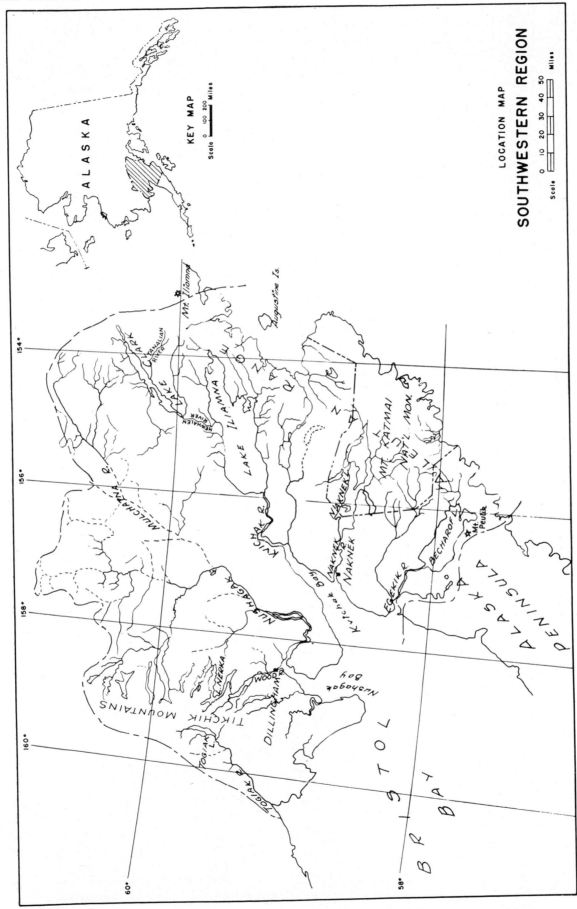

KEY MAP

Scale

0   100   200 Miles

ALASKA

LOCATION MAP

SOUTHWESTERN REGION

Scale

0 10 20 30 40 50 Miles

not been made, but there appear to be excellent possibilities of low-head hydroelectric development by tunneling through the ridge to a power plant at Cook Inlet. The high tidal range in the inlet should be considered in a project here.

Kvichak River, draining Lake Iliamna, is 60 miles long with the lower half affected by tides. It is navigable by launches and barges from Bristol Bay to the lake.

There are no important industries within the basin at present but prospects are very good in the mineral industry, especially in combination with the mineralization on the southeast slopes of the Alaska Range. Copper looks most susceptible of future development but prospecting has also revealed the presence of silver, placer gold, oil and gas showings, and oil shale.

The basin is near areas of recent volcanic activity and there is some possibility of utilizing volcanic energy. Mount Iliamna and nearby Augustine Island issue steam, but there is no direct evidence of favorable geothermal conditions within the basin. A sulphur spring on the shore of Lake Iliamna issues cool water.

Nushagak River Basin

The Nushagak River basin embraces an area from Bristol Bay 220 miles northeastward to the divide with the Kuskokwim basin. It has a width of 100 miles between the Tikchik Mountains to the west and the Kvichak River basin to the southeast. Most of the basin is of a low coastal plain character with only isolated hills. The northwest side of the basin is featured by 12 "finger" lakes emerging from rugged hill slopes. Lake Nerka, with an area of 78 square miles, is the largest of the lakes, which average 34 square miles. The lakes were formed by Ice Age glaciers that carved the preexisting valleys far below sea level. The outlet ends of the lakes are in the coastal plain and it is unknown if sufficient head can be developed for power production, though they have not been examined in the field. The lakes, reached by the Nushagak and Wood Rivers, are spawning grounds for the salmon that form the important fishing industry of Bristol Bay.

Togiak River Basin

Little is known about the details of the Togiak River basin. The basin is located southeast of the delta of the Kuskokwim River. It is 80 miles long and 30 miles wide, trending northeast-southwest. Togiak River, with no important tributaries, drains into Bristol Bay. The headwaters are in a mountainous area with some peaks rising above 5,000 feet. The mountains have been glaciated, resulting in many lakes within the basin. Togiak Lake, largest of these, is 15 miles long. The lack of adequate information on the basin precludes any discussion of development of the stream.

YUKON-KUSKOKWIM REGION

Most of Alaska is a plateau lying between the Alaska Range on the south and the Brooks Range on the north. The major portion of this area is drained by the Yukon River and the Kuskokwim River, the two largest streams in Alaska. Only a portion of the vast power potentialities of the region have been reconnoitered.

Kuskokwim River Basin

The Kuskokwim River is the second largest stream in Alaska in both length and drainage area. The basin, 500 miles long and averaging 100 miles in width, trends northeast-southwest, paralleling in part the lower course of the Yukon. The northeastern two-thirds of the basin is a broad lowland with topographic continuity northward into the Kantishna basin and southward into the Nushagak basin. The drainage divides into both these basins at elevations less than 800 feet. This part of the Kuskokwim basin is enclosed by the Alaska Range on the southeast and the dissected plateau forming the Kuskokwim Hills on the northwest.

The principal feature of this section is the vast plain, covered with swamps and tundra, sloping gently northwestward. The plain was built up by outwash from the glaciers of the Ice Age and sediments from the present tributaries and has forced the main stream into the slopes of the Kuskokwim Hills. The stream meanders near the base of the hills for more than 200 miles to Sleitmut, where it abruptly assumes a course westward for 80 miles. In this section the valley narrows abruptly from 100 miles to an average of about 1 mile. After leaving the hills, the stream flows over the large featureless delta built jointly with the Yukon River.

There are no outstanding tributaries to the Kuskokwim. The largest of these originate in the Alaska Range and flow northwestward to join the main stream near the Kuskokwim Hills. These include the South Fork, Big, Swift, Stony, and Hoholitna Rivers. The principal tributaries from the Kuskokwim Hills are the Takotna, Holitna, George, and Aniak Rivers. The largest settlements in the basin are Bethel, near the mouth, and McGrath, at the confluence with the Takotna.

The entire basin is within the region of permanently frozen ground. It is not implied that all of the ground

Damsite near Georgetown, Alaska, on Kuskokwim River. A reservoir here would have great power possibilities.

remains frozen through all seasons, for the amount and distribution of ground ice is a function of the nature of the soil, ground-water conditions, topography, and other modifying factors. It is likely that artificial drainage and cultivation can modify some areas of permafrost to excellent farm land.

The present economy of the area is based on trapping and mining in the upper basin and fishing and trapping in the lower basin. The mineral resources include placer gold and tin, mercury, and antimony vein deposits, and some coal in the Kuskokwim Hills. Platinum is obtained from placer workings in the lower basin. No commercial farming is practiced in the basin.

Until extensive surveys are made, the potential economic development of the basin is difficult to predict. The extent of presently arable lands and of the areas that may be reclaimed by irrigation or drainage is

unknown. Subject to extensive surveys of the lands and the mineral resources, the principal potential use of the water of the basin is power development. The prospective uses for the power are limited to industries in other basins and to those that may be attracted by abundant power.

Kuskokwim River Site

Although some sites for development of power may exist on some of the tributaries, consideration has been given to only one large development on the main stream. There are several possible sites for dams in the stretch of the river that flows through the Kuskokwim Hills. The best site is situated about 8 miles upstream from the village of Crooked Creek. The floodplain is 1,500 feet wide abutting directly on moderately steep bedrock slopes on both banks. The alluvium of the floodplain is of unknown depth and character, but is probably relatively impervious and of moderate bearing capacity. An earthfill dam to create a reservoir with a surface elevation 300 feet above the river bed would have a crest length of 3,000 feet. A reservoir at that elevation would have a surface area of 1,800,000 acres and a total capacity of 230,000,000 acre-feet of which 40,000,000 acre-feet would be active storage. It would take 10 years to fill the reservoir. A power plant at this site could produce more than 4,800,000,000 kilowatt-hours of firm energy each year.

In consideration of a dam height of optimum value it should be realized that a considerable part of the area covered by the reservoir may be more valuable as farm land or placer property. The most economical dam height also depends on the exact height of the saddles to the Kantishna and Nushagak basins and on the length of time required to fill the reservoir.

Yukon River Basin

The Yukon is one of the great rivers of North America, ranking fifth in length and in size of basin area. Heading in British Columbia within 30 miles of the Pacific Ocean it flows northwest 900 miles to enter Alaska at the town of Eagle. The river crosses and recrosses the Arctic Circle near Fort Yukon, veers to the southwest, and flows through a many-mouthed delta into the Bering Sea, having traversed 1,400 miles and fallen 800 feet in its course across Alaska. The mouth of the river is more than 300 miles inside the Bering Sea winter ice field. Features of the basin are the Yukon Flats on and near the Arctic Circle with an area of 10,000 square miles, and the coastal lowland and delta region, extending inland about 100

Damsite at mile 356 on Nenana River.

miles from the Bering Sea. Over half of the total drainage area of 330,000 square miles lies in Canada. The potential power resources of the region are vast and undeveloped. More than 16,000,000,000 kilowatt-hours of firm energy could be produced each year at sites on the main stem of the Yukon River alone. This is equivalent to an annual discharge of 8,000,000 barrels of oil from the Yukon River into the Bering Sea.

During several months in the summer, the sea and the river are open to navigation, and river steamers carry freight and passengers as far up the Yukon as Whitehorse, Canada, a distance of 1,960 miles. Tanana River, the principal tributary, is navigable for large steamers to Nenana, and for small steamers, except during periods of low water, to Fairbanks. During high water the Tanana is navigable as far as the mouth of Delta River. Porcupine River is navigable; a launch can be chartered at Fort Yukon to Rampart House in Yukon Territory near the International Boundary. Down the Yukon at the town of Koyukuk, connection is made with boats operating on the Koyukuk River to Bettles. Covered freight barges are pushed by the steamers.

The Yukon, like every river, has a personality that must be studied and understood before control is attempted. Here the difficulty is ice. There are two seasons in the north country, the "closed" season when the Yukon is frozen over and the "open" season when it is open to navigation. Any time after October 1, but usually in November, slush ice forms in the river and slowly bridges into a stationary sheet, reaching a maximum thickness in April. In May the melting snow causes the river to rise rapidly and thus the ice breaks. Jams are frequent, and huge blocks of ice 3 to 8 feet thick pile up and push out on the banks until the obstruction moves or a new channel forms. In the upper part of the river 10 days are usually required for all the ice to pass a given point.

One of the peculiarities of the basin is the high ratio of runoff to precipitation which averaged more than 65 percent for the years 1911–13. Principal reasons for such high runoff are short growing season, sparse vegetation, receding glaciers, low evaporation, and ground that is perpetually frozen to bedrock except for a surface layer that thaws in the summer.

Fairbanks is the most important town in the basin. The four divisions for discussion of potential power

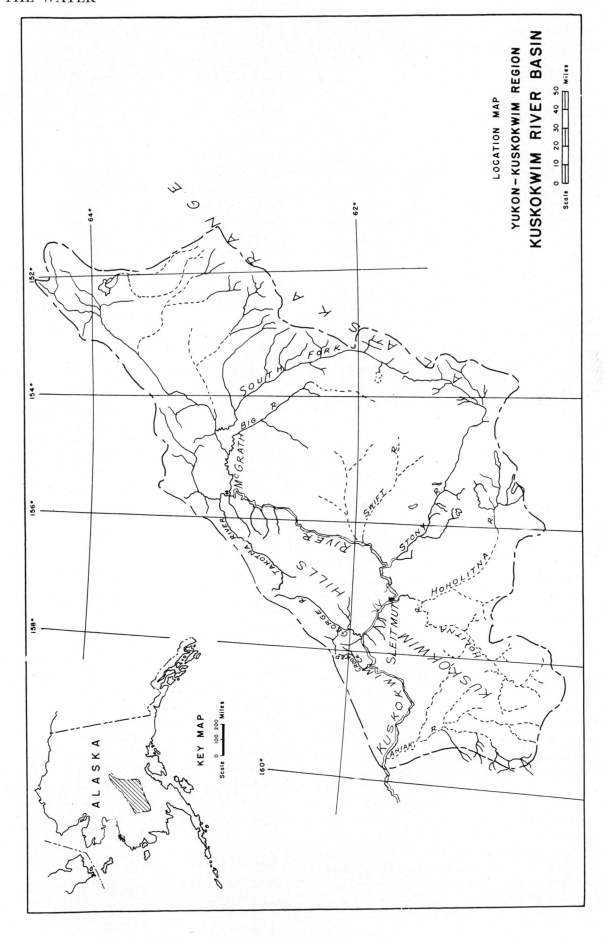

LOCATION MAP
YUKON–KUSKOKWIM REGION
KUSKOKWIM RIVER BASIN

development are: Upper Yukon River Area, Yukon Flats Area, Tanana River Basin, and Lower Yukon River Area.

Upper Yukon River Area

At the upper end of the basin, only a few miles from the Pacific Ocean, the glaciers astride the Coast Range that separates Alaska and British Columbia mark the beginning of the Yukon. The difference in elevation between top and toe of the glaciers on the Yukon Slope is more than 5,000 feet. The melt cascades into a group of parallel glaciated valleys to form several of the most beautiful lakes in Canada. These lakes—Atlin, Fantail, Tagish, Tutshi, and Bennett—have a total surface area of about 500 square miles. The general elevation of the lakes in this region is 2,100 feet above sea level and their drainage area is 5,000 square miles. The physical conditions are favorable for regulating nearly 6,000,000 acre-feet of the flow of Lewes River and diverting the water to power plants on the Taiya River near Skagway. The plan was discussed previously under the Juneau Area of the Southeastern Region.

White River Basin

White River is the first important tributary of the Yukon which drains a portion of Alaska. Heading on the north slope of the St. Elias Range, the river flows generally northward from Alaska to the Yukon River in Canada. Less than half of the drainage area is in Alaska. Runoff is heavy, but the only possible dam sites are in the canyon just across the International Boundary in Canada.

Fortymile River Basin

Crossing the border from Alaska, the Fortymile River joins the Yukon in Canada. Most of the round-shaped basin drained by its North and South Forks is in Alaska. Below the confluence of the forks the river enters a long canyon section. Reconnaissance maps show good topography for dam sites in **V**-shaped canyon sections, but photographs and descriptions indicate possible difficulties with a heavy overburden of gravel. Field investigation, however, would no doubt reveal some feasible dam sites. A dam on the main stem, in a canyon below the mouth of Steel Creek, would be 375 feet high with a 2,000-foot crest and would impound 2,900,000 acre-feet of active storage. A power plant at this site would produce more than 250,000,000 kilowatt-hours of firm energy each year.

Eagle-Circle Development

This development is named for the two villages of Eagle and Circle, located on the Yukon River 10 miles and 150 miles, respectively, below the International Boundary. Reconnaissance maps indicate a constricted section on the river in the reach between 50 miles and 37 miles upstream from Circle. The possibility of finding a dam site in this section is unknown. Extensive investigations would be necessary to determine ice storage requirements in the reservoir before any estimate could be made of a potential economical dam height. Such studies might disclose the necessity of storing the break-up ice from 900 miles of the river upstream in Canada plus that from tributaries. Any studies of this site should be integrated with additional studies on the Rampart site, downstream, and the possible diversion of waters from the Lewes River, upstream.

Yukon Flats Area

At Circle the Yukon River enters a valley that is 200 miles long and from 40 to 100 miles wide. This is the Yukon Flats. The climate is severe with wide extremes in temperature between summer and winter. From 2 to 20 miles wide, the river in this stretch has many new and old channels with innumerable islands. The stream gradient is less than 1 foot per mile.

A number of years ago an agricultural experiment station was operated at Rampart in the lower end of the valley. From results obtained it is known that thousands of acres are suitable for agricultural production. There are more than eight million acres below an elevation of 1,000 feet, but hundreds of lakes cover from one to two million acres.

Porcupine River Basin

Fort Yukon, the largest settlement in the flats, is located one mile north of the Arctic Circle at the confluence of the Yukon River and the Porcupine River. The latter river is an artery of commerce for northeastern Alaska and a means of access to the MacKenzie River delta country in Canada. Midway upstream it crosses the International Boundary in a canyon 75 miles long. Some 30 or 40 miles of the canyon are in Alaska. Available data are insufficient to determine potentialities for control and development, but eventually this section of the river should be investigated.

Chandalar River Basin

The Chandalar River heads on the south slope of Brooks Range and flows south to join the Yukon 20 miles

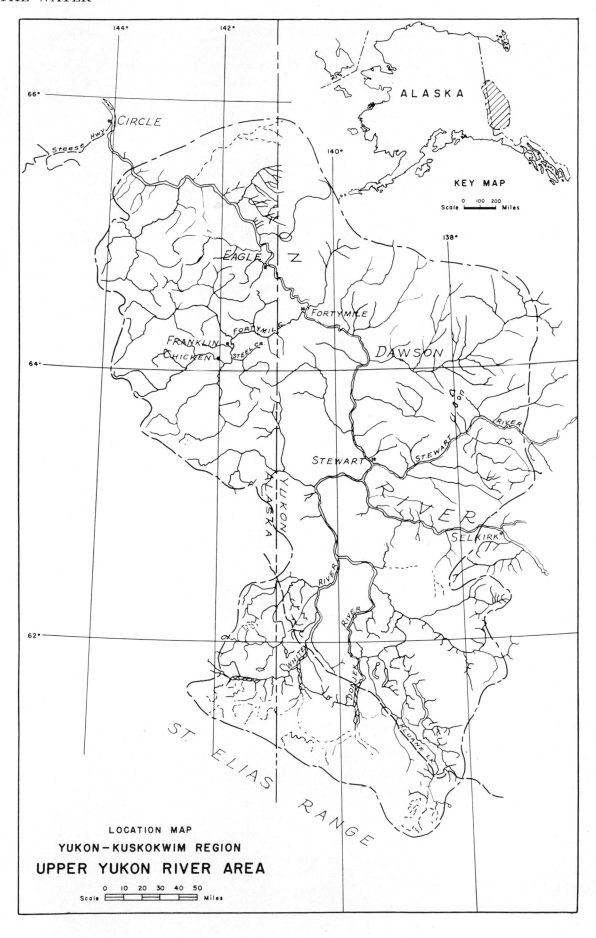

LOCATION MAP
YUKON–KUSKOKWIM REGION
UPPER YUKON RIVER AREA

Scale 0 10 20 30 40 50 Miles

downstream from Fort Yukon. Data are unavailable for an estimate of power potentialities. Promising mining development exists at the headwaters near the village of Chandalar between North Fork and Middle Fork, 120 miles by trail from the Yukon River.

Rampart Site

At the village of Stevens 85 miles north-northwest of Fairbanks, the Yukon Flats suddenly narrows and ends at the head of a constricted river section 100 miles long. Midway down this stretch is Rampart, a town of 1,500 people during the "Klondike Rush" but now reduced to less than 200 people. Downstream from the town of Rampart, canyon walls hug the Yukon River nearly to the mouth of the Tanana River, giving rise to the name of "Lower Ramparts."

Reconnaissance topography indicates several potential dam sites in "Lower Ramparts," but the best site probably will be found about 31 miles downstream from the village of Rampart. If field inspection of the geology and topography confirm earlier reconnaissance, this site on the Yukon River would easily be one of the major potential hydroelectric power developments in North America. Rampart dam would block the mouth of the Yukon Flats, making a vast reservoir of the area. Unlike the Columbia River, which has scarcely enough storage capacity for complete regulation, the Yukon River would have so much capacity in the flats to limit the height of a dam at the Rampart site. A dam 290 feet high with a crest length of 2,500 feet, would create a reservoir with an active storage capacity of 130,000,000 acre-feet. The annual firm generation of the power plant would exceed 8,800,000,000 kilowatt-hours. Development at this site should be coordinated with power potentialities both upstream and downstream. Use of river regulation for improvement of navigation should also be investigated.

Tanana River Basin

The principal tributary of the Yukon is the Tanana River, which is formed by the confluence of the Chisana River and the Nabesna River near the International Boundary. The Alaska Highway meets the river at this junction and follows it downstream to the town of Fairbanks, second largest city in the Territory.

Chisana River Basin

The Chisana River heads in glaciers on the northeast slopes of the Wrangell Mountains. The stream flows northeast for 60 miles, where it abruptly turns towards the northwest and traverses another 50 miles to its confluence with the Nabesna River. Reconnaissance topography indicates a possible dam site between Chivolda Creek and Sheep Creek, about 22 miles below Chisana Glacier. At this site, designated Chisana River No. 1, a dam 230 feet high with a crest 1,500 feet long would impound 510,000 acre-feet of active storage capacity. A power plant would produce more than 40,000,000 kilowatt-hours of firm energy each year.

The tailwater from this site would be diverted into a series of tunnels with a total length of 26 miles which would terminate midway between Stone Creek and Lick Creek just above the maximum pool elevation of the potential Nabesna reservoir. The flow of Stuver Creek would be collected enroute. At the outlet of the tunnel, a power plant known as Chisana River No. 2 would have a yearly firm output in excess of 200,000,000 kilowatt-hours.

Nabesna River Basin

The Nabesna River also originates in the glaciers of the Wrangell Mountains and flows northeast for 75 miles to its junction with the Chisana. Two miles above the mouth of the Cheslina River, a dam 200 feet high would have a crest length of 2,500 feet and would create a reservoir having an active capacity of 1,500,000 acre-feet. Using the regulated flow of the Nabesna and the diverted flow of the Chisana, a power plant at this site would produce more than 120,000,000 kilowatt-hours of firm energy annually.

Field inspection of the Chisana and Nabesna Valleys might reveal unfavorable geological conditions for dam construction, but there is also the possibility that better sites than those herein described could be located. In consideration of these sites, attention should be given to ultimate needs for irrigation of potential agricultural lands in lower Tanana Valley; flood protection for the Alaska Highway, city of Fairbanks, farms and other downstream property; draining of innumerable swamps annually filled by flood waters; and navigation on the Tanana River.

Nenana River Basin

The Nenana River originates in glaciers located on the northern slopes of the Alaska Range and then flows north to join the Tanana River at the village of Nenana. The Alaska Railroad follows the valley for the greater part of its length. Healy, situated near Mount McKinley National Park, is the coal mining center of the Nenana District and is one of a limited number of sites

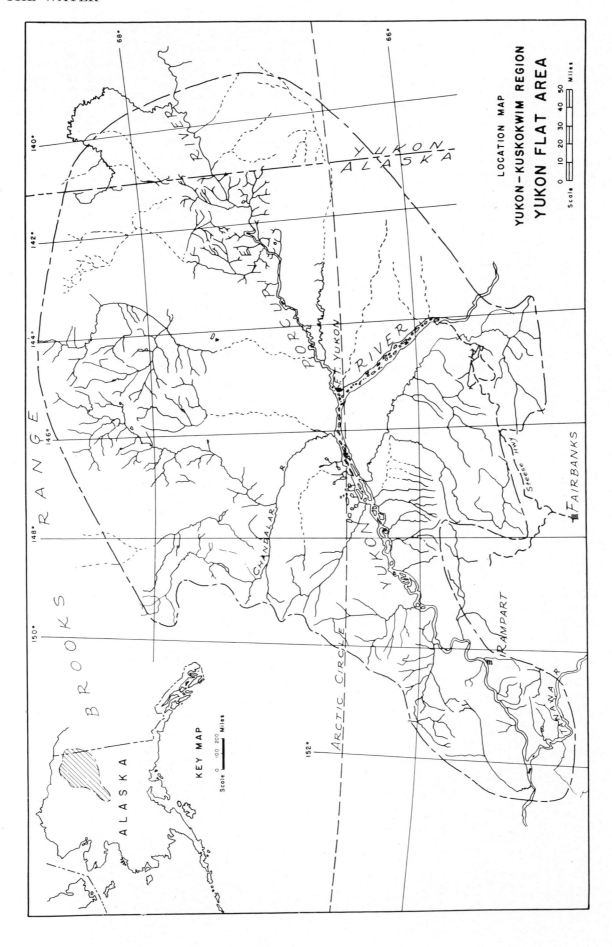

LOCATION MAP
YUKON–KUSKOKWIM REGION
YUKON FLAT AREA

Scale
0 10 20 30 40 50 Miles

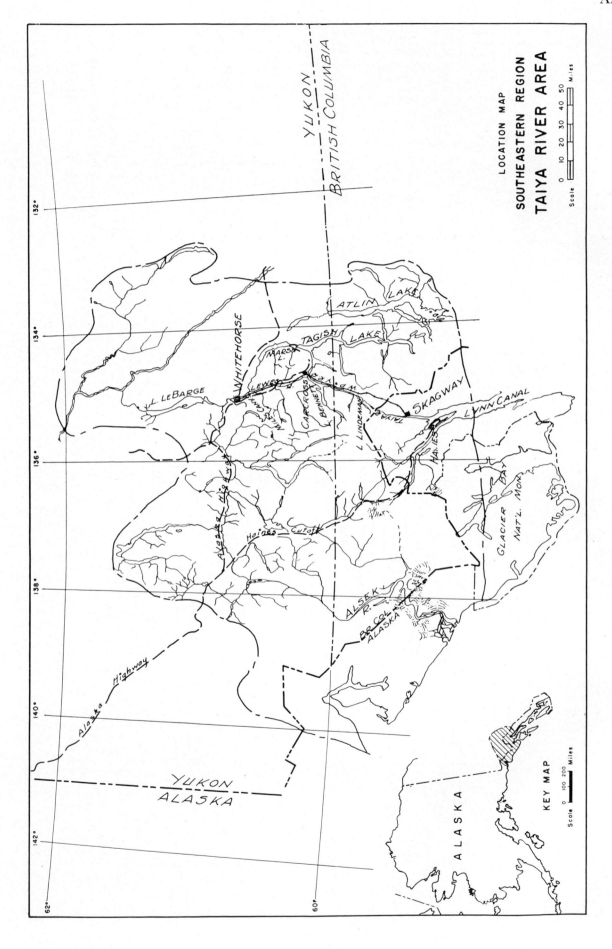

LOCATION MAP

SOUTHEASTERN REGION

TAIYA RIVER AREA

Scale
0 10 20 30 40 50
Miles

KEY MAP

Scale
0   100   200   Miles

considered for a synthetic fuels plant. The plant would require substantial amounts of electric power and regulated cooling water.

There are a number of possible plans for development of power and other uses of the stream and its tributaries. Maximum development, however, would involve consideration of expensive railroad relocation and the possibility of sacrificing the scenic value of portions of the valley. The railroad is not only a transportation route between Anchorage and the interior, but also the only access to the adjacent national park. With these limitations in mind the following plan of basin development is tentatively outlined.

Six miles southeast of Windy railroad station a 290-foot dam with a 1,000-foot crest would impound 550,000 acre-feet of active storage. The power plant, Nenana River No. 1, would have an annual firm production of more than 60,000,000 kilowatt-hours. The tail water could be diverted through a 9-mile tunnel to a power plant near Carlo, Nenana River No. 2. Annual generation at this site would exceed 70,000,000 kilowatt-hours of firm energy. The river could be diverted again 2 miles further downstream through a 9-mile tunnel to a power plant, Nenana River No. 3, above McKinley Park station. This plant would produce at least 80,000,000 kilowatt-hours of firm energy each year. The tailwater from this plant would again be diverted through a 20-mile tunnel to the slope southeast of Ferry station. Before entering the penstocks, the flow would be supplemented by diversion from the Toklat River, the East Fork of Toklat River, and the Teklanika River. A total of 26 miles of tunnel would be required for these diversions, and a 300-foot dam on the Teklanika would impound 550,000 acre-feet of active storage. Using the total flow, a power plant designated Nenana River No. 4 would have an annual firm production in excess of 320,000,000 kilowatt-hours.

Main Stem of Tanana River and Other Tributaries

Although the Tanana River falls more than 1,000 feet from the mouth of the Nabesna River to the confluence with the Yukon River, development of the main stem appears to be difficult except by means of relatively low dams. There is a report of a contracted section called Mason Narrows just above the mouth of the Volkmar River; no topography is available to substantiate this report.

On down the Tanana Valley, the Robertson, Johnson, Gerstle, and Delta rivers have large flows and steep gradients, but there are no readily discernible storage sites on available topographic maps. An exception is a possible small development on the headwaters of the Delta River near Isabel Pass, 4 miles west of the Richardson Highway. If power were needed in that vicinity, storage were required for irrigation of Tanana River Valley lands near the village of Big Delta, or flood protection were required for the Richardson Highway or other property, a project here might prove feasible. Investigation should also be made of a possible site on the Chena River for the multiple purposes of power production, irrigation of lands near Fairbanks, flood control protection for that same city, and municipal and industrial water supply.

From Big Delta downstream to the Yukon is the potential 4-million-acre Tanana Valley agricultural district. At present only a small amount of land is being cultivated in the valley, amounting to about 2,000 acres in the vicinity of Fairbanks. The Fairbanks area is served by the Alaska, Richardson, and Steese highways, Tanana River steamers, and the Alaska Railroad. The Geological Survey is doing field work on permafrost studies in this area.

Lower Yukon River Area

From the confluence with the Tanana to the Bering Sea the Yukon meanders over a broad valley under a low gradient. Though locally partially constricted there are no favorable conditions for power development on the main stem. The greatest immediate need in the Lower Yukon is the improvement of the channels for navigation. Without upstream regulation of flow the cost of maintenance is high.

The Koyukuk is the only important tributary to this section of the river. It drains a large portion of the south slopes of the Brooks Range to the north. No reconnaissance has been made of the basin, and only a small section has been topographically mapped. The Alatna River tributary will be mentioned subsequently in connection with the Kobuk Basin, but no other data are available to make possible an evaluation of the water resources of the basin.

SEWARD PENINSULA REGION

A land mass projects 200 miles from the center of western Alaska, separated only by the Bering Strait from Siberian mainland 56 miles away. North and south the Seward Peninsula is 140 miles across the broad portion. Relief in the interior is strong with the Bendeleben, Kigulaik, and Darby Mountains rising to elevations of 2,500 feet, and individual peaks reaching more than 3,500 feet. Most of the peninsula is tundra that seldom thaws more than a few inches below the surface. Precipitation on the mountain slopes total as much as 40 inches a year while low elevation tundra flats receive only several inches. Ratio of runoff to precipitation is unusually high.

Nome, the largest community, was the scene of an early-day gold rush. Dog team races held each year from Nome on the Norton Sound northeast across the peninsula to Candle on Kotzebue Sound and return are world famous. Much of the region is suitable for grazing of reindeer, and that industry, confined by Federal control to native ownership, numbered herds totaling more than a half million animals at one time. The gold coast stretches for 300 miles along Norton Sound with deposits in streams, deltas, and beaches, thinly disseminated in permanently frozen sand and gravel. Elsewhere on the peninsula are deposits of bismuth, antimony, silver, lead, graphite, tin, tungsten, mercury, platinum, and coal. Strategic mineral deposits assure the region of increasing activity in extractive industries.

Conservation of water resources ultimately will be desirable for utilization in extractive industries and for municipal supplies and power production. Principal rivers are the Koyuk and the Fish draining the south slope, the Kuzitrin and the Kruzgamepa flowing westward from the interior and joining to empty into the Imuruk Basin, thence into Bering Strait, and the Kiwalik that empties into Kotzebue Sound. Several small streams are important because of present utilization for mining and municipal supplies.

Unfortunately, there are no readily discernible potential hydroelectric power developments of major importance. Ultimate development of mineral resources will probably require importation of power in addition to development of limited local power sources.

Koyuk River Basin

The Koyuk River, with a basin area of 2,000 square miles, drains the southeastern part of the peninsula and runs into Norton Bay of Norton Sound. Information is scant but the only likely dam site probably would be found one mile above the confluence of Peace River with the Koyuk.

Fish River Basin

Draining the south slope of Bendeleben Mountains and the west slope of Darby Mountains, the Fish River has a basin area of more than 2,000 square miles. Actually there are two large basins, one drained by the Fish and the other by the Niukluk River, a tributary. Locale of important mineral deposits, the water of the Niukluk and tributary creeks has been used extensively for hydraulic mining.

On upper Fish River is an oval valley 10 miles long and 15 miles wide. Leaving the valley the river drops down a narrow stretch 10 miles long and less than a mile wide with abrupt walls. A dam in this section, 140 feet high with a crest length of 5,000 feet, would impound 1,250,000 acre-feet of active storage. The annual firm energy production would be at least 40,000,000 kilowatt-hours.

Kuzitrin River Basin

The Kuzitrin River with its tributary, the Kruzgamepa River, drains the central portion of Seward Peninsula and flows west into Imuruk Basin, a freshwater extension of Grantley Harbor of Port Clarence. Near Bunker Hill is favorable topography for a dam and reservoir. Further reconnaissance would be necessary to determine the ultimate potentialities of this site; it is considered an alternate to the Tuksuk site downstream on the Kuzitrin. The reservoir created above Bunker Hill would provide water transportation to several mining camps in the basin.

Salmon Lake Site

Kruzgamepa River, the southern tributary of the Kuzitrin, drains 475 square miles of mountainous area. In its precipitous headwaters are several small potential power developments, one of which is especially worthy of consideration.

A small multiple-purpose project could be developed with storage at Salmon Lake on the upper Kruzgamepa River. An 80-foot dam at the outlet of this lake would have a crest length of about 1,000 feet and would impound 180,000 acre-feet of active storage. From the upper end of the lake, a 6-mile tunnel would carry water to Nome River. A buried conduit would convey the combined flows of Salmon Lake and upper Nome River a distance of 16 miles to a short tunnel and a 5,000-foot penstock leading to a power plant on the Snake River. An annual firm generation of more than 40,000,000 kilowatt-hours would be possible at this site. The water would be discharged into the Snake River at a high enough elevation for gravity diversion by downstream mining interests for use in thawing frozen ground prior to dredging operations. At present a substantial amount of energy is being consumed in pumping water for this purpose. The buried conduit from Nome River to Snake River would be in frozen sedimentary formations throughout most of its length, and a large portion of the construction would be on steep sidehills. Considerable study will be necessary on water temperatures and temperature losses in transmission

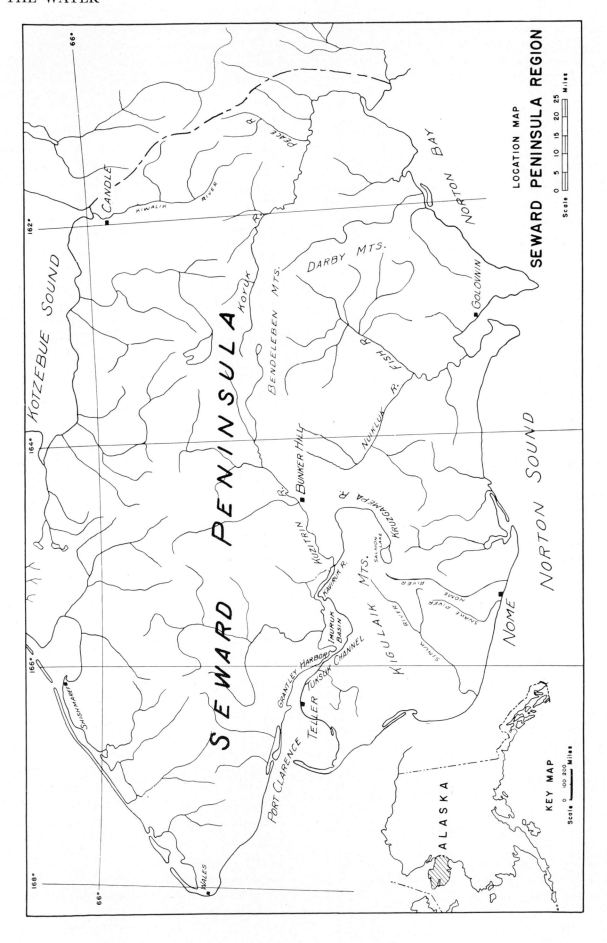

LOCATION MAP

SEWARD PENINSULA REGION

Scale

0   5   10   15   20   25   Miles

KEY MAP

Scale

0   100   200   Miles

in order that the conduit may be designed to prevent freezing during the severe winters. Investigation should also be made of the possibility of diverting the upper Sinuk River to the upper Nome River.

Tuksuk Site

A potential power site exists in Tuksuk Channel, which joins Imuruk Basin with Port Clarence. A topographic map indicates that the water surface could be raised 100 feet by a dam with a crest length of 2,500 feet. It would require 9 years to fill the reservoir, which would cover 250,000 acres and have an active storage capacity of 4,500,000 acre-feet. A power plant at this site would produce in excess of 120,000,000 kilowatt-hours of firm energy each year. The site on the Kuzitrin at Bunker Hill is considered an alternate to this development. More detailed studies may indicate the desirability of coordinated operation of both power plants.

Kiwalik River Basin

The Kiwalik River drains 800 square miles on the north side of Seward Peninsula, flowing into Kotzebue Sound near the village of Candle. There is a possible dam site just above Candle, but the runoff of the stream is so small that a power development at this location was not considered.

ARCTIC REGION

The Brooks Range forms an east-west mountain barrier extending completely across the northern portion of the Territory. The land to the north is the Arctic Slope. It is an isolated and barren desert, almost uninhabited by man or beast, in which precipitation averages only 5 inches annually. The slope is treeless except for the high mountain sides and the willow-lined lower river reaches. The tundra-covered terrain is impassable by ordinary means during the brief summer, but during winter months transportation presents no unusual difficulties. Most of the Eskimo inhabitants are nomadic and move along the coast in search of seal, walrus, and whales which are reasonably plentiful in the Arctic Ocean. The only village of any consequence is Barrow, which is the most northerly inhabited point in North America.

The slope is not wasteland. It is capable of supporting a substantial number of reindeer herds that would be valuable for meat and hides. Large areas are unexplored and may contain strategic mineral deposits. Naval Petroleum Reserve No. 4, covering 35,000 square miles, is the world's largest exclusive oil claim. Oil that has the color of honey, smells like gasoline, and pours at 70° F. below zero has been found in a test bore hole. Exploration has been underway since August 1944; however, the field has yet to be proved.

South of the Brooks Range lie the Kobuk and Noatak Rivers, draining an area about the size of Seward Peninsula. The only settlements in the vicinity are several small villages, the largest of which is Kotzebue on Baldwin Peninsula.

Future development of regional water resources would depend on the extent of the needs of the extractive mineral industry for hydrolectric power and for industrial uses. Construction and operation of hydraulic works would be complicated by low temperature and snow, but engineering experience gained on dam sites at high elevations of the Rocky Mountains in the States would be valuable in this region. The major obstacles would be location and transportation of suitable materials.

Kobuk River Basin

The Kobuk River basin lies between the Noatak River basin on the north and the Yukon River basin on the south. The river delta, covering more than 150 square miles on Hotham Inlet of Kotzebue Sound is interlaced with multiple channels. It is 450 miles to the headwaters but the lower 400 miles of channel have a gradient of only 1 foot per mile. Available topography is insufficient for the location of favorable dam sites in this stretch. Reconnaissance, however, might reveal sites in unsurveyed portions.

The upper 50 miles of the stream is precipitous with many rapids and small gorges. The most favorable dam site appears to be in the "Lower Gorge," 25 miles below the mouth of the stream draining Walker Lake. A dam in this canyon would be 225 feet high and would have a crest length of 1,500 feet. Water would extend up to Walker Lake, creating an active reservoir capacity of 2,000,000 acre-feet. The drainage area tributary to this site is rather small. There is, however, a possibility of diverting the flow of the Alatna River, a tributary of the Koyukuk River, at a point above the mouth of Helpmejack Creek. This possible diversion would be subject to greater potential use farther downstream on the Alatna or the Koyukuk. Using the Alatna water along with the Kobuk runoff, a power plant at the Kobuk River site would generate more than 110,000,000 kilowatt-hours of firm energy each year.

Noatak River Basin

At the extreme northwestern tip of the continent, the Brooks Range spreads giant fingers of mountains tapering down to meet the Arctic Ocean. The valleys between the outstretched fingers are individual river basins. The Noatak River basin, encompassing more than 12,000 square miles, lies between the De Long Mountains on the north and the Baird Mountains on the south. The basin is divided into upper and lower valleys by a series of canyons in a 70-mile stretch midway down the river.

In the headwaters of the river below Midas Creek near the 157th meridian, the topography appears favorable for a dam site. The river flow, however, is probably insufficient to render any sites economically feasible above the tributary Aniuk and Cutler rivers. In the lower section there are five sites for potential dams and power plants.

The first dam site is located near the 160th meridian, just above the mouth of the Nimiuktuk River. A 200-foot dam would have a crest length of 2,500 feet and would impound 3,100,000 acre-feet of active storage. The potential annual production of this power plant, Noatak River No. 1, would be more than 120,000,000 kilowatt-hours annually. The second power plant, Noatak River No. 2, would be situated 15 miles below the mouth of the Nimiuktuk River and would generate at least 130,000,000 kilowatt-hours of firm energy each year. This development would require a dam 160 feet high, for creation of head only, regulation being provided by coordinated operation with Noatak River No. 1.

Seven miles west of the 161st meridian a 240-foot dam with a crest 1,200 feet long would create a reservoir with 650,000 acre-feet of active capacity. This power plant, Noatak River No. 3, would have a firm output in excess of 230,000,000 kilowatt-hours annually. The next dam downstream would create 140 feet of power head, with no active reservoir storage space. The annual firm production at Noatak River No. 4 would be more than 160,000,000 kilowatt-hours.

Just before the Noatak River empties into Kotzebue Sound, it is constricted by the Igichuk Hills in a canyon section 8 miles long. A 130-foot dam at the lower end of this canyon would have a crest length of 1,800 feet and would impound 1,700,000 acre-feet of active storage. The output of the power plant, Noatak River No. 5, would exceed 150,000,000 kilowatt-hours of firm energy each year.

The river would be completely regulated by the active storage provided in the three reservoirs and the available head above Site No. 4 would be fully utilized.

The total energy potentiality at these five sites exceeds 600 million kilowatt-hours a year. The heart of Naval Petroleum Reserve No. 4 on the Arctic Slope is within transmission range of these potential power plants. Likewise the Candle District on Seward Peninsula lies 110 miles south of the Igichuk Hills with only the 8,000-foot-wide neck of Hotham Inlet of Kotzebue Sound intervening.

Colville River Basin

At least a dozen rivers drain the area north of the Brooks Range, but lack of topographic maps precludes an estimate of potential power development. An exception is the Colville River, the largest stream on the Arctic Slope. It flows eastward and parallel to the Brooks Range for more than 200 miles, with many tributaries joining it at right angles from the mountain slopes. Leaving the mountains the river flows northward, crossing the comparatively flat tundra to discharge into Harrison Bay of the Arctic Ocean. Reconnaissance topography indicates reasonably favorable dam sites at several locations.

On the main stream and on the tributary Awuna River there are possible dam sites near the 156th meridian. These two reservoirs could regulate water for diversion below their confluence to a power plant on the Kigalik River. This development, however, appears less favorable than a larger development downstream.

At the 154th meridian, a dam 160 feet high with a crest length of 3,000 feet, would create an active storage capacity of 3,200,000 acre-feet. This space would regulate the runoff of the Colville River and of the tributary Killik River, which could be diverted into the main stem reservoir by construction of diversion works and a short aqueduct.

Water would be released from the Colville reservoir into a tunnel 7 miles long that would convey the water to a tributary of Maybe Creek, tributary to Ikpikpuk River. In the Ikpikpuk basin, one, or possibly two power plants, depending on local conditions found on reconnaissance, would generate more than 380,000,000 kilowatt-hours of firm energy each year. Although final releases of water would be made at an elevation of 600 feet above sea level, there appears to be no possibility of downstream power production on the Ikpikpuk River because of the low river gradient and the lack of a dam site.

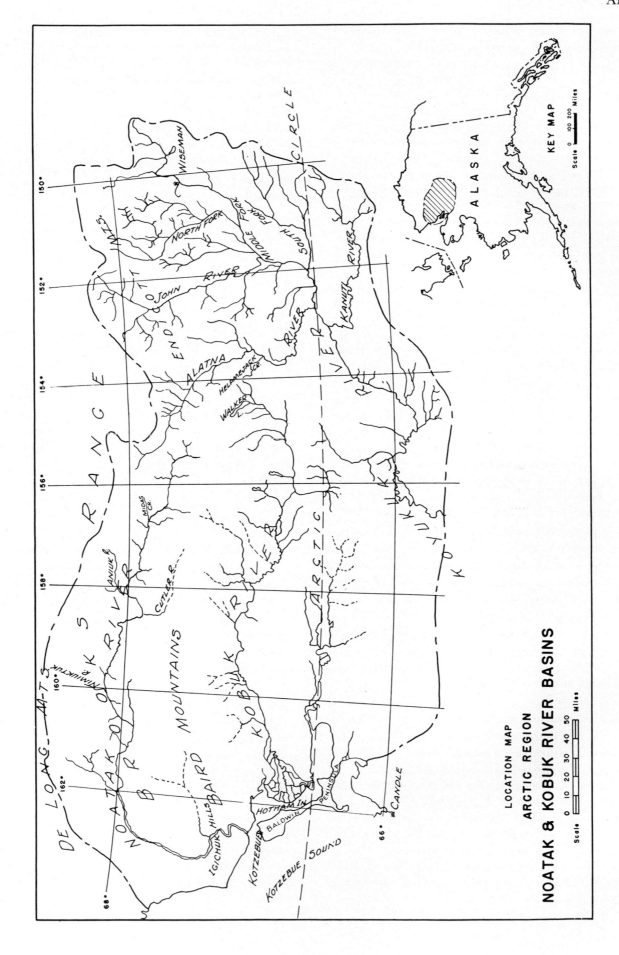

LOCATION MAP

ARCTIC REGION

NOATAK & KOBUK RIVER BASINS

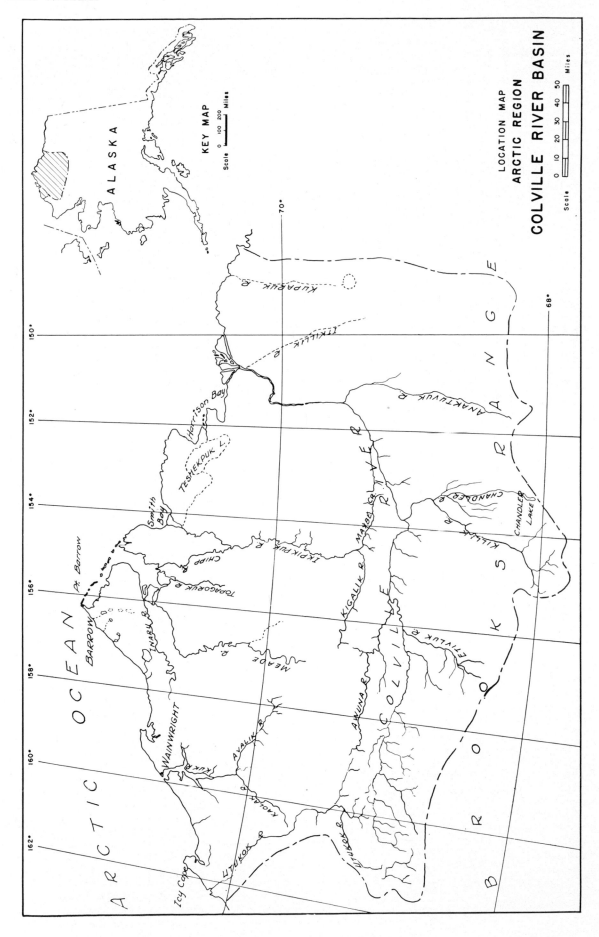

KEY MAP

Scale 0 100 200 Miles

LOCATION MAP
ARCTIC REGION

COLVILLE RIVER BASIN

Scale 0 10 20 30 40 50 Miles

Wealth
From Water

"The age of light metals is here.   This presents one serious question: Are the low-cost power resources of the Nation great enough to produce these wonder metals in sufficient quantities? . . .

"Alaska's power potentialities may well be the decisive factor in the world struggle for supremacy in production of light metals."

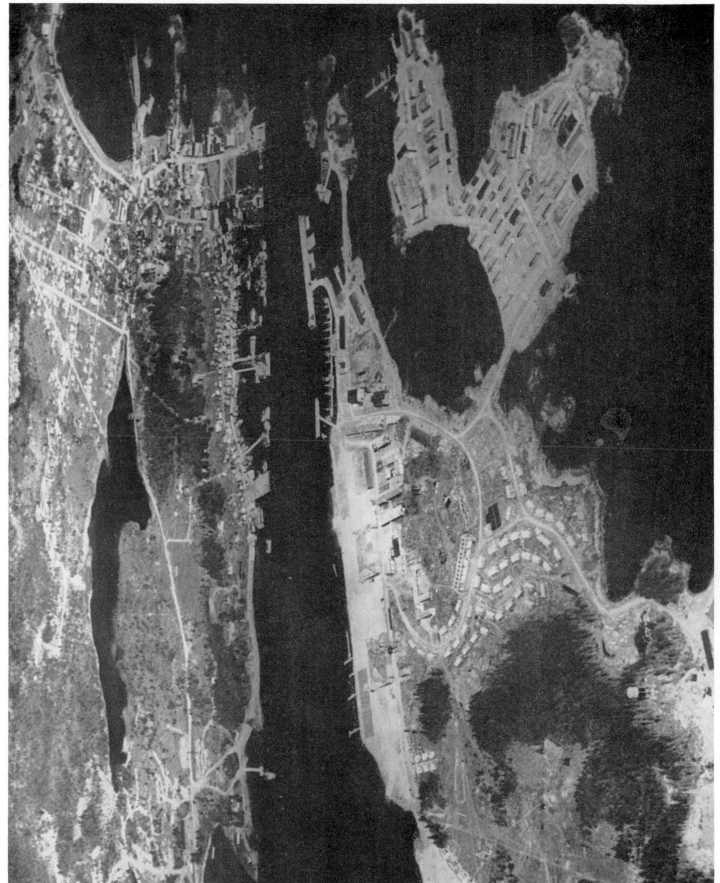

Sitka and Japonski Island, one of the oldest communities in Southeastern Alaska.

CHAPTER VI

Wealth From Water

Alaska's future potential wealth staggers the imagination. It is incalculable. A portion of the wealth to be created with proper use of water resources, can be approximated.

It must be realized the following information is very general, suitable only for reconnaissance purposes. It will require considerable modification or even major revision when more definite data have been accumulated. A serious attempt has been made to keep the estimates of monetary value conservative.

Alaska's potential hydroelectric generation exceeds 50,000,000,000 kilowatt-hours annually. How much is it worth? Customers having constant demand for exceptionally large block of power, such as the light metals industry, might receive a firm power rate less than 3 mills per kilowatt-hour. The small user with irregular demands would be supplied at a much higher rate. It is estimated that the weighted average of all sales would be 4 mills per kilowatt-hour.

Fifty billion kilowatt-hours would bring in $200,000,-000 in gross sales each year.

Alaska's potential agricultural lands are sufficient to meet the needs of its developing economy. Estimates of the ultimate potential acreage vary widely, but an estimate of about 5,000,000 acres appears to be a fair appraisal of the area that may be physically suitable for cultivation and crop production. Due to a diversity of economic factors, however, the acreage which may be economically feasible for agricultural production may not exceed 2,000,000 acres. Almost all of this land would require clearing, and much of it might require irrigation or drainage for optimum production. At present agricultural lands produce annually an average gross income of about $75 per acre. Pasture lands have a much lower annual income, but lands devoted to vegetable crops have produced annual incomes in excess of $250 per acre. Using the present average annual gross income of $75 per acre and the estimated area of 2,000,000 acres, the gross income from agriculture would approximate $150,000,000 per year.

It should be mentioned that only a portion of the potential income from agriculture should be attributed directly to development of water resources, the remainder being attributable to other factors of production, such as the land and application of fertilizers.

Floods now cause recurring damage to property as well as endangering lives in Alaska. Flood control benefits which would result from multiple-purpose river control systems have not as yet been evaluated. Likewise, benefits resulting from potential improvement of inland waterway navigation have not been evaluated. These matters require future study by the Corps of Engineers.

Recreational benefits resulting from multiple-purpose projects would be considerable, but require extensive study by the National Park Service and the Fish and Wildlife Service before any estimate of monetary value could be made.

Water for municipal and industrial purposes will increase in importance as the Territory develops. Benefits would result from construction of a multiple-purpose project to serve the Fairbanks and the Nome areas but an estimate must await further study.

The age of light metals is here. This presents one serious question: Are the low-cost power resources of the Nation great enough to produce these wonder metals in sufficient quantities? Even now aluminum production is severely restricted owing to lack of low-cost power in the States. Most light metal producers are combing the country for potential power sources which could be developed to supply energy at less than 3 mills per kilowatt-hour. There are only a few remaining undeveloped sites in the United States capable of generating energy at such low-cost. This has resulted in light metal producers turning toward Canada. Recently, they have been eyeing Alaska's power potentialities.

Alaska's power potentialities may well be the decisive factor in the world struggle for supremacy in production of light metals.

Supersonic scientific research in the States has been severely restricted for lack of electric energy. Two years ago the War Department announced they desired 9,000,000,000 kilowatt-hours of electric energy to power a supersonic wind tunnel. This quantity of power is twice the full output of Hoover Dam or Grand Coulee.

Even the division of the project into two widely separated units, each requiring 4,500,000,000 kilowatt-hours did not solve the power supply problem.

Alaska's potential power may provide the answer.

There are few places on the earth's surface where such fantastic quantities of power can be made available as in Alaska. Power requirements of the entire project could be met at either Anchorage, Fairbanks, or Juneau. It was estimated that a city of 25,000 persons would be constructed in conjunction with such a research center.

What indirect benefits would accrue to Alaska's development of low-cost power sources for use in manufacturing and mining? Such benefits would be so far-reaching as to be incalculable, but a partial determination of the true value of the energy is possible.

Considering, first, indirect benefits in manufacturing, the Statistical Abstract of the United States discloses revealing information on the economics of manufacturing in the States during 1939. The list of manufactures was screened to eliminate those not likely to have a corresponding development in Alaska and statistics compiled for the following:

Lumber and timber basic products.
Furniture and finished lumber products.
Paper and allied products.
Chemicals and allied products.
Products of petroleum and coal.
Leather and leather products.
Stone, clay, and glass products.
Iron and steel and their products.
Nonferrous metals and their products.

The average worker in these industries used 16,100 kilowatt-hours of electric energy, equivalent to an average demand of more than 10 horsepower.

After spending $4,200 for raw or semifinished materials, electric energy, and wages, the value of finished products totaled $7,400 per worker. The true value of electric energy at the disposal of the average worker is readily seen when data show that one kilowatt-hour of energy, plus 7¾ minutes of the worker's time turned 26 cents worth of raw or semifinished materials, electric energy, and wages, into finished products valued at 46 cents. Without electric energy this same average worker would have been practically helpless. Electric energy enabled the worker to create over and above his wage, 20 cents of wealth with each kilowatt-hour.

Similarly, for every kilowatt-hour of electric energy used in mining in the States during 1939, minerals worth 85 cents were extracted.

Should Alaska develop mining and manufacturing to the point where 150,000 persons are gainfully employed in mining, and 600,000 in manufacturing, power requirements would be 11,000,000,000 kilowatt-hours and value of products would be $5,700,000,000 a year predicated on statistical averages for the States in 1939.

With the development of Alaska's economy the benefits that would result from development of Alaska's agricultural lands would be far-reaching. The standard of living would be materially raised. Under present conditions many foods are so expensive as to be out of reach for many people. This is particularly true of eggs, milk and green vegetables, all of which could be produced in Alaska. With a plentiful supply of food available at substantially lower cost, the Territorial Department of Health believes the elimination of diet deficiencies would result in improvement of the health of many Alaskans.

The Commander-in-Chief of the Alaskan Command stated: "To the extent that civil facilities are developed to a level which will permit a self-sustaining economy and a full development of the natural resources of the Territory, the expenditures for purely military works may be reduced. The benefit to the National economy of such a reduction in military expenditures is obvious.

"A review of the various programs proposed for implementation by the Department of the Interior, indicates that a number of these would, if implemented, strengthen the internal economy of Alaska, and thus tend to reduce the investment in military works without a corresponding reduction in defense capabilities.

"Among these projects are the provision of housing and community facilities, the improvement of transportation, the development of hydroelectrical power, increase in agricultural development, and the encouragement of capital goods industry."

This is conclusive proof of important potential benefits for the defense of Alaska and the Nation.

GROSS RETURNS

Based on the generation of 50,000,000,000 kilowatt-hours annually and the development of 2,000,000 acres of agricultural land, the annual gross returns would be:

Power sales_____ $200,000,000
Agricultural income_____ 150,000,000

These would be accompanied by annual benefits associated with the related purposes of flood control, navigation, recreation, and municipal water supply. No attempt has been made to evaluate these associated benefits.

FURTHER INVESTIGATIONS

Before this great "Wealth From Water" can be realized, multiple purpose river control systems must first be constructed. However, the Congress could only act after engineering and economic investigations were completed for individual projects and feasibility reports submitted. It would be a sound investment for the Government to continue engineering and economic investigations for the orderly and comprehensive development of Alaska's water and land resources. Millions for detailed plans will produce billions in benefits.

Cooperating
Interests

"The various agencies of the Department of the Interior having an interest in development of Alaska's natural wealth have teamed together in the preparation of this reconnaissance report ... Their cooperation is ... practical, and essential, as evidenced in this chapter which presents their specific comments and programs.

"Other Federal and Territorial agencies that are involved in development of the resources of Alaska have likewise cooperated with the Bureau of Reclamation and their reports appear as part of this chapter."

Juneau, capital of Alaska.

CHAPTER VII

Programs of Cooperating Interests

The fullest cooperation and harmony among all Federal and Territorial interests are essential for intelligent comprehensive development of America's northernmost possession—a land so vast that it constitutes an empire.

Only through a pooling of the separate functions and the knowledge and the "know how" of all governmental bodies operative in Alaska can needless duplication, wasted time, wasted money, and failure to integrate today's program with that of tomorrow be avoided.

To that end, all the various agencies of the Department of the Interior have worked as a team in the preparation of this report. This teamwork is manifested in the specific comments and programs comprising the bulk of this chapter.

Even more gratifying, however, is the cooperation evidenced in the form of program planning by other Federal agencies vitally involved in developing the resources of Alaska. These agencies have been willing to consider the needs of the Bureau of Reclamation and to so direct their programs that the required data could be obtained. The recent establishment of the Alaska Field Committee of the Department of the Interior and the Inter-Agency Committee on the development of Alaska has in a large measure been responsible for this unified effort.

It was to be expected that the Territorial Government of Alaska from the Governor down would cooperate to the extent of their funds and personnel available. They have.

Strategically situated as it is, Alaska is all-important to national defense. Military interests, accordingly, are of commensurate importance to and in Alaska. The official statement of Lt. Gen. N. F. Twining, Commander-in-Chief, Alaskan Command, in cooperation with this report and the program it envisages is therefore doubly significant.

Although the cooperating programs of all other agencies, Federal and Territorial, are confined to this chapter, their influence and importance are reflected throughout the report.

ALASKA DEPARTMENT OF AGRICULTURE

In considering agriculture in Alaska it is well to remember that most of the Territory lies in the north temperate zone. Too often the impression is given that Alaska is almost wholly within the Arctic Circle.

The three main factors influencing farming are: (1) temperature, (2) precipitation, and (3) soil. All of these vary widely. For example, recorded temperatures in Central Alaska range from 99° to −72° F. Precipitation at Point Barrow is but 4 inches, while on the Baranof Islands 248 inches per year is the record. The soil ranges from very fine sand through silt and loam to muck and peat.

Garden and field reports, covering 50 years of farming and gardening from all parts of Alaska from Point Barrow to Umnak, show that a wide variety of crops of excellent quality can be grown.

The one inescapable conclusion, based on past records, is that the conditions preventing development of agriculture in Alaska are *economic*, not *agricultural*. This will be discussed in detail later in this report.

There are three main agricultural regions—Matanuska Valley, Tanana Valley, and Kenai Peninsula. These are so considered, primarily, because of large areas of land suitable for cropping. There are many smaller areas as favorably situated in regard to climate and soil.

The extent of the various areas suitable for agricultural purposes is not definitely known. Estimates range up to 7,500,000 acres that can be cropped immediately upon clearing, and an additional 58,500,000 acres suitable for farming and grazing when cleared and drained.

Only brief mention can be made in this report of outstanding features of several farm areas.

Southeastern Alaska

As is well known, this is a heavily timbered region. The temperature is comparatively mild in both summer and winter. In fact, it is very similar to the coastal regions further south and this condition is reflected in the type of vegetation at such points as Juneau and Ketchikan. The precipitation is quite heavy. This, together with the cool temperatures during the summer, precludes the possibility of certain types of agriculture such as grain growing. Many garden crops, however, do exceedingly well and excellent gardens are to be seen in many places along the coast. Bush fruits flourish. The mountains, however, crowd the coastline so closely that no large areas are suitable for field crops. We can see, therefore, that farming is limited to small areas, to dairying, and to poultry husbandry. Because of the mild temperatures, ornamental plants thrive and make it possible to have very lovely home landscaping.

Southwestern Alaska

Lower temperatures and less precipitation are not conducive to heavy plant growth and in many places there is no timber at all. We find grass in great evidence which indicates at once that livestock could become one of the principal forms of farm endeavor. Hardy crops of various types such as potatoes and a general line of garden vegetables can be grown. However, summer temperatures are also too low to make grain growing a success. Dairy and poultry production are of importance and beef cattle will increase in importance as the Territory develops. Kodiak Island and the chain of the Aleutians offer potentialities in beef production. Results of the last few years give encouragement to that belief.

Kenai Peninsula

The Kenai Peninsula in many ways is similar to southwestern areas. Much of it is treeless or sparsely timbered. Only the west side of the peninsula is suitable for agriculture, the other part is too mountainous. This western area has received very favorable publicity and bids fair to become one of our leading agricultural areas. One definite handicap of the past is being overcome by the construction of a highway extending from the tip, at Homer, up the west side along Cook Inlet to connect with highways into Anchorage and Seward. Old settlements at such points as Homer, Ninilchik, Kasilof, Kenai, and Hope will take on new activities with the completion of the road.

The mild climate, with natural resources, such as coal, fish, and game, give every reason to believe that a considerable agriculture will be developed. Dairying will undoubtedly have a major part in this program, also poultry and, we believe, beef production. A general line of garden vegetables and potatoes can and are

being grown on the Peninsula at very many places. Attention was focused on this area by the withdrawal of 161,000 acres of public land pending consideration and passage of a bill to establish a colony between Kenai and Kasilof.

Anchorage Area

Approaching the interior, we find an agricultural area around Anchorage. Farming there will be on a small scale, according to present indications. Nevertheless, because of the proximity of a major market, many will find it worthwhile to establish homes on farmable land along the new highway out of Anchorage as well as in other nearby areas such as the Spenard region. Here again we find potatoes, garden produce, and poultry the main types of farming. Many people like to live out of town and commute back and forth, raising much of the produce they eat and a surplus that can be sold.

Undoubtedly, one of the reasons more people do not move out into rural areas is because they are loath to leave behind the city conveniences, particularly those provided through the use of electric current. This will be emphasized later in this report.

Matanuska Valley

The town of Palmer in the Matanuska Valley, sometimes spoken of as the "Banana Belt" of Alaska, is located 50 miles from Anchorage Actually, the climate is much too cold to even approximate this term but, nevertheless, the mild weather enjoyed there has made it possible to grow many kinds of vegetables, fruits, and grain. A great impetus to farming in this valley was given by establishment of a government sponsored colony in 1935. Farming has prospered there. Palmer is truly one town in Alaska wholly supported by agriculture. Dairying has taken front rank. At present, there are some 38 small dairy farms listed as grade "A". The milk produced and sold constitutes a considerable portion of the income of the farmers there. Sales of milk and cream in 1948 amounted to $250,519. Garden produce, sold through the cooperating association, totaled $127,600. In addition, a large amount was sold by independent growers. There could be considerable expansion of farm activity in this valley.

Tanana Valley

This is the most extensive agricultural area in Alaska, comprising approximately 7,000 square miles. On the valley floor the soil ranges from coarse sand to very fine sand and is well adapted to production of hay, vegetables, including potatoes and small fruits. The slopes on the hills adjoining the valley are composed of a soil a bit heavier; this is known as a silt loam and is of a brownish color. It is retentive of water and fairly fertile. The southerly slopes, especially, are well adapted to the production of hay, quality potatoes, and to ripening cereal crops such as wheat. The climate is strictly continental showing extremes from a summer high of 99° to a winter low of −66° F., giving a range of 165°. The average precipitation is lower than any of the areas that have been discussed and averages 11.65 inches. There is, therefore, a lack of sufficient moisture some years to produce good crops. Usually, the summers are only moderately warm and are very conducive to the production of general farm crops. The winters can be quite cold and by some are considered a drawback because good housing is required for livestock as well as for humans. Also, here we find permafrost which again is considered detrimental to crop production by some. Settlement in the Tanana Valley, while it has been going on for a number of years, has developed rather slowly as will be pointed out later.

There are other regions well suited to general farm purposes such as in the Yukon Valley, in the Koyukuk, the Kuskokwim, the 40-mile area in the interior, and Unalakleet.

To recapitulate, it will be noted that the coastal areas have the most equable climate and considerable precipitation, beginning at the southeastern part of Alaska. In the southwestern, precipitation is less and there is a little more winter. The Kenai Peninsula precipitation is more pronounced and, while general farming is practiced, grain crops cannot be ripened successfully. Farther north, in the Matanuska Valley the precipitation tapers off, summer temperatures are somewhat higher, and grain can be ripened as well as other crops. The Tanana Valley, north of the Alaska Range, has even less precipitation with higher summer temperatures and much colder winters. Diversified farming can be carried on here quite acceptably because grain can be ripened, without question, which will serve as a feed for livestock and poultry. Vegetables and hay can also be produced as well as in southern regions, except that at times there is a shortage of moisture. It is interesting to note that farther north there is still less precipitation so that at Rampart on the Yukon, where an experiment station was established years ago, and continued until 1925, the annual precipitation was 9.94 inches. At the extreme northern tip of Alaska it is about 4 inches per annum. It is evident that the weather is a vital factor to consider by those who want to farm in Alaska. In other words, if one desires to do grain farming, the interior is the best place. Dairying can

be done acceptable in the Kenai Peninsula or in the Matanuska Valley. For those who prefer beef cattle production, the lower parts of the Kenai Peninsula, Kodiak Island, and some nearby islands and also some of the Aleutians offer the best possibilities.

Permafrost

A great many people are apprehensive that the perpetually frozen subsoil in Central Alaska is an unfavorable condition for crop production. Actual growing tests indicate that permafrost is neither stimulative nor retarding in its effect. Immediately after the land is cleared, it is exposed to the sun and the ground thaws. The surface down as far as thawed becomes very wet and gives the impression that the land is swampy and poorly drained. This, of course, is particularly true on the bottom lands. It is true that this wet ground is cold and not conducive to good plant growth but after cultivating for a year or two, the frost recedes from 6 to 8 feet down. The water settles, some of it evaporates, and some of it is used by the growing crop. Consequently, the land loses its boggy aspect and because the sum total of the loss of soil moisture exceeds the average summer precipitation of only 7 inches, the inevitable result is that the subsoil becomes depleted of water. Crop plants from then on are strictly dependent on the water that moves down from the surface. Because the ground freezes down several feet every winter and has to thaw before planting, it is immaterial whether the ground is permanently frozen underneath or simply frozen 6 or 8 feet. In either case, spring planting proceeds equally well and the crops likewise grow equally well.

Very little has been said up to now about livestock production. It would be impossible, after seeing the vast areas of grassland in Alaska, to be skeptical about the possibility of beef cattle production. There are thousands of square miles of good grasslands in various parts of this Territory. The total extent of the areas are not definitely known.

It is believed, with the increase of population both in the United States and Alaska, and the lessening of desirable rangeland in the States both in acreage and productivity, that the livestock man is going to come to Alaska to raise beef. There is no denying the fact that the Americans prefer beef to any other meat and as long as there is land available they are going to insist on beef as a large part of their diet. It is estimated that in the United States proper the per capita consumption of beef plus veal is 75 pounds per annum. According to import figures, the Alaska consumption of beef per capita is even greater. It is logical to assume that the time will come when Alaska will produce much of its own beef. Conditions in some places may seem rather rugged for wintering over beef cattle stock, but such is also true of the Great Plains where blizzards sometimes cause heavy loss of stock. There are instances, well authenticated, of horses, mules, and cows living over on the natural range for one or more winters in the interior. The buffalo herd in the Big Delta country gives excellent evidence that they can forage the year-around and find conditions congenial to a normal increase in numbers.

From the experience of dairymen in various parts of Alaska it is noted that dairy cows can be kept in good health and in a high state of production both in the interior and on the coast. With dairying, it is more a question of the economy of production than one of survival. As agriculture increases, more home-grown feed could be utilized at a saving to the dairyman. So far, dairying has been a reasonably profitable form of farming. As competition increases, it will be necessary to produce more economically than at present. There is a good demand for fluid milk; in fact, the demand exceeds the supply so the dairyman is not forced to produce butter or byproducts.

Other forms of livestock enterprise, such as sheep production, have been carried on in a small way and in places have proven successful. The Aleutian Islands offer good opportunities along that line and it is likely that more people will run sheep on some of these grassy islands. It is well-known that the wool clip from the Islands brings a premium price on the market because of superior quality and freedom from extraneous material.

More attention will also be given to pork production as more extensive farming is done. There are several hog ranches now in operation and as home-grown feed becomes available more hogs will be raised. Hogs should be a part of most farm enterprises because, of all farm animals, hogs are the most economical meat producers.

The same applies to poultry. Poultry has developed into a considerable business. The gross receipts for the Territory from poultry are estimated to be $150,000 for the current year, in spite of the fact that shipping strikes seriously curtailed the amount of feed available for the laying hen.

Aids to Farm Settlement and Development

While considerable progress has been made over a term of years in determining what crops can be produced here and marketed, the fact remains that, with the exception of the Matanuska colony which was government financed and sponsored, farming has developed quite slowly. The reasons for this are fairly obvious.

Desirable land is available in 160-acre homestead tracts in the several areas outlined. But for a settler to establish himself on a tract of land and develop it to the extent of providing himself and a family with a reasonable income requires years of hard work and some privation—also, a considerable outlay of money.

A great deal of consideration has been given lately as to how these early years of privation under pioneering conditions can be ameliorated. Assurance must be given the homesteader so he can offer his family a reasonable amount of comfort and convenience. Most conclusions have been that financing of some sort, such as a Federal loan, is necessary. In that way, land can be cleared, some essential building done, and crops raised and sold. The loan, of course, should be on a long-term basis and at a low interest rate. Good roads are also essential.

Even after this is accomplished what makes life tolerable on the farm are some of the conveniences enjoyed by urban dwellers. These conveniences can come mainly through the use of electricity. There is no one thing that presents such great possibilities to the average homesteader as electric current, because so many uses can be made of it in the house, in the barn, and in the field.

Such uses are too well known to be detailed at great length but we would like to enumerate a few. We might mention irrigation as a great aid to many of the crops grown, especially in the interior and Matanuska Valley. The total summer precipitation is seldom sufficient to produce maximum crops and some years is greatly deficient, particularly for such crops as potatoes, garden vegetables, and small fruits such as raspberries and strawberries. Electric pumps would be a great convenience in supplying irrigation water.

Another possible use of electricity is in the form of heating cables laid underground to serve hot beds and gardens. This would greatly extend the productive season of vegetables. As it is now, the season is quite short. If a few weeks could be added in the spring and in the fall, the use of fresh vegetables could be increased both for home use and for sale. The extent to which underground heating cables could be used would, of course, depend at how low a rate the electricity could be supplied. Obviously, with the rates prevailing at present, heating the ground with cables is out of the question.

The production of greenhouse crops could be greatly extended if low-cost current was available to use for lighting purposes. During the summer there is an abundance of light. In the fall and winter, however, the light becomes definitely deficient and of too low actinic value to serve in growing such crops as tomatoes and lettuce. Heat could also be supplied by use of

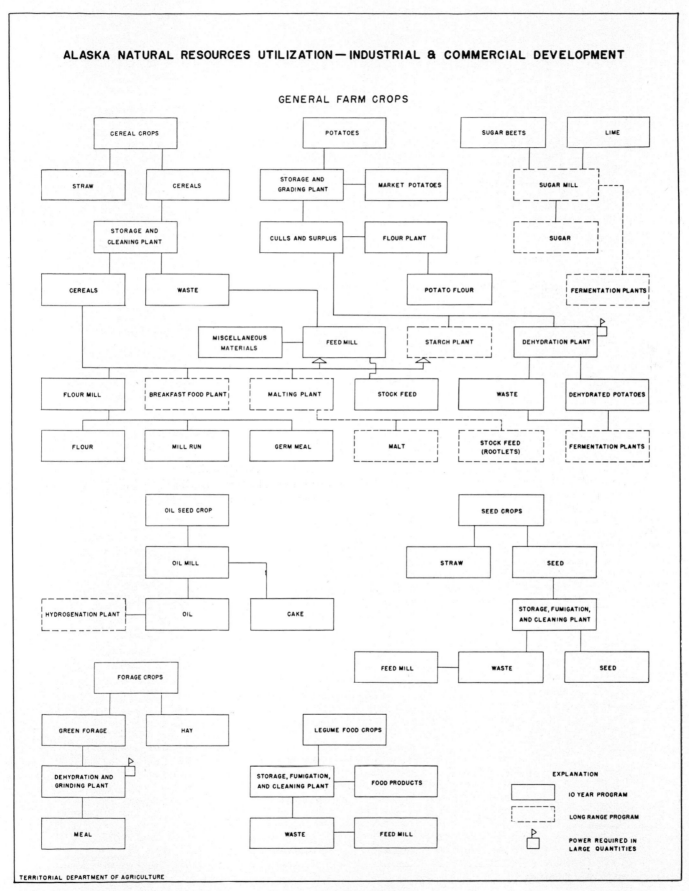

ALASKA NATURAL RESOURCES UTILIZATION—INDUSTRIAL & COMMERCIAL DEVELOPMENT

GENERAL FARM CROPS

AGRICULTURAL GROUP

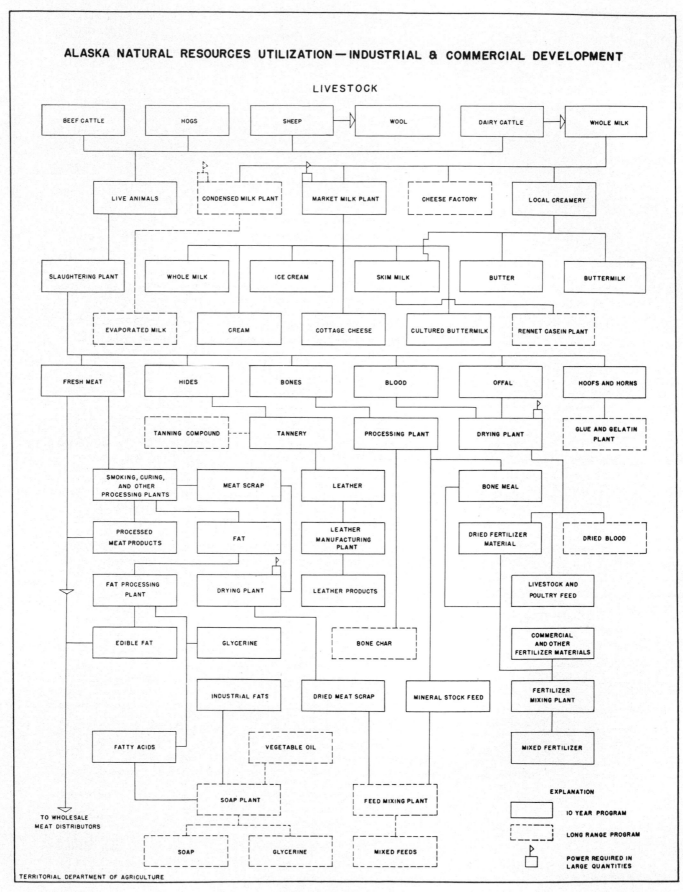

ALASKA NATURAL RESOURCES UTILIZATION—INDUSTRIAL & COMMERCIAL DEVELOPMENT

AGRICULTURAL GROUP

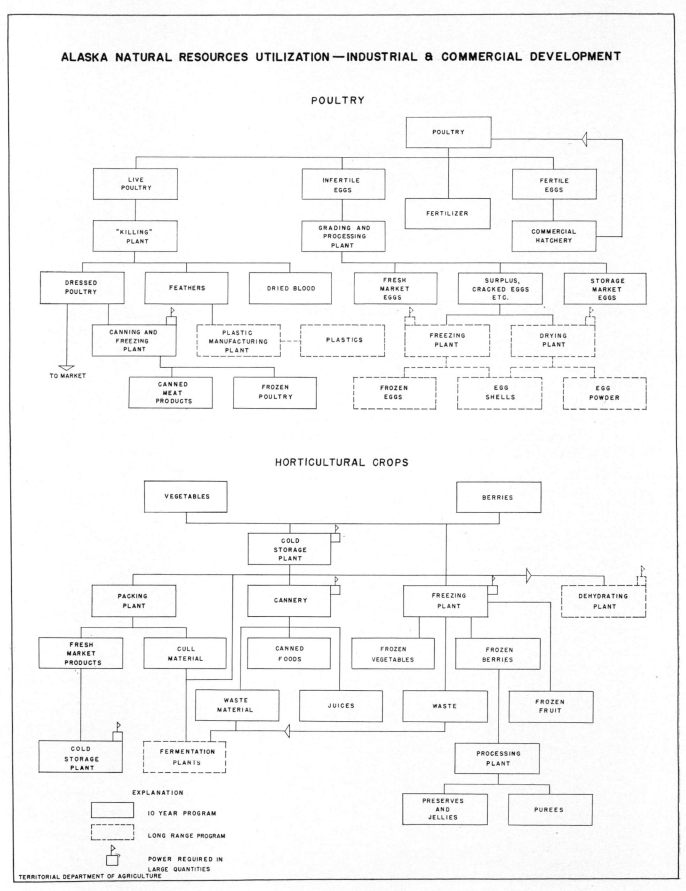

ALASKA NATURAL RESOURCES UTILIZATION—INDUSTRIAL & COMMERCIAL DEVELOPMENT

POULTRY

HORTICULTURAL CROPS

EXPLANATION

10 YEAR PROGRAM

LONG RANGE PROGRAM

POWER REQUIRED IN LARGE QUANTITIES

TERRITORIAL DEPARTMENT OF AGRICULTURE

AGRICULTURAL GROUP

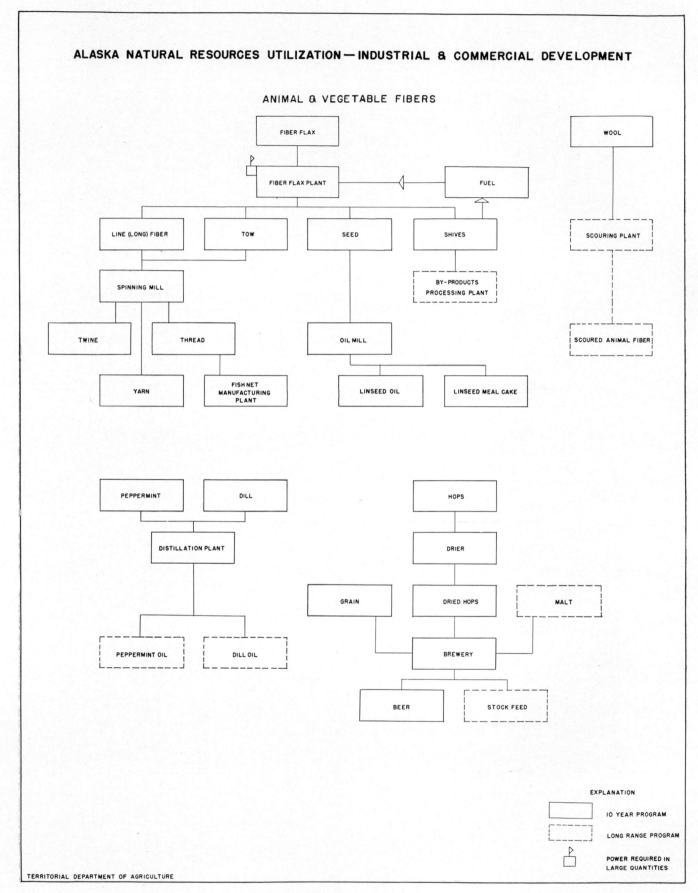

ALASKA NATURAL RESOURCES UTILIZATION — INDUSTRIAL & COMMERCIAL DEVELOPMENT

ANIMAL & VEGETABLE FIBERS

AGRICULTURAL GROUP

TERRITORIAL DEPARTMENT OF AGRICULTURE

electricity provided it is cheap enough to compete with other heating systems.

In the house, one of the convenient ways of preserving fruit and other food items is the quick-freeze method. This method has been denied to the pioneer woman and will continue to be denied until electricity at a low rate is available. It would add a great deal of convenience to the homemakers as well as make it possible to serve fresh foods throughout the year, to have a quick-freeze unit in the kitchen.

To stimulate the establishment of farm homes, we might sum up by saying: (1) Make available a reasonably adequate sum of money on a long term basis and at a low interest rate to be used for land clearing, erection of necessary buildings, and possibly purchase of machinery and livestock. (2) Make available electricity at a low enough rate to make its use economical to do many things conveniently and efficiently on the farm and in the home. (3) Make it possible to have water for irrigation purposes when and if needed. (4) Provide a good telephone system. (5) Build roads connecting homesteads to main highways.

Settlement by a Government sponsored colonization project could be the answer to the above. There is such a bill in Congress and land withdrawals have been made at Dunbar (32,437 acres) near Fairbanks and in the Kenai-Kasilof area (161,000 acres) on Kenai Peninsula. Under such a colonization plan the new settlement would be supplied with these conveniences, and if the benefits were extended, as they should be, to the older settlers, much of the hardship attendant to homesteading in Alaska would be eliminated.

ALASKA DEPARTMENT OF MINES

Nearly every known mineral is present in unknown quantity in some part of Alaska. The widespread mineralization leads to the conclusion that the mining industry is potentially the most important to the Territory in the immediate future. Markets for the products of other industries such as farming, power, timber, et cetera would follow the development of the mining industry. Indications warrant the belief that the value of our mineral production should be several times the present rate ($18,378,000 in 1947). The economy of the second and fourth divisions ordinarily depends almost entirely on mining, although the situation is at present temporarily altered by extensive Government construction projects under way in those divisions. Many sections of Alaska are of value only for the minerals they contain. No part of it should be restricted to prospecting and development of the mineral resources. Minerals are of value only to the extent they are utilized, and their extraction does not necessarily adversely affect scenic attractions or other uses for the areas involved.

A mineral deposit must be located before it can be evaluated or developed. No mining industry can long endure or expand without the discovery of new deposits. Prospecting is necessary, but it is practically dormant in Alaska at the present time. It is estimated that less than 75 full- and part-time prospectors were active in Alaska during 1948, in spite of the fact that very few qualified persons will deny that Alaska offers the most favorable field for the discovery of new mines of any part of the United States. Among the reasons for the decline in prospecting are the following:

1. Inability of the prospector to earn a grubstake through winter employment. Several of the former large mining companies offered employment to prospectors during winter to finance prospecting during the open season, but such is no longer the case.

2. Unwillingness of private capital to grubstake prospectors due to uncertain and delayed returns. Grubstaking is much less today than a number of years ago.

3. Hesitancy of venture capital to come into Alaska, take over and develop prospects that are discovered. This is mainly because of unsettled conditions such as irregular, unreliable American shipping by water at high rates, which has so deteriorated during the past few years that it is practically a farce; Government reservations and threats of more, et cetera.

4. Lack of experienced prospectors with proper training. Many persons are interested in prospecting but do not possess sufficient knowledge to intelligently engage in the search for mineral deposits.

5. Rewards are not commensurate with efforts required to locate a mineral deposit of commercial tenor. Considerable time must elapse before a prospect is developed to a point where financial returns may be expected. A living may be attained through less arduous labor under more favorable living conditions in other lines of endeavor.

6. The romance of prospecting has largely been eliminated by the passing of the bonanza days in Alaska when the discovery of high-grade, surface mineral deposits could be expected.

Early development of the natural resources of Alaska, with resultant increase in population, seems to be well justified under present conditions. Foremost among plans toward this end should be the development of its mineral resources. Accomplishment of this purpose can only be attained by encouraging and reviving prospecting from its present stagnant state. Government subsidy seems to offer a solution, inasmuch as assistance from private sources seems inadequate. Canada has for a number of years carried out a program for assisting prospectors with apparent success. The British

Columbia system includes educational and financial aid. A number of favorable discoveries have resulted, at least one of which had been brought into production by 1945. A bill was introduced at the 1945 session of the Alaska Legislature, providing for assistance to prospectors with Territorial funds. Its need was freely admitted by the legislators, but it failed to pass by a small margin, presumably on account of lack of funds to carry out the terms of the Act. The bill was drawn up after careful study and was designed to provide assistance similar to that available to the British Columbia prospector.

During the 3 biennia 1927 to 1933, the Legislature provided $20,000 to be expended each biennium under what was termed the "Prospectors' Aid Act." Under the terms of this act, not to exceed $150 per annum for transportation only could be allotted to any one prospector. Although no discoveries of commercial mineral deposits were reported by prospectors who received assistance, the expenditure was probably justified by information of value to future prospectors on little-known areas, contained in reports submitted by prospectors, which reports were required by regulations governing the administration of the Act. More effective results would probably have resulted, had it provided for fully financing a fewer number of carefully selected prospectors in areas known to have favorable possibilities for new discoveries.

Preference in any plan for subsidizing prospectors should be given to those who have continued this type of activity in spite of handicaps. There are a few old-time prospectors remaining whose experience and familiarity with the country would be invaluable in training the younger generation. Mining claims staked by a subsidized prospector should become his property as an incentive to diligence. Taxes and additional wealth created by a very few producing mines resulting from the program would more than repay the cost. Services of prospectors who show lack of interests or adaptability should immediately be discontinued to avoid adverse effects on other prospectors in the party. Government and Territorial geologists and mining engineers are already available in the field to assist in appraising and laying out development plans for any new mineral discoveries made by subsidized prospectors. Free assaying and identification services are available at the public assay offices of the Territorial Department of Mines for samples submitted in connection with prospecting activity in the Territory.

Should metallic and nonmetallic minerals be found in sufficient quantities to warrant development, the following industrial flow-diagrams are presented. These diagrams portray graphically what full utilization of Alaska's mineral resources would mean to the Territory's future economy.

WEATHER BUREAU

The climate of Alaska is sufficiently unlike that of any of the 48 States to warrant careful scrutiny of any assumptions to be made regarding weather influences under which social and economic development in Alaska will be undertaken. Such assumptions would ordinarily rest on the broadest possible base of factual evidence. The facts in this case are embodied in the 6,000,000 Alaskan weather observations which have accumulated in the repositories of the Weather Bureau over the past 15 years.

The value of a well-organized and well-functioning weather service is recognized by all agencies that are interested in the economic development of the Territory of Alaska. Aviation, agriculture, grazing, forestry, water-power development, placer mining, forest-fire protection, and the conservation of wildlife and salmon can be planned more intelligently if information on weather and climate is obtained from an adequate system of meteorological stations carefully distributed over the vast Territory.

An inventory of the natural resources of a country would be incomplete without including its climate, for climatic conditions, as much as topography, geographic position, and other economic aspects, have an important bearing on the occupation and development of a region. Climate is not only basic to land resources and to land use, but it affects man in many other ways—his housing, clothing, occupation, forms of government, and manner of living.

The relation of such climatic elements as temperature, precipitation, sunshine, and the length of the growing season to animal and vegetable life, and hence to man's occupancy of land, is too obvious to need special consideration. In a report to the President of the United States some time ago his Science Advisory Board aptly stated: "In whatever way we think of the land, or whatever land it is that claims our attention, that land is conditioned by the sky under which it lies, by the climate which is proper to it."

Suitable meteorological service is essential in the development of the water and power resources in Alaska. Adequate rainfall data must be collected, and analyzed for the full development and use of water and associated land resources, including irrigation drainage, flood control, navigation, hydropower, municipal and industrial water supply, and other related purposes.

An adequate meteorological service is vital to safe and efficient aviation. Air transportation is playing an important part in the development of Alaska, where distances are great, topographical features rugged, and weather conditions extreme. Such a service requires a large network of observing stations with well spaced upper-air observations and forecast centers at important

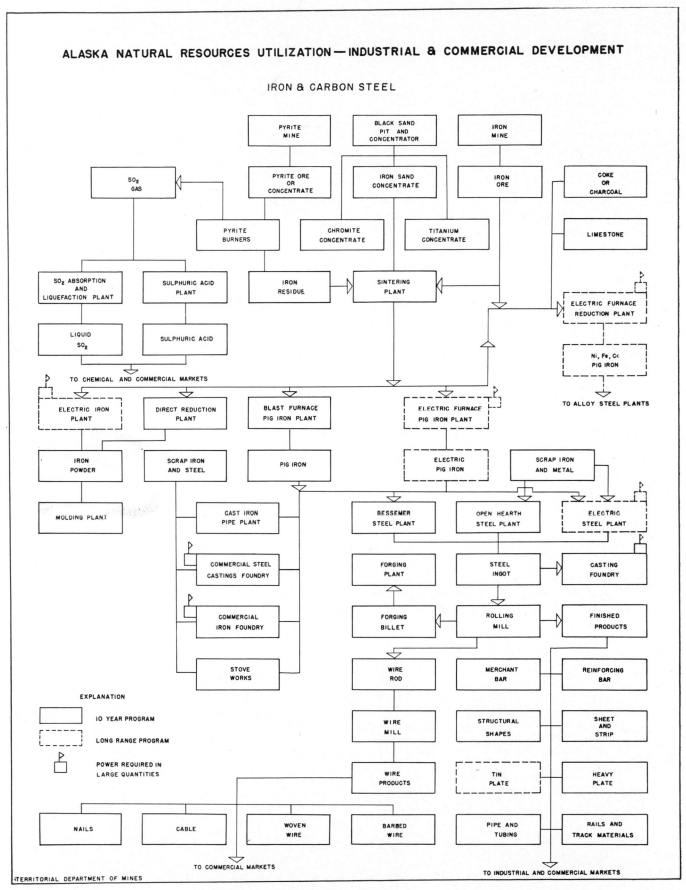

FERROUS METALS GROUP

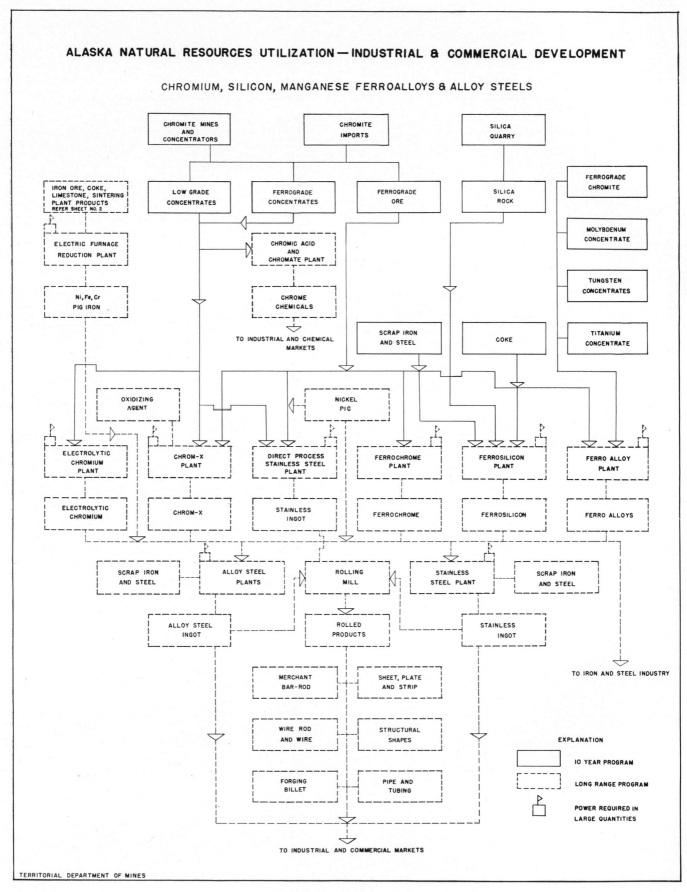

ALASKA NATURAL RESOURCES UTILIZATION — INDUSTRIAL & COMMERCIAL DEVELOPMENT

CHROMIUM, SILICON, MANGANESE FERROALLOYS & ALLOY STEELS

FERROUS METALS GROUP

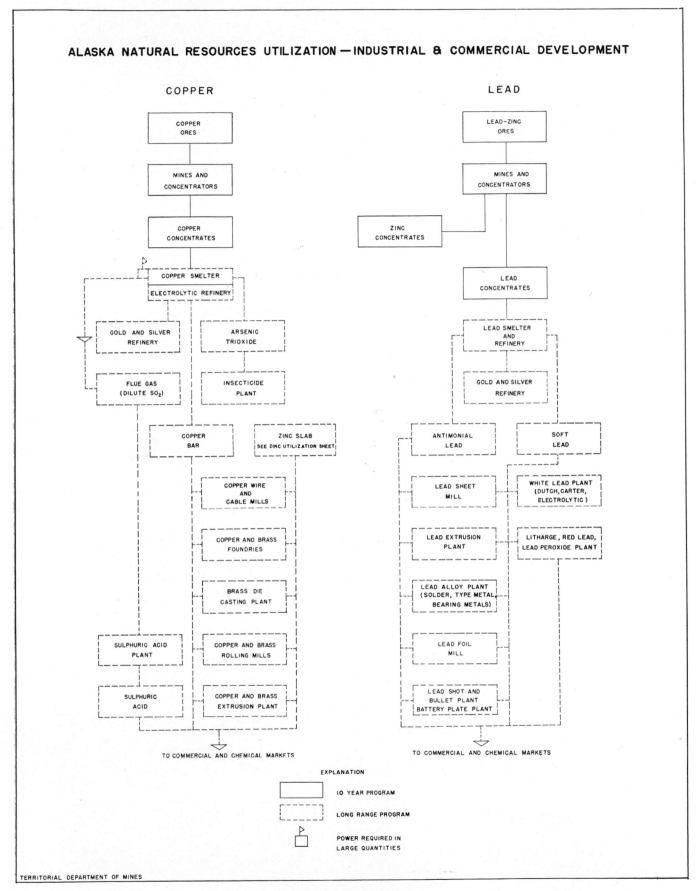

ALASKA NATURAL RESOURCES UTILIZATION — INDUSTRIAL & COMMERCIAL DEVELOPMENT

NONFERROUS METALS GROUP

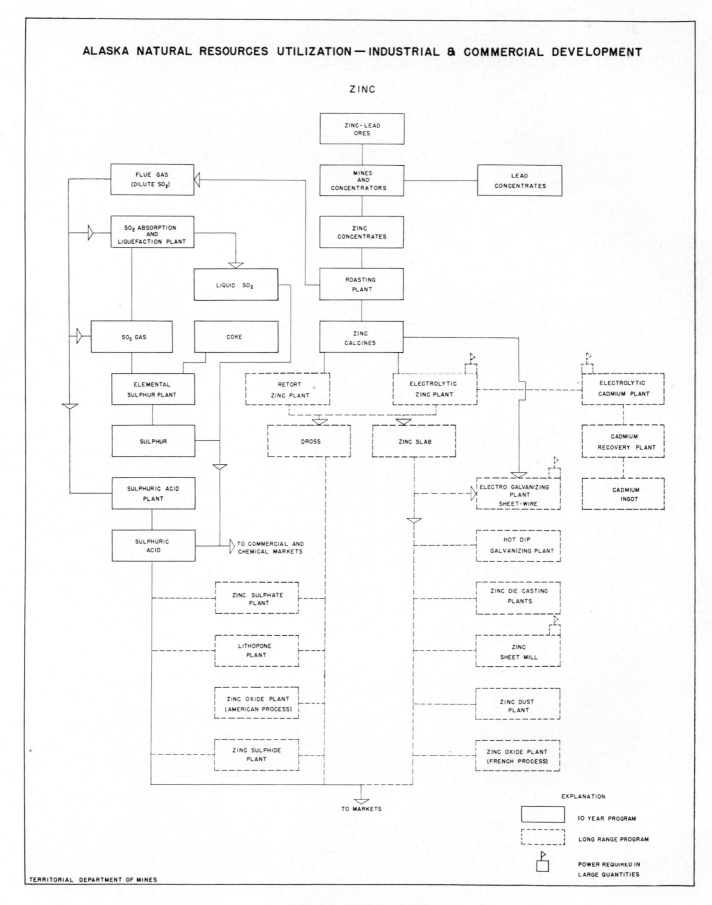

ALASKA NATURAL RESOURCES UTILIZATION — INDUSTRIAL & COMMERCIAL DEVELOPMENT

ZINC

NONFERROUS METALS GROUP

TERRITORIAL DEPARTMENT OF MINES

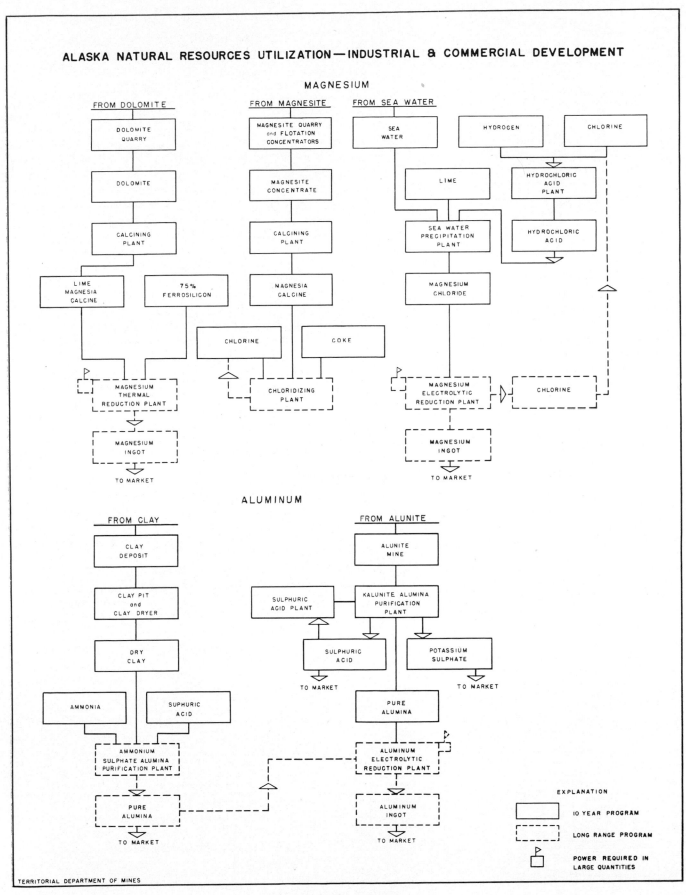

ALASKA NATURAL RESOURCES UTILIZATION—INDUSTRIAL & COMMERCIAL DEVELOPMENT

LIGHT METALS GROUP

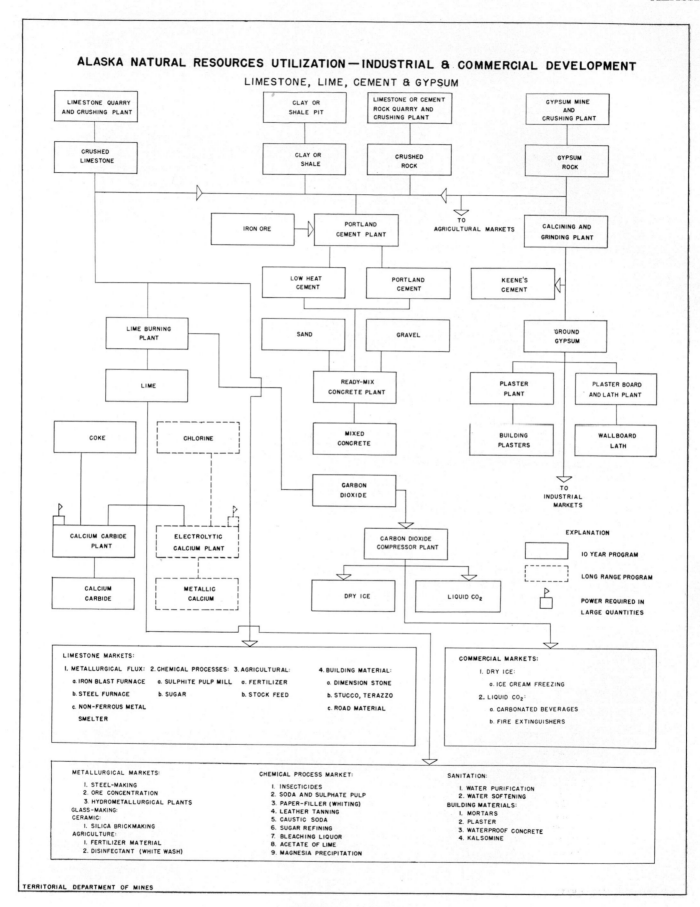

ALASKA NATURAL RESOURCES UTILIZATION—INDUSTRIAL & COMMERCIAL DEVELOPMENT

LIMESTONE, LIME, CEMENT & GYPSUM

NONMETALLIC GROUP

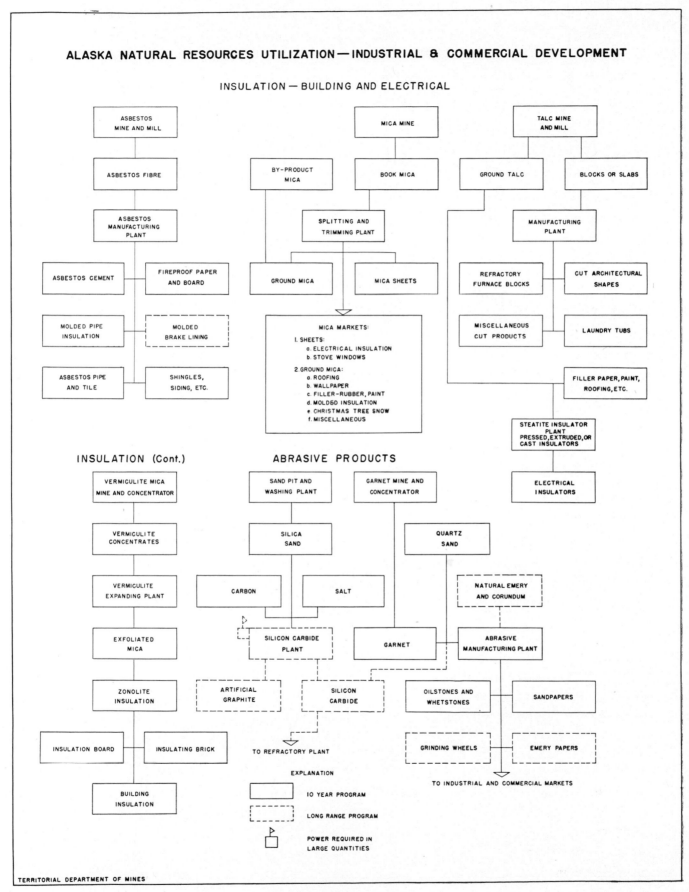

ALASKA NATURAL RESOURCES UTILIZATION—INDUSTRIAL & COMMERCIAL DEVELOPMENT

NONMETALLIC GROUP

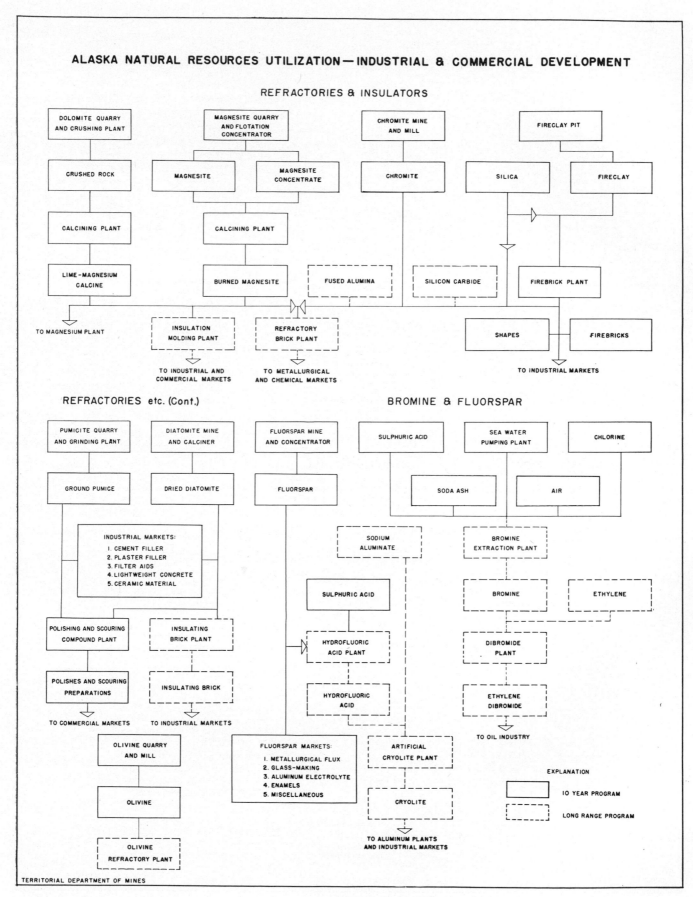

ALASKA NATURAL RESOURCES UTILIZATION—INDUSTRIAL & COMMERCIAL DEVELOPMENT

REFRACTORIES & INSULATORS

REFRACTORIES etc. (Cont.)

BROMINE & FLUORSPAR

TERRITORIAL DEPARTMENT OF MINES

NONMETALLIC GROUP

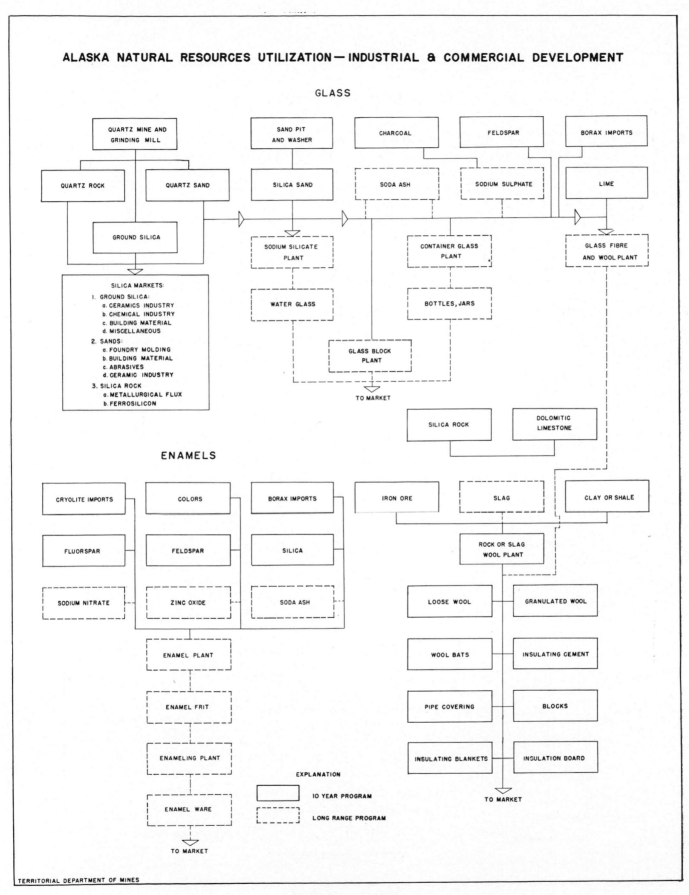

ALASKA NATURAL RESOURCES UTILIZATION—INDUSTRIAL & COMMERCIAL DEVELOPMENT

GLASS

NONMETALLIC GROUP

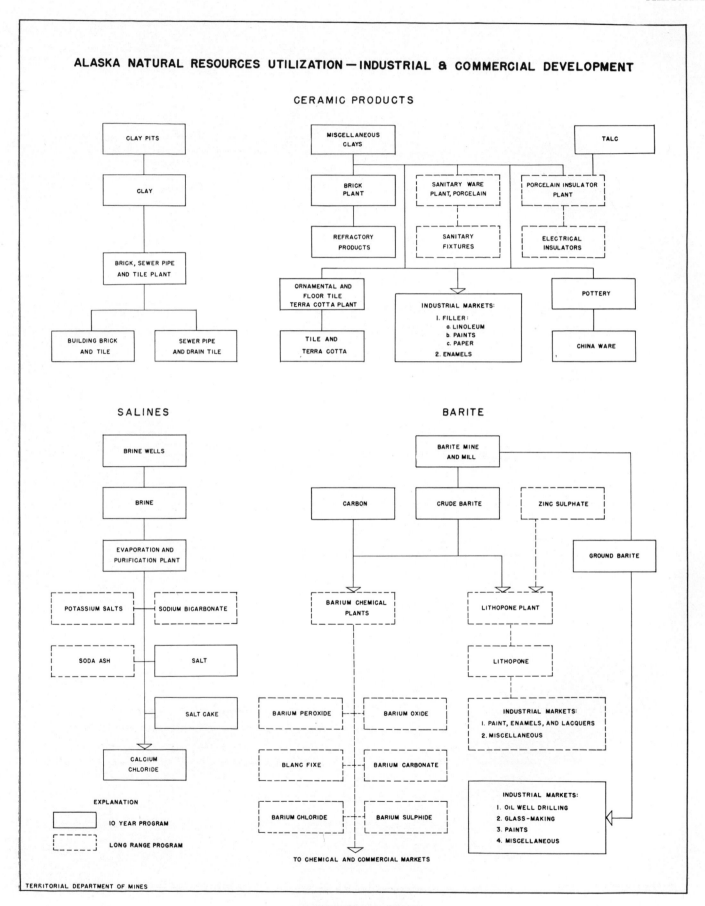

ALASKA NATURAL RESOURCES UTILIZATION — INDUSTRIAL & COMMERCIAL DEVELOPMENT

CERAMIC PRODUCTS

SALINES

BARITE

EXPLANATION

10 YEAR PROGRAM

LONG RANGE PROGRAM

TERRITORIAL DEPARTMENT OF MINES

NONMETALLIC GROUP

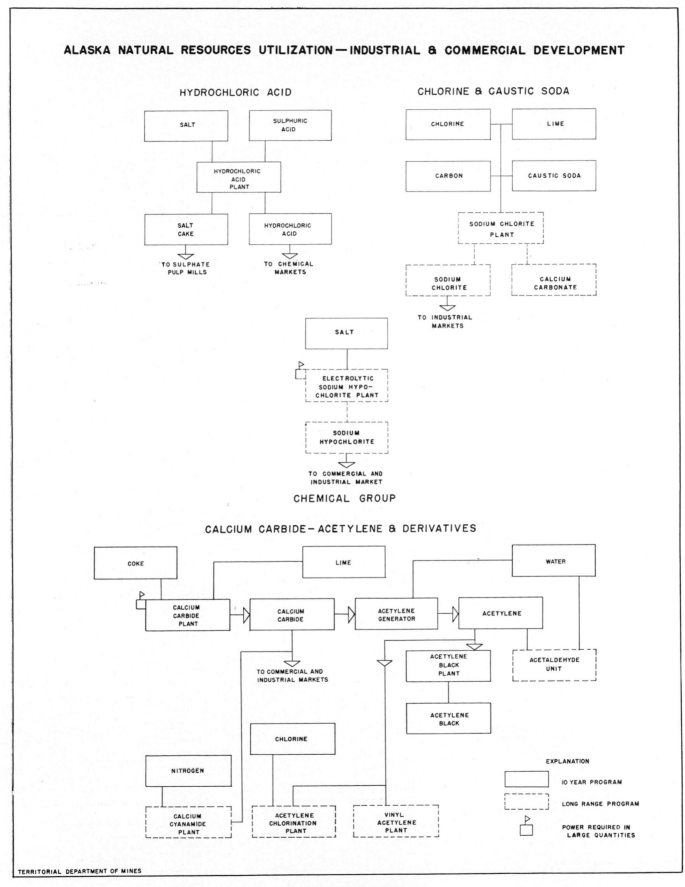

ALASKA NATURAL RESOURCES UTILIZATION — INDUSTRIAL & COMMERCIAL DEVELOPMENT

HYDROCHLORIC ACID

CHLORINE & CAUSTIC SODA

SALT

SULPHURIC ACID

HYDROCHLORIC ACID PLANT

SALT CAKE

HYDROCHLORIC ACID

TO SULPHATE PULP MILLS

TO CHEMICAL MARKETS

CHLORINE

LIME

CARBON

CAUSTIC SODA

SODIUM CHLORITE PLANT

SODIUM CHLORITE

CALCIUM CARBONATE

TO INDUSTRIAL MARKETS

SALT

ELECTROLYTIC SODIUM HYPO-CHLORITE PLANT

SODIUM HYPOCHLORITE

TO COMMERCIAL AND INDUSTRIAL MARKET

CHEMICAL GROUP

CALCIUM CARBIDE — ACETYLENE & DERIVATIVES

COKE

LIME

WATER

CALCIUM CARBIDE PLANT

CALCIUM CARBIDE

ACETYLENE GENERATOR

ACETYLENE

TO COMMERCIAL AND INDUSTRIAL MARKETS

ACETYLENE BLACK PLANT

ACETALDEHYDE UNIT

ACETYLENE BLACK

CHLORINE

NITROGEN

CALCIUM CYANAMIDE PLANT

ACETYLENE CHLORINATION PLANT

VINYL ACETYLENE PLANT

EXPLANATION

10 YEAR PROGRAM

LONG RANGE PROGRAM

POWER REQUIRED IN LARGE QUANTITIES

TERRITORIAL DEPARTMENT OF MINES

NONMETALLIC GROUP

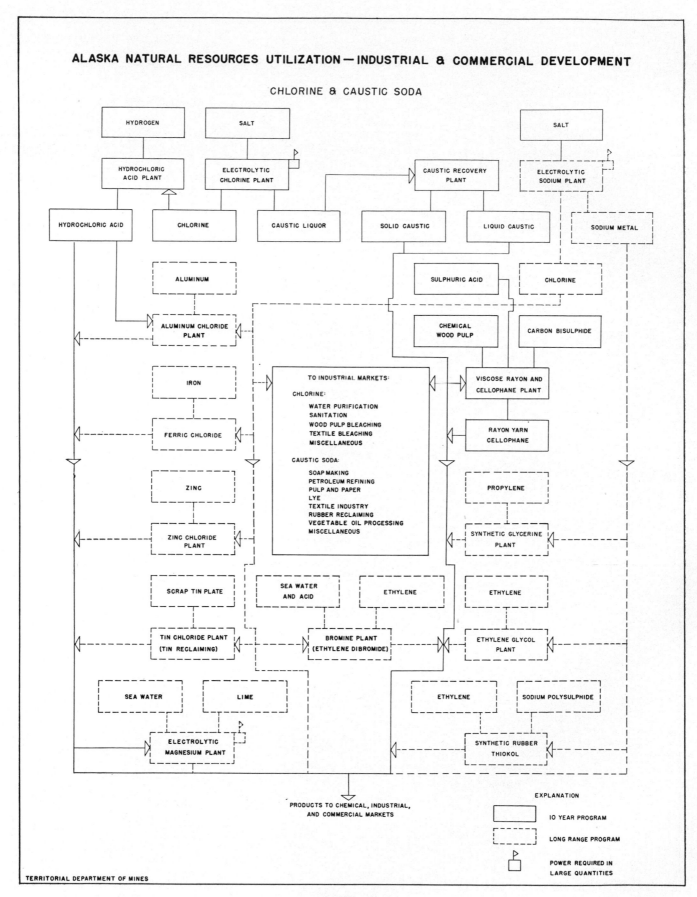

ALASKA NATURAL RESOURCES UTILIZATION—INDUSTRIAL & COMMERCIAL DEVELOPMENT

CHLORINE & CAUSTIC SODA

CHEMICAL GROUP

TERRITORIAL DEPARTMENT OF MINES

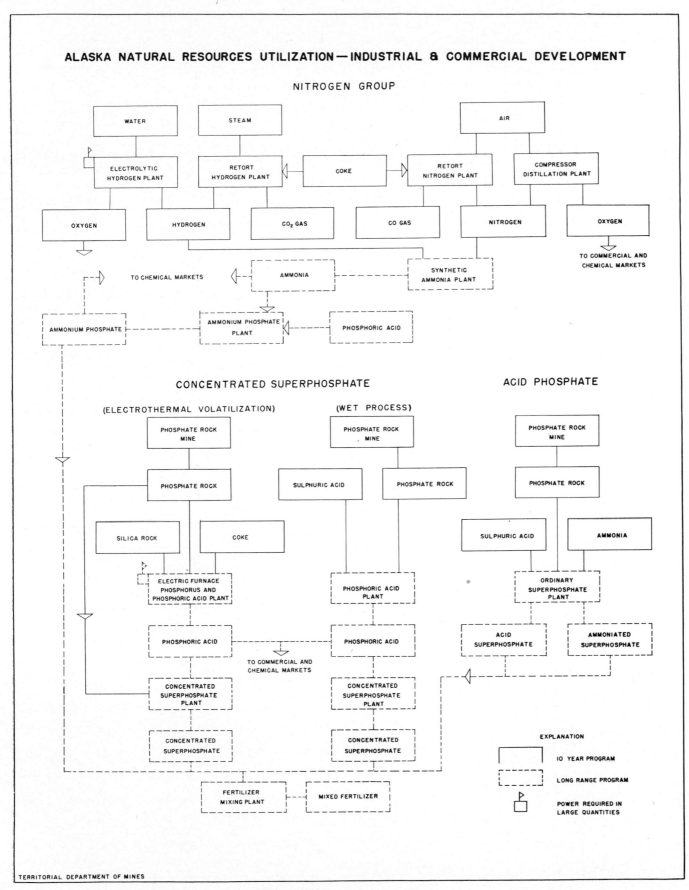

ALASKA NATURAL RESOURCES UTILIZATION—INDUSTRIAL & COMMERCIAL DEVELOPMENT

CHEMICAL GROUP—FERTILIZER

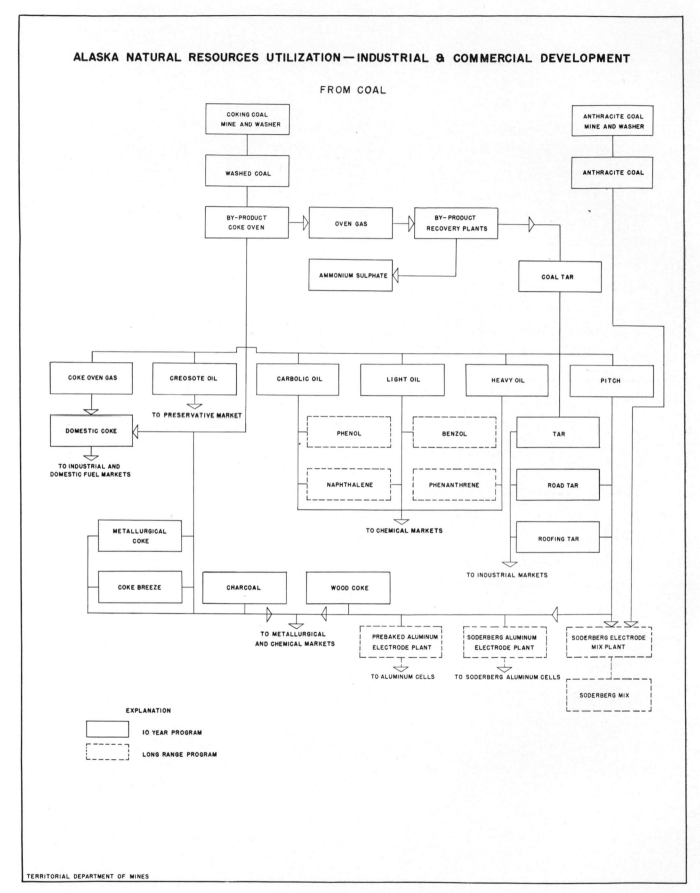

ALASKA NATURAL RESOURCES UTILIZATION—INDUSTRIAL & COMMERCIAL DEVELOPMENT

FROM COAL

INDUSTRIAL CARBON GROUP

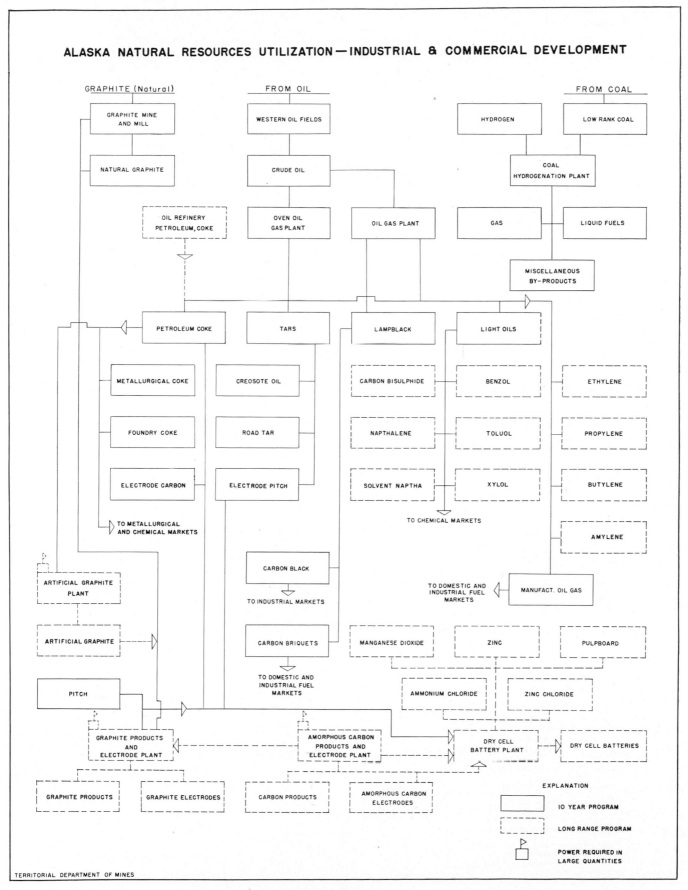

ALASKA NATURAL RESOURCES UTILIZATION — INDUSTRIAL & COMMERCIAL DEVELOPMENT

INDUSTRIAL CARBON GROUP

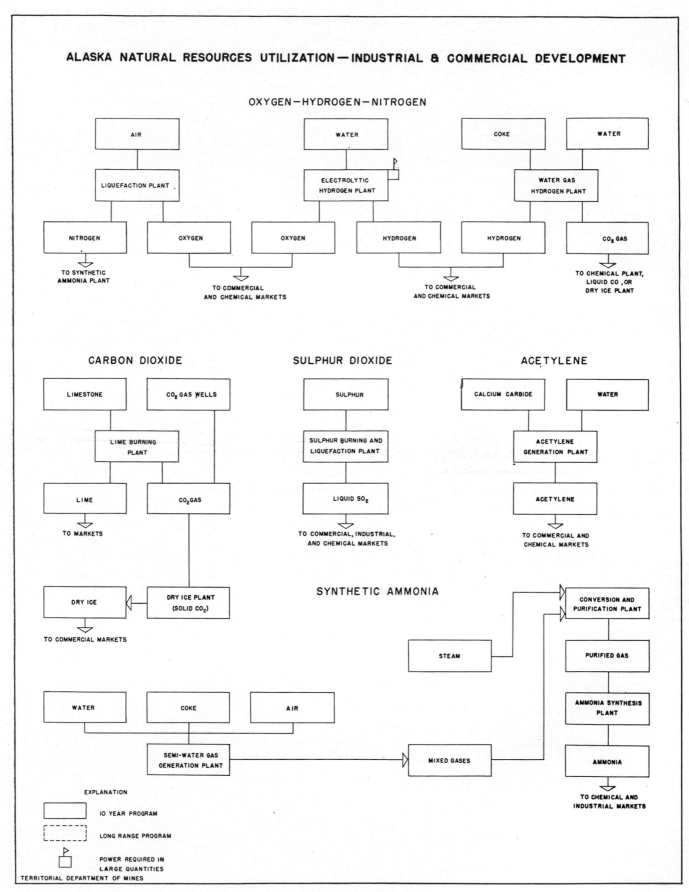

ALASKA NATURAL RESOURCES UTILIZATION—INDUSTRIAL & COMMERCIAL DEVELOPMENT

INDUSTRIAL GAS GROUP

terminals where airline operators and pilots can obtain the latest weather information, examine weather maps and upper-air charts and consult with meterologists.

Historical

The earliest meteorological observations were begun at Sitka by Russian missionaries in 1828. The meteorological work at Sitka was taken over by Russian Government officials in 1842 and continued until 1867 when the Territory was acquired by the United States. However, aside from this record and a couple of others of a fragmentary nature made at mission stations, there appears to have been no effort during the Russian occupancy to make systematic weather records.

Soon after the organization of the United States Weather Bureau under the Signal Corps of the Army, by Joint Congressional Resolution, February 9, 1870 (16 Stat. L., 369), weather observations were begun by the surgeons at several Army-post hospitals. Thereafter a few additional stations were established, with 13 in operation by 1890, but these early records were made generally near the coast and no data became available for the interior until the 80's and then only fragmentary in nature.

After the transfer of the Weather Bureau to the Department of Agriculture in 1890, observational work was extended as rapidly as conditions permitted, and by 1920 weather reports were being received from 73 stations. However, in Alaska, as in the States, the bulk of climatological records is obtained through cooperation with interested persons who make observations without compensation for their service and, because of sparse settlement in most sections, limited communication facilities, and often lack of permanency in residence, it has been difficult in many cases to maintain continuity of records for a sufficient length of time for the data to be of material climatological value. The station mortality and observer turnover are extremely large. Current climatological records for Alaska have been printed in both monthly and annual summaries and earlier data, up to 1921, are summarized in considerable detail in Weather Bureau Bulletin W.

Forecasting activities in Alaska necessarily could not begin until it was possible to secure current daily observations from scattered places in the Territory by cable, telegraph, and radio. Local forecasts for Juneau and vicinity were first issued in 1917, and were extended later to the area traversed by the Alaskan Railroad to Fairbanks and the Tanana Valley. In May 1919 Juneau was designated as the district forecast center.

The first observation obtained by radio was from Nome on November 1, 1907, followed by Eagle on June 24, 1909, Kodiak and Dutch Harbor on May 1, 1915, and St. Paul on August 8, 1915. Prior to these dates observations were secured regularly from places on or contiguous to the Seattle-Alaska cable. When the forecast service began in 1917 observations were available at Juneau daily or twice daily from 10 places in Alaska. These reports were cabled also to Seattle and distributed to the various forecast centers. They proved to be of incalculable value in connection with the forecasting service in the United States.

By the time that the service for airways was inaugurated in 1931 there were 13 such stations transmitting observations daily or twice daily. They, with an increased number of observations each day, have formed a fundamental source of data used in providing service to aviation since that time.

In 1931 there were 13 stations transmitting synoptic observations daily, or twice daily, in Alaska. The first service for aviation was inaugurated in the same year, with an appropriation of $26,695. For several years thereafter no material change was made in the service to aviation.

The first plans for an expansion began as a cooperative movement early in 1936 on the part of the Department of the Interior, War Department, Post Office Department, and Department of Agriculture (Weather Bureau), involving plans for the relief and development of Alaskan aviation. While the request for funds for this project by the Department of the Interior for the improvement of Territorial possessions was not approved by the Bureau of the Budget in that year, these plans were, in general, followed later when funds became available.

A statement as to the need of aviation and general weather service within Alaska was included in a report to Congress, as requested in the concurrent Congressional Resolution No. 24, approved August 21, 1937. This report, by the Alaskan Resources Committee, entitled, "Alaska—Its Resources and Development" was presented to the President in December 1937 for transmission to the Congress. The staff report on "Meteorology and Climatology," prepared by representatives of the Weather Bureau and a member of the Army Air Corps, proposed a weather-reporting service consisting of four airway district forecast centers, 7 upper-air reporting stations, and 82 additional synoptic reporting stations. The committee pointed out that the advantageous use of weather reports is dependent upon the ability of the Weather Bureau to organize meteorological observation stations and the effectiveness and expedition with which observations can be obtained from such stations. Hence adequate communication facilities, particularly radio, are vital in carrying out a meteorological program in Alaska. This committee indicated the necessity of full cooperation by radio stations, personnel of the Signal Corps (Army), Navy, and Bureau of Air Commerce (later C. A. A.).

In April 1938 an interdepartmental committee was organized for the purpose of putting into effect recommendations submitted by the National Resources Committee with respect to weather service in Alaska. A Weather Bureau representative served on that committee, and at the first meeting on May 2, 1938, plans were drawn up for 9 primary airports and 21 secondary landing fields, with the Weather Bureau presenting an estimate for consummation of the project.

The first evidence of fruition of plans of the Interdepartmental Committee was the transfer of $131,500 from the Army Air Corps to the Bureau for use in establishing five radiosonde and pilot balloon stations in Alaska, namely: Point Barrow, Nome, Bethel, Anchorage and Ketchikan. The War Department considered data from these stations as essential for accurate forecasting in Alaska for activities of the Army Air Corps. They were established before the close of the fiscal year 1941, increasing the number of radiosonde stations to seven, since two had been previously established at Fairbanks and Juneau. At the request of the Secretary of War the Weather Bureau set up in its budget for the fiscal year 1942 funds for continued operations of these five stations.

The Chief of the Army Air Corps, outlined "The Minimum Requirements for Safety of Air Corps Operations in the Fairbanks Area," with respect to weather service, and listed the need for 18 additional stations for hourly reporting from 7:30 to 19:30 o'clock with 13 additional stations reporting at 3-hourly intervals, plus a continuance of reports from existing stations within the Territory. He further indicated that additional airway weather service would be required as soon as communication facilities would enable transmission of reports from other points.

As of January 1, 1941, 7 first-order stations were operating in Alaska from which radiosonde and pilot balloon observations were available, 16 second-order hourly reporting stations, and 97 airway reporting stations. Juneau was designated as the general supervising station for the Territory and direct supervision of activities within specified areas was assigned Fairbanks, Anchorage, and Nome. On August 2, 1941, the Army Air Corps requested that weather reporting service in Alaska be further expanded, with minor modifications. This was accomplished.

On April 24, 1942, the Navy requested that a weather reporting station be placed on St. Matthew Island. As this was not practicable because of lack of facilities, a radiosonde station was opened at Gambell on St. Lawrence Island instead.

Due largely to the requirements of wartime aviation implemented in part by the transfer of funds from the War Department, there was steady growth in the network of stations. Toward the end of the war there were forecast centers at Juneau, Anchorage and Fairbanks with the administrative work of the region (number 8) centered at Anchorage. Ten combination raidosonde and pilot-balloon and two pilot-balloon stations were in operation by the Bureau, supplemented by others operated by the Army. There were nearly 150 airway weather stations including those reporting on-call and others taking observations for forecast maps. The C. A. A. also took observations at a small number of their communication stations.

Close liaison was maintained during the war with the A. A. F. and the C. A. A. and changes in observing stations, programs, instrumental equipment and the transmission of reports were worked out to the mutual benefit of all concerned.

The establishment and maintenance of a network of reporting stations in Alaska has been difficult because of limited communications and transportation facilities and the lack of observer personnel in some communities. Transportation difficulties were greatly reduced by the development of landing fields and installation of air-navigation aids by the C. A. A. Closely associated therewith has been the development of radio communication facilities by that agency. However, the lack of communication facilities has been one of the Bureau's primary problems in obtaining reports from points off the airways, where it has been necessary to rely upon overloaded radio-communication facilities operated by the Signal Corps in some cases, or upon radio facilities operated by the Bureau of Indian Affairs personnel, or by some individual in the community. In many cases transmission of reports has been unsatisfactory.

Current Activities

The Weather Bureau maintains a climatological service for Alaska with headquarters at Anchorage. The regional director at that station supervises the collection of weather reports, many of which are obtained from cooperative observers without cost to the Government. These reports consist of daily records of temperature, precipitation, snowfall, and other weather elements. At the present, cooperative stations are in operation at 24 locations. Six of these stations are closely grouped in the agricultural region of the Matanuska Valley. In addition, meteorological records from all first and second order Weather Bureau stations and all C. A. A. and military observing points are processed for climatological purposes. These reports are summarized and published in considerable detail

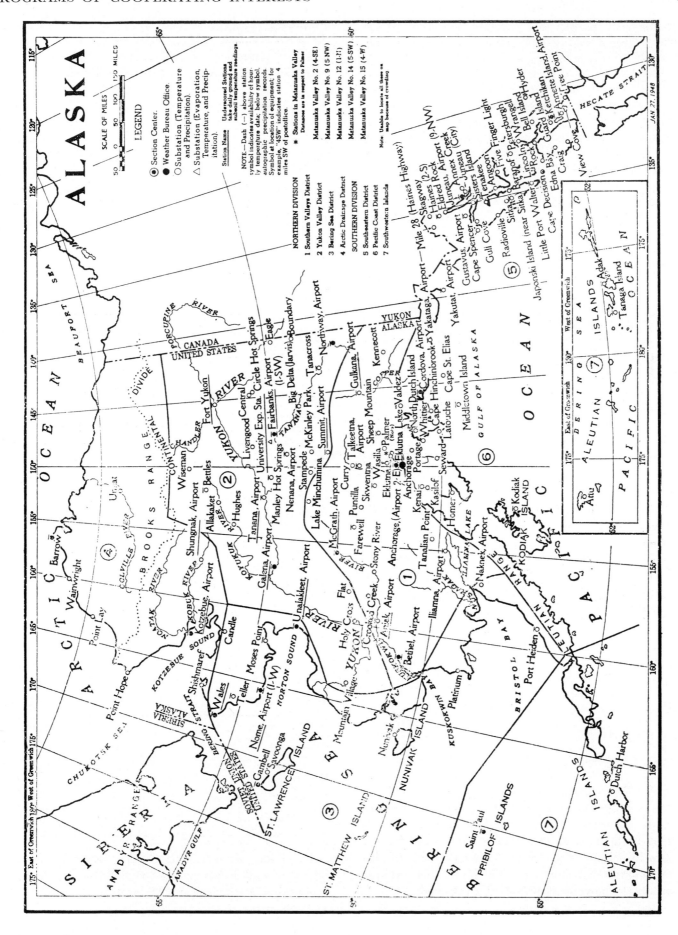

for the several months and for the year as a whole. Printing of the climatological reports is done at Seattle, Wash.

The civil airway weather service in Alaska is under the supervision of the Weather Bureau Regional Office at Anchorage. At the present there are 17 first order Weather Bureau offices in Alaska. Radio observations of temperature, humidity and winds aloft are made at six of these stations; radio observations of temperature, humidity and visual observations of winds aloft are made at seven stations; and visual observations of winds aloft are made at three stations. All these stations participate in the regular surface observational program as well.

Forecast service in Alaska is handled by forecast centers at Anchorage, Fairbanks, and Juneau. Airway and general weather forecasts are distributed by all three centers and marine forecasts are added from the Anchorage and Juneau centers.

The basic net of first order stations is supplemented by additional stations manned by the following agencies:

1. Twenty-nine second-order Weather Bureau stations. These stations are operated by paid noncommissioned employees of the Weather Bureau and furnish synoptic and/or airway observations.

2. Thirty-one communications stations of the C. A. A.

3. Eleven stations of the U. S. Coast Guard.

4. Five stations of the U. S. Navy.

5. Fifteen stations of the U. S. Air Forces and additional weather reconnaissance flights.

6. Four cooperative airway stations.

Reports from all stations are gathered at collection points and consolidated for inter-Alaska distribution by the radio and radio teletype circuits of the C. A. A. Reports from selected stations are relayed to national and international weather exchanges.

Storm warnings are issued as required and broadcast for public information. Fire weather forecasts are issued seasonally.

Climate of Alaska

General Climate Controls

The Arctic Slope is dominated by the Arctic Anticyclone at all seasons although areas of low pressure break into this region in summer. The interior is dominated by high pressure in the long winter and by low pressure in summer. Lows are able to penetrate into this region mostly in summer. The Pacific coastal area encounters the movement of lows at all seasons.

Climatic Regions

For the purpose of this report, Alaska is divided climatically into four regions: the Pacific Drainage, the Bering Coastal Area, the Arctic Slope, and the Interior Valleys.

The Pacific Drainage

Temperatures along the coast are generally cool and mild. The moderating influence of the ocean is a large factor in the control of temperature. Average January and July temperatures illustrate this point:

TABLE 42.—*Average temperature °F.*

	January	July
Juneau	28	57
Kodiak	30	54
Matanuska	13	58

Kodiak, with the greatest marine influence, has a range of 24° between mean temperatures of January and July, and Matanuska, more inland, has a range of 45°. The winters are not colder than many places in the United States, summers are definitely cool.

Precipitation is generally rather heavy with the maximum in autumn and winter. Moist air moving in from the Pacific is forced to drop much of its moisture on the windward side of the mountains in crossing this barrier. An idea of the variation between months and between stations can be obtained from the following tabulation:

TABLE 43.—*Average monthly precipitation, inches*

	Ketchi-kan	Juneau	Cordova	Anchorage	Matanuska
January	13. 6	7. 2	9. 6	0. 8	0. 9
February	11. 2	5. 5	10. 6	. 7	. 8
March	12. 1	5. 5	9. 3	. 6	. 6
April	10. 9	5. 4	9. 4	. 4	. 5
May	8. 4	5. 2	9. 1	. 5	. 7
June	6. 6	4. 0	6. 0	. 7	1. 1
July	8. 1	5. 1	8. 9	1. 6	1. 9
August	11. 6	7. 4	13. 7	2. 6	2. 7
September	12. 2	10. 2	19. 9	2. 6	2. 5
October	20. 2	11. 4	22. 6	2. 2	1. 8
November	20. 0	9. 2	15. 2	1. 0	1. 0
December	15. 9	7. 6	13. 2	. 9	1. 1
Annual total	150. 8	83. 7	147. 5	14. 6	15. 6

Ketchikan, Juneau, and Cordova are representative of individual locations on the windward side of the mountains, Anchorage and Matanuska, the leeward side.

Precipitation usually falls steadily, seldom heavy and seldom showery. Thunderstorms are rare.

Snowfall is governed by the same factors as precipitation in general, temperature permitting. The magnitude of the snowfall can be judged from the following average monthly amounts:

TABLE 44.—*Average monthly snowfall, inches*

	Ketchi-kan	Juneau	Cor-dova	Anchor-age	Mata-nuska
January	10. 0	28. 1	28. 1	12. 1	8. 4
February	7. 1	23. 8	25. 1	8. 7	7. 8
March	4. 7	14. 9	25. 7	7. 7	6. 8
April	. 6	4. 6	11. 2	2. 9	2. 5
May	. 4	. 1	. 2	. 2	0
June	0	0	0	0	0
July	0	0	0	0	0
August	0	0	0	0	0
September	0	. 1	0	0	. 4
October	. 2	1. 5	3. 4	5. 2	2. 7
November	1. 9	9. 1	10. 0	11. 2	7. 1
December	7. 4	25. 0	25. 0	10. 4	10. 3
Annual total	32. 3	107. 2	128. 7	58. 4	46. 0

Relative humidity is rather high, varying somewhat with the precipitation. Dense fog varies from 1 to 3 days a month in the winter, is infrequent in summer. Cloudiness is prevalent: Anchorage has 180 cloudy days a year, Juneau 262. Sunshine is correspondingly deficient: Anchorage averaging 45 percent of the possible amount, Juneau 29 percent.

The Bering Coastal Area

Mean temperatures vary on the average from the fifties in summer to zero or below in winter depending somewhat on distance from the ocean. The fact that the ocean is frozen for several months tends to lessen its moderating influence in winter. The following average temperatures are characteristic:

TABLE 45.—*Average temperature °F.*

	January	July
Nome	3	50
Holy Cross	0	57

Nome is on the coast thus having the moderating influence of the ocean, and is protected somewhat by mountains from the cold north winds. Holy Cross farther inland has a greater range of temperature.

Precipitation is rather scant in this area with its maximum in late summer and autumn. Monthly distribution is shown in the following tabulation:

TABLE 46.—*Average monthly precipitation, inches*

	Nome	Holy Cross
January	1. 1	1. 4
February	. 8	1. 0
March	. 8	1. 3
April	. 7	. 6
May	. 6	. 7
June	1. 1	1. 2
July	2. 5	2. 7
August	3. 2	3. 7
September	2. 7	2. 9
October	1. 6	1. 6
November	1. 0	1. 2
December	1. 1	1. 3
Annual total	17. 2	19. 6

Precipitation is of a steady type rather than showery. There is an average of only one thunderstorm a year at Nome The greatest precipitation ever recorded in 24 hours at Nome is only 2.30 inches.

Snow has fallen in every month with the possible exception of July. In the winter months all precipitation is snow. Average snowfall by months is:

TABLE 47.—*Average monthly snowfall, inches*

	Nome	Holy Cross
January	10. 8	20. 5
February	8. 9	12. 8
March	10. 2	12. 5
April	5. 1	7. 1
May	1. 3	1. 2
June	. 2	T
July	0	0
August	T	0
September	. 4	. 3
October	3. 6	5. 8
November	8. 5	13. 0
December	10. 8	18. 0
Annual total	59. 8	91. 2

Relative humidity is rather high, but at winter temperature is of little practical significance. At Nome light fogs occur 5 or 6 days a month, except in summer when they are about twice as frequent. Fogs are probably a little less frequent farther inland. Cloudiness is general: 185 days a year at Nome are cloudy. Cloudiness is somewhat less away from the coast. The clearest season is winter. Nome averages only 42 percent of possible sunshine.

Arctic Slope

Temperatures are kept low by northerly winds during all seasons. The average July temperature at Barrow is 40° F. In contrast Nashville, Tenn., has an average January temperature of 39° F. The average January temperature at Barrow is −17° F. For comparison, the lowest temperature ever recorded at Washington, D. C., is −15° F. Although the Arctic Ocean is frozen months at a time, it has some moderating influence, and temperatures vary more away from the coast than they do at Barrow.

Precipitation is slight—less than some deserts in lower latitudes. There is a slight maximum of precipitation in late summer as shown by the following tabulation for Barrow:

TABLE 48.—*Average monthly precipitation, inches*

	Barrow
January	0. 2
February	. 2
March	. 1
April	. 1
May	. 1
June	. 3
July	. 9
August	. 7
September	. 5
October	. 6
November	. 3
December	. 3
Annual total	4. 3

Snowfall occurs in all months.

TABLE 49.—*Average monthly snowfall, inches*

	Barrow
January	2. 6
February	2. 7
March	2. 0
April	2. 7
May	1. 8
June	0. 4
July	1. 0
August	0. 7
September	3. 0
October	7. 9
November	4. 3
December	3. 9
Annual total	33. 0

The Interior Valleys

Temperatures in this area have the greatest variability of anywhere in Alaska. Fairbanks has had extreme temperatures of 99° F. and −66° F. Differences between January and July are shown in the following tabulation:

TABLE 50.—*Average temperature °F.*

	January	July	Difference
Fairbanks	−11	60	71
Fort Yukon	−21	58	79
Tanana	−12	58	70

Even though the winters are as cold as those along the Arctic Ocean, the summers are warm enough for hardy plants to thrive.

Precipitation is light but has a decided late summer maximum.

TABLE 51.—*Average monthly precipitation, inches*

	Alla-kaket	Eagle	Fair-banks	Fort Yukon	Ruby	Tan-ana
January	0. 7	0. 4	1. 0	0. 4	1. 5	0. 8
February	. 8	. 4	. 5	. 4	1. 0	. 7
March	. 6	. 4	. 7	. 3	. 8	. 6
April	. 4	. 4	. 3	. 2	. 4	. 2
May	. 6	. 8	. 6	. 5	. 9	. 8
June	1. 3	1. 5	1. 4	. 8	. 9	1. 2
July	2. 2	1. 8	1. 9	1. 1	3. 1	2. 4
August	2. 0	2. 0	2. 0	1. 2	3. 2	2. 5
September	1. 5	1. 3	1. 3	. 6	1. 9	1. 7
October	1. 1	. 8	. 8	. 6	1. 1	1. 1
November	. 8	. 5	. 7	. 4	. 9	. 7
December	. 8	. 4	. 6	. 3	. 9	. 6
Annual total	12. 8	10. 7	11. 8	6. 8	16. 6	13. 3

A small portion of the summer rainfall is of the shower type and is associated with thunderstorms. Most of the precipitation, however, falls as slow, continuous precipitation. The greatest precipitation in 24 hours at Fairbanks was 2.33 inches.

Snowfall, because of the extreme cold, is frequently in small, dry, powdery flakes that blow and drift easily.

TABLE 52.—*Average monthly snowfall, inches*

	Alla-kaket	Eagle	Fair-banks	Fort Yukon	Ruby	Tan-ana
January	13. 4	8. 4	17. 9	7. 8	17. 3	10. 0
February	12. 9	5. 4	8. 5	6. 9	11. 6	9. 5
March	11. 1	5. 5	7. 5	3. 8	10. 8	8. 1
April	5. 0	3. 6	1. 8	1. 6	2. 6	2. 5
May	. 6	. 5	. 4	. 5	1. 3	. 5
June	0	T	. 1	0	0	T
July	0	0	0	0	0	T
August	T	. 2	0	. 1	0	0
September	1. 1	1. 7	. 5	1. 3	. 5	. 9
October	8. 5	8. 1	9. 5	7. 2	7. 9	7. 6
November	11. 7	9. 2	10. 8	7. 7	10. 8	5. 8
December	12. 4	10. 1	9. 6	5. 1	12. 2	8. 6
Annual total	76. 7	52. 7	66. 6	42. 0	75. 0	53. 5

Relative humidity is rather high for a place with so light precipitation. However, this is of little significance at the temperatures prevailing most of the year. Light fog occurs at Fairbanks on an average of 50 days a year, the winter months having 1 day in 3 or 4 with light fog. This region has the most fair weather of any portion of Alaska, but is still rather cloudy compared to most places in the United States. Fairbanks has 100 clear days a year, 163 cloudy, and 46 percent of the possible sunshine.

Length of Days in Alaska

Because of its position so far north, the length of day varies much more between summer and winter than in the United States. At the Arctic Circle on the shortest day in winter the sun rises to the horizon in the south at noon, then setting. Farther south it rises correspondingly longer but farther north it does not rise on this day. For instance, at Fairbanks, about 2.5 degrees south of the circle, on December 21, the sun rises at 9:58 a. m. and sets at 1:40 p. m. At Barrow, about 4 degrees north of the circle, the sun has not risen since late November and will not be seen again until late January.

In summer the days are as long as they were short in winter. At the Arctic Circle on the longest day the sun dips to the horizon at midnight, then rising. Farther south the sun goes below the horizon, farther north the sun does not reach it. At Fairbanks on June 21 the sun rises at 12:57 a. m. and sets at 11:48 p. m. At Barrow the sun has not gone below the northern horizon since early May but circles the sky, being highest in the south at noon and lowest in the north at "midnight." The sun first sets at Barrow early in August. This is as much a "land of the midnight sun" as is northern Norway. Accompanying figures show the length of day throughout the year at Juneau, Anchorage, and Fairbanks.

Climate of Potentially Agricultural Area

The Matanuska Valley and some adjacent area has climatic conditions as favorable for agriculture as some areas in the Dakotas and Montana. The average growing season, as measured from the last killing frost in spring to the first killing frost in autumn, is near 100 days.

TABLE 53.—*Average growing season*

	Date of last killing frost	Date of first killing frost	Growing season, days
Seward	May 18	September 27	132
Anchorage	May 25	September 12	110
Talkeetna	June 14	August 25	72
Bismarck, N. Dak	May 10	September 22	135

Summer temperatures are cool but the long days stimulate plant growth.

TABLE 54.—*Average monthly temperature,* °F.

	Seward	Anchorage	Matanuska	Talkeetna	Bismarck, N. Dak.
January	23	12	13	8	8
February	27	19	18	17	12
March	31	24	24	21	25
April	36	35	37	34	43
May	44	45	47	45	55
June	51	54	55	55	64
July	55	57	58	58	70
August	54	56	56	55	68
September	49	48	48	46	58
October	40	36	37	34	45
November	31	22	22	20	28
December	25	13	14	10	16

Precipitation is most abundant in late summer and autumn, late for many crops. However, early soil moisture is available from melting snow, and the moisture requirement of plants is reduced by the cool temperatures. (See tabulation of precipitation under "Pacific Slope.")

In the interior valleys climatic conditions are a little more critical. The growing season is 90 days or less. However, temperatures are a little higher than in the Matanuska Valley, and the days are a little longer.

TABLE 55.—*Average growing season*

	Date of last killing frost	Date of first killing frost	Growing season, days
Allakaket	June 13	August 6	54
Fairbanks	May 29	August 26	89
Fort Yukon	June 1	August 21	81
Holy Cross	May 31	August 29	90
Tanana	June 3	August 26	64

TABLE 56.—*Average monthly temperature,* °F.

	Allakaket	Fairbanks	Fort Yukon	Holy Cross	Tanana
January	−20	−11	−21	0	−12
February	−12	−1	−16	5	−4
March	−3	10	0	13	6
April	18	29	22	26	25
May	41	47	43	42	44
June	56	58	58	54	57
July	58	60	61	57	58
August	52	55	55	54	53
September	40	44	42	44	41
October	20	27	21	30	24
November	−7	3	−6	12	1
December	−17	−7	−20	1	−10

Precipitation, although not heavy, is almost ideally distributed. There is little during the winter when it is of little practical significance to agriculture. Summer rains begin in June and are usually heaviest in July and August, the growing season. Precipitation is generally adequate for agriculture. (See tabulation under "Interior Valleys.")

Figure 8 shows the average length of the growing season in Alaska. Figure 2 shows the average temperature in July and figure 6 the average precipitation for the year. Areas with average temperatures below 50° F. in July will support only limited vegetation.

Snowfall

Snowfall in Alaska has a relative distribution quite similar to that for the rainfall, being heavy along the Pacific coast, with decrease northward to a minimum along the Arctic coast. The average annual amounts vary from over 100 inches in southeastern sections of the Territory to between 80 and 100 inches in most of the Bering Sea area, 40 to 60 in the interior valleys, and to less than 40 in the Arctic region. Barrow records snowfall in every month of the year. The Pacific coast, in general, has about 4 months without any snow, the Bering Sea coast 3 months, the interior 2 months, and the far north no month without at least a trace of snow. In the interior June and July are the months without snow, while in the same latitude along the Bering Sea, July and August are generally snow-free, illustrating the effect of the cool sea in retarding the spring and early summer rise in temperature.

Deficiencies

Although there was a considerable expansion in the Weather Bureau's services in Alaska during the recent World War, the anticipated future development of Alaskan resources must be paralleled by suitable additional meteorological services. Pending such expansion, however, every effort should be made to utilize to the fullest extent the climatological and hydrologic records already available. There is at present, a backlog of more than 6 million unprocessed weather observations in Alaska. These observations are records of such weather elements as rainfall and snowfall amounts, highest and lowest temperatures, wind directions and speeds, humidity pressure, ceilings and visibilities, and other weather phenomena.

When properly processed, these data can reveal the all-important story of weather and climate in Alaska. They can supply the basis for determining design values, the calculation of safety factors, and the calculation of "weather risks," all of which must be known in the intelligent planning of the development of municipal water supply, water power, irrigation, and flood control in Alaska, as well as the planning of development of Alaskan agriculture, industry, aviation, and other civil activities. The data that these observations will reveal when properly processed are also of utmost importance in planning military defenses and operations.

The Weather Bureau is planning a 5-year program for placing these weather observations on punched cards. Once the data are on punched cards they can be tabulated and retabulated in many ways to meet the various requirements of the water and power resources planners, as well as the requirements of agriculture, industry, aviation, the military and others. If funds become available for this program, the Weather Bureau will then be able to make its store of unprocessed climatological and hydrologic data for Alaska available for whatever planning and investigative studies may be required by the end of the 5 year period.

Alaska, notwithstanding its extensive area and decided contrasts of climate, due to its topography, adjacent waters and geographic location, has only 136 climatological stations as compared with a total of 517 in the States of Iowa, Kansas, and Nebraska, the area of which is only about one-third of that of Alaska.

There is great need for complete weather observations and records from far-flung places which are not now obtainable because of isolation, sparse habitation, or lack of communications. In most of these places it would be necessary to erect suitable buildings, provide meteorological, radio, and other equipment and to employ observers, operators, etc. It would, of course, be prohibitive to incur the expense of such installations for weather reports alone. However, when other government agencies have need for service at such locations, cooperation and division of cost could bring about the desired results.

The Weather Bureau should operate a river and flood service in Alaska. To do this, it would be necessary to install complete facilities for conducting such a river and flood forecasting service. A number of reporting stations would need to be established at various points on the Yukon, Tanana, and other rivers. Two or more should be equipped to record stream flow and to transmit the record to the principal forecasting centers. It would also be necessary as a part of this project to inaugurate snow and ice surveys. Such surveys could best be made by utilizing airplane flights and air photography, and by establishing a short wave radio communication system.

Illustrations

The pertinent climatic features of Alaska are portrayed in the following accompanying figures:
1. Mean temperature for January.
2. Mean temperature for July.
3. Absolute maximum temperature for year.
4. Absolute minimum temperature for year.

5. Number of days with freezing temperature for year.

6. Mean precipitation for year.

7. Mean snowfall for year.

8. Average length of growing season.

9. Time of sunrise and sunset, Juneau.

10. Time of sunrise and sunset, Anchorage.

11. Time of sunrise and sunset, Fairbanks.

GEOLOGICAL SURVEY

The Geological Survey has the responsibility for a group of activities that are necessary for the appraisal of the potentialities of a partially developed area such as Alaska and for assisting in the development of the area. Such basic investigations are prerequisite to the development of Alaska in an intelligent and effective fashion. These activities include study of the quantity and quality of surface and underground waters; geologic mapping and investigation of mineral resources; topographic mapping; the classification of the public lands for their mineral or nonmineral character and for their water power potentialities; and mineral leasing on the public lands.

Water Resources Investigations

Our modern economy depends to a high degree upon the adequacy and safety of water supplies for domestic, municipal, and industrial purposes, and for irrigation and power. Available water resources will have a profound effect on the economic growth and development of Alaska. The demonstrated key position of water resources in the economic development of the United States predicts they will prove no less significant in the future development of the Territory of Alaska.

Accurate knowledge of this vital resource—knowledge of stream flow, underground waters, and the quality of waters—obviously is indispensable to the consideration of any project involving its control and utilization. There is a wide fluctuation from season to season and from year to year in the quantity and quality of water in surface streams, and to a lesser extent in the underlying ground-water reservoirs. Only systematic, reliable records will permit an accurate appraisal of water supplies and of their long-time trends and cycles. Without such basic information, designs may not be adequate, money may be wasted in construction, and projects may not be operated effectively.

Information on the water resources of Alaska has been collected intermittently by the Geological Survey and other agencies subsequent to 1906. However, only in Southeastern Alaska are there records that cover

periods of more than a few years and, even in Southeastern Alaska, only a few of the records are over a considerable period of time. Available records thus fall far short of presenting the complete understanding of water resources needed for purposes of development of plans outlined. The records have been collected largely to serve current needs for some local and regional planning and local development; they do not provide a balanced and comprehensive coverage of the Territory. Hence, they provide inadequate information on which to base detailed specifications for many of the water-development projects. Elimination of major deficiencies in the basic data is the primary objective of the investigative program of the Geological Survey.

Surface Water Investigations

Stream-gaging stations are established and operated to disclose the amount, seasonal variation, trend, and distribution of runoff. The records obtained provide information needed in connection with the present investigations by Federal and Territorial agencies and for administration of several local projects. They provide, subject to the limitations of the available data, an inventory of water resources for planning further development and aid in the solution of problems of water.

Past stream-gaging programs of the Geological Survey and the Forest Service have provided a limited amount of information at various locations in the Territory. The present and proposed programs of the Geological Survey will provide a general coverage on many of the larger streams and particularly those susceptible of early development. In many cases intermittent discharge measurements only are available and, in the vicinity of proposed major projects, the detail and duration of stream-flow data may be insufficient to furnish the information needed for preparing final designs. The gaging program is being extended whenever and wherever feasible to provide the additional basic data required.

Water-supply investigations in Alaska were started by the Geological Survey in 1906. Initial studies were made on the Seward Peninsula. Subsequently the investigations were extended to the Fairbanks district in 1907, the Circle district in 1908 and the Fortymile and Seventymile districts in 1910. These investigations, which were in the placer districts, were discontinued in 1912. The results of these studies were summarized in "Water Supply Papers 314, Surface Water Supply of Seward Peninsula, Alaska, and 342, Surface Water Supply of Yukon-Tanana Region, Alaska." A water-power reconnaissance was conducted in South-Central Alaska in 1913, the results of which are summarized in

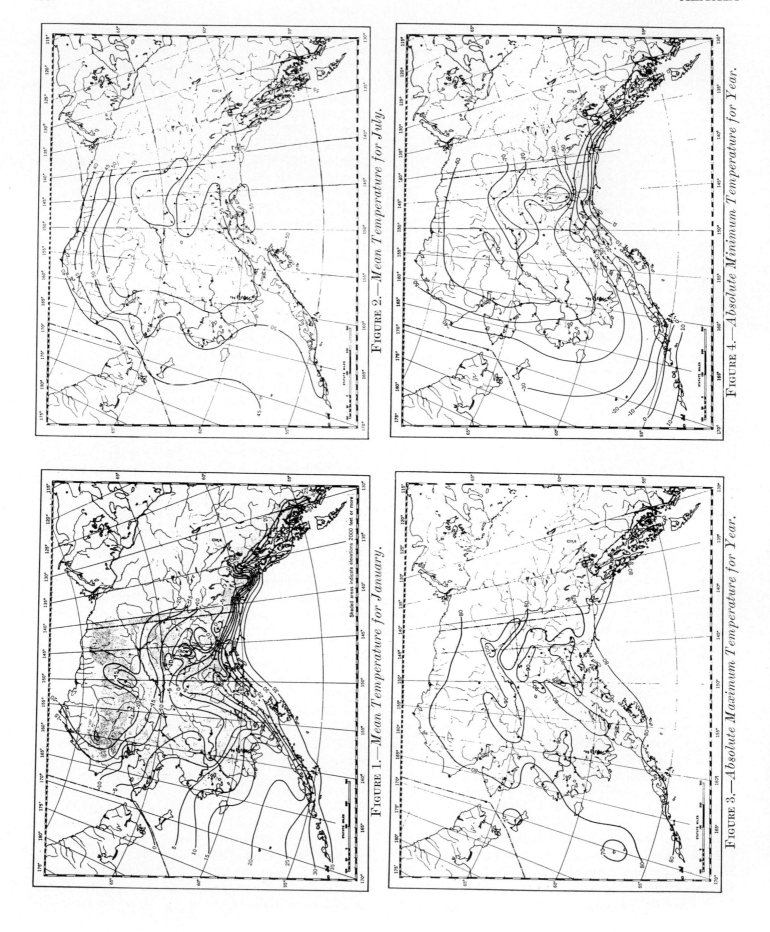

FIGURE 1.—Mean Temperature for January.

FIGURE 2.—Mean Temperature for July.

FIGURE 3.—Absolute Maximum Temperature for Year.

FIGURE 4.—Absolute Minimum Temperature for Year.

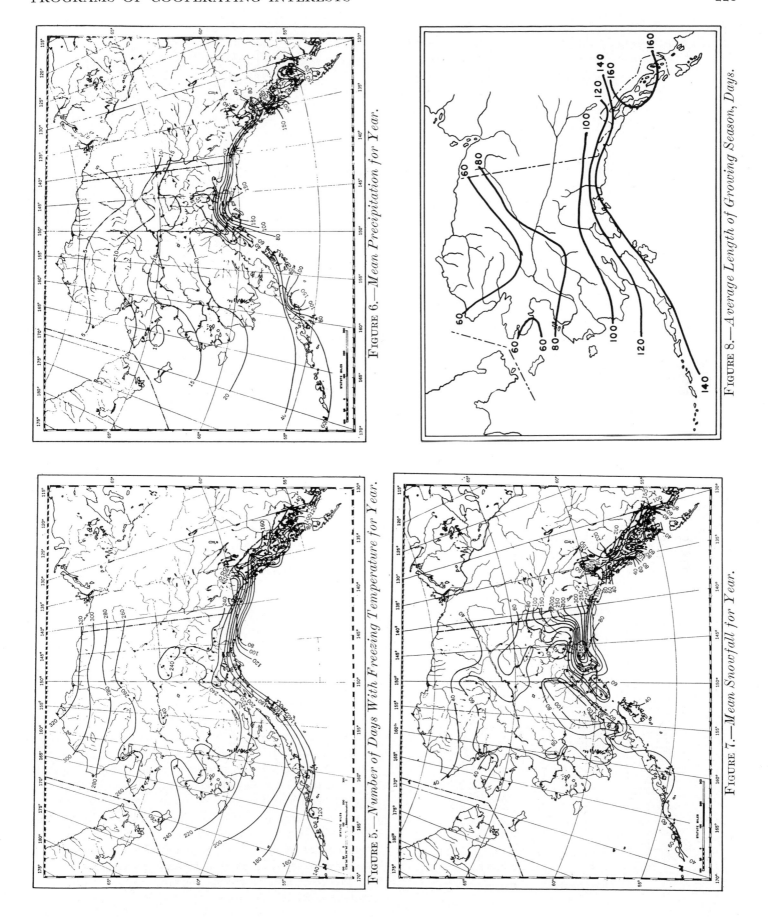

FIGURE 6.—Mean Precipitation for Year.

FIGURE 8.—Average Length of Growing Season, Days.

FIGURE 5.—Number of Days With Freezing Temperature for Year.

FIGURE 7.—Mean Snowfall for Year.

"Water-Supply Paper 372, A Water-Power Reconnais-sance in South-Central Alaska." In 1915, as a result of urgent need for information on the water-power re-sources of Southeastern Alaska, the Geological Survey and the Forest Service established a comprehensive stream-gaging program in that region. Subsequent to 1920 and until 1946 the Forest Service continued limited investigations alone or in cooperation with private groups investigating possibilities for development of the pulp and paper industry. The results of studies in Southeastern Alaska prior to 1946 are summarized in Geological Survey Bulletins 642, 662, 692, 712, 714, 722, and 836, and in the Federal Power Commission-Forest Service reports, "Water Powers of Southeastern

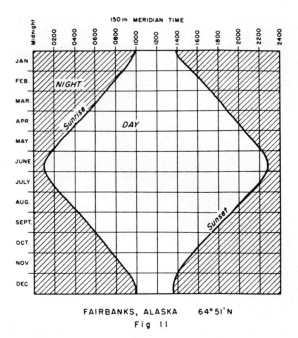

FAIRBANKS, ALASKA   64° 51' N
Fig 11

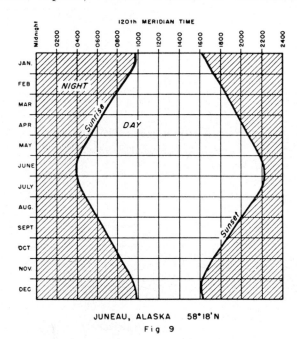

JUNEAU, ALASKA   58° 18' N
Fig 9

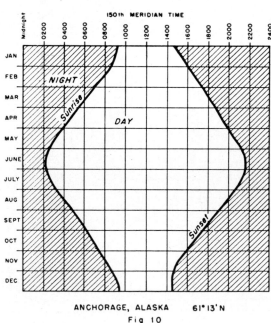

ANCHORAGE, ALASKA   61° 13' N
Fig 10

Alaska," published in 1924 and "Water Powers of Southeast Alaska," published in 1947.

The number and distribution of gaging stations and miscellaneous stream-flow measurement points at the time the Geological Survey's present program was initiated in 1946 and at the present time are as follows:

TABLE 57.—*Number and distribution of gaging stations*

Area	Gaging stations [1]		Miscellaneous measurement points [2] 1948
	1946	1948	
South Central and Interior Alaska.	0	17	29
Southeastern Alaska	3	16	13
Total	3	33	42

[1] As of September 30.
[2] Gaging stations may be established at many of these locations.

Records for many of the stations indicated are of very short duration and investigations must be con-tinued for several years before reasonable deductions as to annual and seasonal variations can be made. How-ever, correlation of the short-term records and the re-sults of miscellaneous discharge measurements with continuous records of long duration will tend to assure full usefulness of the available data. The results of investigations will be published annually in preliminary reports and may be summarized at 5-year intervals.

In order that some of the major deficiencies in stream-flow data may be overcome and water resources de-velopments advanced, the program of surface-water in-vestigations will be extended and expanded as rapidly as facilities and resources permit. Many additional gaging stations are necessary, particularly at sites of prospective and feasible projects, and the improvement and rehabilitation of existing installations should be advanced as rapidly as possible. The programs of the past several years have been too limited in scope and extent to permit investigations of floods. It is therefore most desirable that the characteristics of recent notable floods be studied.

Ground-Water Investigations

The more important specific objectives of ground-water investigations include the securing of information on (1) the sources and amounts of perennial ground-water outflow through springs (which affords dry season stream flow), (2) the extent of areas from which ground water is or may be withdrawn for use in significant amounts, (3) the perennial yields and the quality of ground water available in those areas, and (4) the potential interference between utilization of surface water in streams and utilization of ground-water.

Ground-water data, when available, serve many purposes. They facilitate judicious development of domestic, municipal, agricultural and industrial water supplies, indicate possibilities for irrigation in areas remote from perennial surface sources and, in interior Alaska, may be useful in defining the location, extent and effects of permafrost.

Ground-water investigations in Alaska have been very limited. Prior to 1947 essentially the only ground-water data available were those obtained from logs for drilled water wells. A systematic investigation of the ground-water resources of the Fairbanks area was started by the Geological Survey in 1947 with an inventory of wells, supplemented in 1948 by the drilling of exploratory test holes, to obtain much-needed data on the deeply buried strata and their hydrologic characteristics, the character and distribution of subsurface materials, and the water-bearing character and distribution of permafrost, and quantitative determinations of the permeability of water-bearing sands and gravels. Ground-water reconnaissance has been performed in several scattered locations in the Territory. The relative urgency of the water supply problems precludes estimates of perennial yield in the near future. The results of the ground-water studies will be published in special reports as significant phases of investigations in specific areas are concluded.

A systematic inventory of the ground-water resources of pertinent areas in Alaska is proposed, which will include (1) canvassing existing wells to secure descriptive data, (2) geologic mapping and test drilling to determine the extent and characteristics of water-bearing zones, (3) determining the extent of ground-water withdrawals, (4) conducting pumping tests on selected wells to determine the water-yielding properties of formations, and (5) making periodic observations of water levels in selected observation wells to evaluate changes in ground water storage in relation to recharge, natural discharge, and withdrawals. The first stage of the proposed inventory would be of a reconnaissance character to fix the general pattern of ground water occurrence and to define fundamental problems in the Territory. Later stages would involve intensive study of critical problems.

Quality of Water Investigations

Knowledge concerning the quality of waters is as important as data on the amounts available. Data regarding temperature of the water are of peculiarly practical interest. The sediment transported by streams may create significant problems in the design of diversions and conduits and of reservoir siltation. The chemical character of waters, changes in chemical concentration and character following use for industrial and agricultural purposes, and changes in quality that take place during storage in lakes and reservoirs all give rise to problems of providing satisfactory water supplies for industrial, domestic and irrigation purposes. The wide variation known to exist in the chemical character of ground-waters makes dependable information on the quality of those waters particularly important. Securing data on both ground- and surface-waters which will help solve problems of the kind suggested is the primary objective of proposed quality of water studies.

Few data on the quality of ground- and surface-waters have been collected in Alaska. During 1947 and 1948 analyses have been made by the Geological Survey of ground-waters in the Fairbanks area and miscellaneous determinations were made at additional locations. In Alaska many of the streams are of glacial origin and carry large quantities of suspended sediments. Determination of the character and volume of sediment transported thus is particularly important in Alaska in connection with reservoir development, runoff retardation and soil-erosion studies.

Proposals for quality of water investigations needed in Alaska would include (1) establishment of a laboratory for analysis of both the chemical quality and sediment content of samples and (2) activation of a comprehensive program for the collection of surface and ground-water samples in areas of interest. Samples would be collected at appropriate intervals; for example, occasional ground-water samples, daily samples of surface-water sources when changes in concentration are to be studied, and, for sediment load computation, at frequent intervals, say hourly, during freshets and rises and occasionally during other periods.

Mineral Deposits

The exploration and exploitation of mineral resources of Alaska have shared with the fur industry in enticing white men to spread over the Territory, even into its most remote and inaccessible parts. The exploitation of mineral resources led to the establishment of many of the major towns (Juneau, Nome, and Fairbanks) as well as many of the smaller settlements. At present, and for many years past, mining ranks second to fishing among the prominent industries in Alaska, although in the recent war and postwar years the construction industry has greatly outranked both. Since the beginning of mining in Alaska in 1880, mineral production has reached a total value of nearly 1 billion dollars.

Gold has accounted for approximately two-thirds of the total value of mineral production. Two-thirds of the gold has been derived from placer deposits, although at various times the annual production of gold from placers and lodes has been essentially equal, and in some years lode production has exceeded placer production. Copper, to the value of one-third of the total value of gold production has been recovered in the Territory principally between 1911 and 1938; and copper production was, in fact, responsible for the all-time maximum annual value of mineral production attained in 1916. Silver, in value amounting to one-sixteenth of the copper and one-forty-fifth of the total value of gold, has been produced as a by-product of placer gold, lode gold, and copper mining. Lead, to the value of $2,800,000, has been recovered as a by-product of lode gold mining. Deposits of lead-silver ores are also known in Alaska that may under slightly different economic or transportation conditions, support mining of these metals alone. Platinum, mercury, tin, antimony, tungsten, and zinc have been recovered from Alaska ore deposits that are workable for these metals themselves. Chromite ore has been mined, but not processed to obtain the metal. Palladium has been recovered from one gold-copper mine in Southeastern Alaska. Other metals which occur in deposits that further development work may yet show to contain commercial amounts include iron, molybdenum, nickel, bismuth, and arsenic. Traces of other metals, such as cobalt, are also known.

The total value of production of these other metals (exclusive of gold, silver, and copper) and nonmetals is approximately one-thirtieth of the grand total of the mineral production.

The value of the coal produced thus far in Alaska greatly exceeds the value of the production of any other nonmetallic mineral material. The value of the total production is about one-ninth of the value of the copper, and one-twenty-fifth of the value of the gold production. Petroleum has been produced at Katalla on the south coast, and exploratory drilling for other oil accumulations has been done or is in progress on the Alaska Peninsula and in Northern Alaska. Gypsum, limestone and marble have been utilized in considerable amount, and clays, asbestos, and jade to a lesser extent. Deposits of abrasive garnet, barite, fluor spar, sulphur and pumice have also attracted some attention. Broken rock for railroad riprap and gravels for roads and other construction are also used.

Gold was the initial mineral resource developed under frontier conditions, especially more readily recoverable placer gold. The deposits mined in earlier years were of the bonanza type and permitted attainment in 1910 of the peak production in terms of quantity of gold. Subsequently, the mining industry settled down to larger scale mining of lower-grade deposits. Boom conditions no longer persisted, and settlements became more stabilized. As improved means of transportation have made some areas more accessible, attention has been more and more focused on the possibilities of mining low-value deposits of other mineral resources. Eventually this trend should lead to more thorough appraisal of deposits that have been recognized but not developed because of the obvious impracticability of obtaining sufficiently low-cost transportation to make mining pay.

Mineral resources are widely distributed in the Territory; few areas, on the basis of exploration to date, can be ruled out as of no interest from this viewpoint. The apparent spotty distribution of well-known mineralized areas in Alaska is largely a result of the emphasis that has so far been placed on placer and lode gold mining. True, there appears to be some segregation or restriction of certain metals to more or less distinct parts of the Territory but search has not yet been thorough enough to prove this, e. g., mercury in the Kuskokwim region, tin in the Seward Peninsula and in the central Yukon region, and chromite in the Kenai Peninsula.

The future of Alaskan mining appears to depend on a more thorough search for workable deposits of more types than have been of interest thus far, on the determination of the character and manner of occurrence of such deposits, and considerable thoroughness in the development of each deposit. Geologic mapping on scales sufficient to permit detailed analysis of geological features that pertain to mineral exploitation, or to other economic or military problems, covers only 0.3 percent of Alaska. An additional 3.2 percent has been mapped on a scale adequate for semi-detailed or reconnaissance analysis of such features. About 45 percent has been covered by exploratory geologic maps;

but 51 percent of the Territory has not been mapped geologically.

The Geological Survey has prepared a plan, coordinated with the Interior Department's Alaska development plan, designed to speed up geologic mapping at reconnaissance or larger scales, and to complete the correlative investigations and interpretations necessary for adequate over-all appraisal of mineral resources.

Several areas under consideration as power sites are known to contain mineral resources. Mining operations are being or have been carried on in some of these. The data acquired to date, however, are inadequate for estimating the significance which the development of sources of low-cost power would have on exploitation of mineral resources.

The mining industry is the only one, among the several principal industries in Alaska, whose ultimate limit of expansion, as determined by reserves available, remains essentially unknown.

Topographic Mapping

The responsibility for the preparation of the topographic quadrangle atlas of Alaska rests with the Geological Survey as the recognized agency of the Federal Government responsible for the topographic mapping of the United States and its territories and possessions. This function is accomplished by means of funds which the Congress annually appropriates for the Geological Survey, supplemented in the past by transferred funds, principally from the Departments of the National Military Establishment.

Topographic maps portray, in symbolized form, the natural and man-made features existing upon the land surface. By their representation of relief and delineation of the works of man such as roads, railroads, dwellings, etc., they offer a means of economically planning engineering projects, evaluating natural resources, planning for conservation, industrial development and recreational projects. By their use, many preliminary surveys prior to location of transportation routes, transmission lines, irrigation channels, etc., can be eliminated.

Alaska has an area of approximately 580,000 square miles, about one-fifth the area of the United States. Of this vast territory about one-half has been covered by topographic surveys, largely of a reconnaissance nature. These reconnaissance maps were generally prepared by plane table methods in conjunction with geological exploration. Where the necessity was urgent and time and funds permitted, larger scales were used for special purposes. These included a number of sheets at 1:62,500 and a few at even larger scales. Much of this work, both large and small scale, has been concentrated in the areas where mining operations have been most

active. This includes the Alaska Railroad belt, the Yukon-Tanana region, portions of Southeastern Alaska and Seward Peninsula. Much of the remainder of the Territory was mapped by exploratory reconnaissance methods and, because of the transportation problems involved, followed the main drainage systems.

The maps published to date by the Geological Survey number more than 50. They incorporate areas that range widely in extent and are not based on any established quadrangle system. Most of them cover irregular areas of geographic or geologic importance.

By agreement between the Bureau of the Budget, the Department of the Army, and the Geological Survey, a standard quadrangle subdivision of Alaska has now been established. All new mapping will be printed on a format based upon this quadrangle grid.

Aerial Photography

The Territory of Alaska is almost entirely covered with aerial photography of some type. Up until 1948, the major coverage has been with trimetrogon photography with added areas covered by nine-lens, tri-lens, and some single-lens photography. From a mapping viewpoint there are serious gaps and most of the photography is suitable only for rather small scale compilation. During the past field season, however, substantial areas in Southeastern, Central, and Northern Alaska were covered with single-lens vertical photography which will lend itself more readily to the compilation of larger scale topographic maps.

Ground Control

The situation with respect to ground control in Alaska is a serious one. Before any large-scale mapping program can be prosecuted, the prerequisite ground control must be established. Performance of the surveys required for primary, secondary, and supplemental control is a major operation even in the United States. In Alaska its magnitude is enhanced immeasurably by the ruggedness and over-all difficulty of the terrain, the short seasons, and probably the most serious obstacle, the lack of extensive transportation and supply routes.

At present there are three major long lines of horizontal control, all adjusted to the 1927 North American Datum. These triangulation nets extend from Southeastern Alaska to the Seward Peninsula, along the 141° meridian, and from Fairbanks to the tip of the Aleutian Islands. In addition there are several shorter lines plus some isolated segments which are not adjusted to the North American Datum.

Vertical control is even less adequate and is concentrated for the most part along the overland transportation routes.

Program

It is generally agreed that the most immediate and important map need for Alaska is the completion of the reconnaissance map series at the 1:250,000 scale. This group of maps can be completed in a period of 5 years or less, thus providing a system of maps which will greatly assist both the civil and military agencies in planning and development activity in Alaska. The method of preparing this series involves the combination of all existing source material, field surveys, large scale maps, land plats, trimetrogon manuscripts, etc., supplemented by additional photo-compilation and revision where needed or advisable. Presently available ground control is generally made to suffice but since it is scant in many areas, any new control will be of value.

The preparation of topographic maps for larger scale publication at 1 mile to the inch has proceeded at a moderate pace in the past, but should be increased in scope during future years, as new photography and ground control becomes available. The 1:250,000 scale map series will be of considerable value in planning operations for large-scale mapping. Primarily because of the current lack of adequate basic control in Alaska it is apparent that, for many years to come, national map accuracy standards will be difficult if not impossible to attain without exorbitant costs.

The need for an adequate series of maps covering the vast area of Alaska stems from a variety of sources. These are the major considerations of the significant geographic position of Alaska; its transportation problems; the development of mineral resources, including petroleum; water resources development; studies of glaciers, volcanoes, and permanently frozen ground; and last, but not least, the opportunity in the Territory for wide-spread settlement. With adequate topographic maps, more favorable settlement areas can be selected, based in part upon initial studies for water resources, proximity of transportation, and sources of food and fuel. Thus will be laid a firm foundation for the efficient, economic development of the Territory of Alaska.

River Surveys

In the United States the construction of reservoirs is usually attended by the relocation of railroads, highways and other improvements, sometimes at a cost exceeding the cost of the dam. In Alaska, as yet only slightly developed, most, if not all, such increased cost can be prevented by obtaining information on the location and extent of such projects now and reserving the sites for future use, and the information required for this purpose can be used also for the selection of the most economical sites and for preliminary plans and estimates for power projects.

The first step in the location of reservoir and power sites is a topographic survey of the river valley and the preparation of maps showing the course and fall of the stream and the configuration of the valley floor and immediately adjacent slopes. From the map, dam and reservoir sites can be selected, capacity of proposed reservoirs can be computed, power projects can be outlined and if the water supply is known, potential water power can be estimated. Water power is abundant in Alaska but because of the wide variation in the flow of the streams due to long cold winters, storage is essential to its utilization in all projects of major size. The river surveys should be followed by geologic examinations at proposed dam sites as foundation conditions are an important element in appraising values of such sites.

So far, few adequate river surveys have been made in Alaska. Eklutna Lake near Anchorage and a portion of Eklutna Creek have been mapped. The United States Forest Service has made many reconnaissance surveys on streams in Southeastern Alaska, but even preliminary planning requires accurate topographic maps of the rivers and lakes on a fairly large scale. A program for river surveys in Alaska therefore would include practically all streams of substantial size. The first projects would be those within easy transmission distance of the larger cities or those well situated for pulp and paper or other plants.

OFFICE OF INDIAN AFFAIRS—
ALASKA NATIVE SERVICE

The native stock in Alaska which constituted nearly half of the total population of the Territory in 1920 and slightly more than half in 1929, was considerably outnumbered by the white population in 1939. At that time there were reported 32,458 Aleuts, Eskimos, and Indians, as against 39,170 white persons. These figures are taken from the Sixteenth Decennial Census.

The Eskimos, numbering 15,576 in 1939, accounted for nearly half of the native stock; the Indians, 11,283 in number, for more than one-third; and the Aleuts made up the remainder, 5,599.

The Indian population comprises several linguistic stocks, of which the Athapascans and the Thlingits, numbering 4,671 and 4,643, respectively, are by far the most numerous.

The following table provides additional detailed information concerning the composition of population:

TABLE 58.—*Composition of population*

Race or linguistic stock	1939	1929	1920	Percent of change	
				1929 to 1939	1920 to 1929
White, total_____	39, 170	28, 640	27, 883	36. 8	2. 7
Native_____	30, 384	18, 460	16, 286	64. 6	13. 3
Foreign-born_____	8, 786	10, 180	11, 597	−13. 7	−12. 2
Native stock, total_____	32, 458	29, 983	26, 558	8. 3	12. 9
Aleut_____	5, 599	[1] 19, 028	2, 942	[1] 11. 3	[1] 14. 4
Eskimo_____	15, 576	_____	13, 698	_____	_____
Indian, total_____	11, 283	10, 955	9, 918	3. 0	10. 5
Athapascan_____	4, 671	4, 935	4, 657	−5. 3	6. 0
Haidas_____	655	588	524	11. 4	12. 2
Thlingit_____	4, 643	4, 462	3, 895	4. 1	14. 6
Tsimshian_____	881	845	842	4. 3	. 4
United States, Canadian, and unknown stocks.	433	125	_____	246. 4	_____
Japanese_____	263	278	312	−5. 4	−10. 9
Other and unknown races.	633	377	283	67. 9	33. 2
All races, total___	72, 524	59, 278	55, 036	22. 3	7. 7

[1] Eskimo and Aleut are included together.

Distribution of the Population

The Eskimos occupy the Bering Sea and Arctic Ocean coast. There are Eskimo settlements several hundred miles inland along the courses of the main rivers emptying into these bodies of water. Scattered groups of Eskimos live as far inland as the north slope of the Brooks Range. They also occupy St. Lawrence, Nunivak, King, and Diomede Islands.

The Aleuts for the most part occupy the Alaska Peninsula, and the Aleutian Islands and Kodiak Island. The Athapascans occupy all of the interior of Alaska. Two of the main branches of the interior Athapascan Indians are the Tinnehs in the Upper Yukon area and the Tanas of the middle Yukon area.

Of the Athapascan groups in Southeast Alaska the Thlingits are the most widely distributed. There are fairly well localized groups of Haidas at Kasaan and Hydaburg and a community of Tsimshians at Ketchikan and Metlakatla.

There is considerable inter-mixing of the racial groups, particularly of the Eskimo and Aleut stock in the Bristol Bay and northern coast of the Alaska Peninsula.

These people are in general great travelers and move about extensively within their own areas as well as migrating to some extent from area to area.

Native Population as Labor Supply

The general intelligence of the native people, their local knowledge, wide variety of aptitude, and eagerness for wage employment, make this population group a valuable labor pool. Some employers currently object to native labor because of allegedly greater absenteeism, lack of skill, and unreliability. Many regard the natives as a "last hired—first fired" class. It can safely be assumed that these alleged disqualifications are largely a part of the over-all social and employment situation rather than due to any characteristics of the natives as a laborer.

A study of very limited data available suggests, but does not definitely conclude, that the number of natives in the 20- to 30-year age group is much smaller than in the corresponding age group among whites.

Since males in the 20- to 30-year age group are an important source of industrial labor the relatively small number in this age group, as compared with the white population, should be taken into account in consideration of the native population as a labor pool.

No attempt has been made to establish the cause for the sharp decline of the size of the native population as compared with the white population beginning with the 20-year age group. Population studies on other groups indicates that improved health conditions in the villages, improved community services and other advantages for the native people may tend to increase the number in the higher age group.

Educational Services

The Alaska Native Service at present operates 85 day schools in villages scattered throughout Alaska. In 10 communities, schools have previously been operated which will be reopened when sufficient appropriations are secured for their operation. A review of requests filed by communities for the establishment of schools indicates that there are approximately 42 communities, each with sufficient number of children to justify the establishment of a school. The Alaska Native Service has a program of establishing schools in these communities over a period of the next 6 to 10 years, depending upon the availability of funds for providing school services to these people. In accordance with past policy, schools would also be established in communities where the need arises should concentrations of population result from a greater industrial use of Alaska's water power and natural resources.

Dog teams travel to regions otherwise inaccessible.

In addition to these day schools the Alaska Native Service operates three boarding schools. Of these, the school at Mount Edgecumbe is equipped for and committed to a policy of providing vocational education for enrollment of 600 young men and women. The policy of the school is to provide training in trades which now exist or may be developed as a result of the over-all industrial and economic development of the Territory. Training is provided at present for marine mechanics, boat operators, heavy duty mechanics and clerical workers. In addition college entrance training is provided for those people interested in higher education for nursing, teaching or vocations requiring professional training.

The Territory of Alaska operates 50 schools in rural areas and 22 schools in the incorporated cities of the Territory. These schools are available to Alaska natives as well as to whites. By mutual agreement between the Alaska Native Service and the Territory a plan is in operation whereby schools now operated by the Alaska Native Service will be taken over by the Territory as rapidly as the availability of funds and

other conditions permit. Any expansion of school services for present or future populations of the Territory should be considered in light of this policy.

Medical Services

The Alaska Native Service operates hospitals at the following places with the accommodations (beds) indicated:

TABLE 59.—*Accommodations (beds) at hospitals*

Station	General	Tuberculosis	Orthopedic	Cribs	Quonsets [1]
Barrow	13			3	1–24 bed.
Kotzebue	13	5			1–24 bed.
Bethel	26	17			1–24 bed.
Kanakanak	20	16			1–24 bed.
Tanana	20	16			
Juneau	25	25			
Mount Edgecumbe	20 (inf)	136	65		

[1] These quonsets are under construction for the care of tuberculosis patients and are expected to be in operation during the latter part of 1949 or early 1950 fiscal year.

Natives use skin boat with outboard motor for transportation between islands.

In addition to the foregoing a 200-bed hospital is now under construction at Mount Edgecumbe. This will be for tuberculosis patients. The Bureau of the Budget and Congress have also authorized a 400-bed institution at Anchorage. This will have 100 beds for general use and 300 beds for tuberculosis patients.

Future plans for construction include the replacement of the hospital at Kotzebue with a 60- to 80-bed unit, additional or replacement construction at Juneau, additional staff quarters at various hospitals and small clinic units at various places or additional space at some of the present hospitals as the need develops. The location of future construction will doubtless be influenced by hydropower developments. Additional quonset space may also be provided in the future if the use of those now under construction proves practical in the handling of tuberculosis cases.

In addition to the resident staffs of the regular hospitals field nurses are located at Bethel, Dillingham, Kotzebue, Nome, Nulato, Uzinki, Wainwright, White Mountain, Wrangell, and Yakutat. Part-time physicians are under contract at Anchorage, Cordova, Fairbanks, Juneau, Ketchikan, Kodiak, Nome, Seldovia, Valdez, and Wrangell. Field nurse positions are also established at Mount Edgecumbe, Savoonga, and Unalakleet but are vacant at the present time.

Cooperative arrangements are in effect with the Alaska Health Department whereby the Native Service supplies funds for per diem care of patients in the Seward Sanatorium operated by the Methodist Mission Board of the States. Cooperative arrangements are also made for public health nurses at Angoon, Hoo-

nah, Hydaburg (including Craig and Klawock), and Naknek.

Land Ownership and Use

The number of natives of Alaska who hold title to the land they use and occupy is very small. With the exception of a few who have been granted homestead allotments under the act of May 17, 1906, practically no individual natives living outside of surveyed townsites have title of any sort to their lands, but hold them by possessory rights only which have not been formally determined. These possessory rights are recognized by Congress and have been specifically mentioned in several acts, beginning with the act of May 17, 1884, which provides, "That the Indians or other persons in said district shall not be disturbed in the possession of any lands actually in their use or occupation or now claimed by them—."

Group land ownership by natives, in the form of recognized reservations, is so small as to be relatively unimportant at the present time. Of the 100-odd reserves under the general jurisdiction of the Alaska Native Service, the majority are for school or other administrative purposes, and only about 20 are primarily for the use of the native inhabitants. Of those, only seven or eight are large enough to provide a sufficient resource base for the people residing thereon.

The native uses of the land are principally for trapping and hunting. In these pursuits they cover large areas, the vast majority of which are tundra and other submarginal types of country good for little beyond producing fur and game. Reindeer are raised by the Eskimos in some areas. Agriculture, logging, and mining are relatively limited in extent among the native peoples.

Agriculture

The native people of Alaska are not agriculturally minded. They originally lived along the coastal areas or along the principal rivers and their economy was based upon fishing and hunting. They used some wild plants and berries for food, but moved about seasonally to take advantage of opportunities to obtain different kinds of game and fur animals and fish for their food and clothing supply. It is only since their contact with white civilization that they have made any attempts to grow agricultural products for food or to produce reindeer for food, clothing, and sale.

The basic economy of the native people still is fishing, with its related activities, and hunting and trapping. However, a few villages are largely dependent upon the production of native arts and crafts and a few are now dependent upon a wage economy for their livelihood with a lesser number dependent upon the reindeer industry. The native people have proved themselves quite adaptable to changed conditions and new industries, and it is believed that where it can be demonstrated to them that they can make a better living or supplement and increase their regular food supply by gardening or the production of livestock that they will increasingly adopt such practices.

The development of Alaska and the encroachment of white civilization have caused changes in the native's economy. In some instances these developments have caused a diminishing of the native's original source of food supply and in others they have created desires and appetites for the white man's food, clothing, and equipment. Reindeer were introduced to offset a loss of other food supplies and gardens have been advocated to supplement native food in some areas.

Gardens have been grown sucessfully in Southeast Alaska, on the Alaska Peninsula, on Afognak, Spruce, and Kodiak Islands, in some areas along the Yukon and Kuskokwim Rivers, at Tanana, Tetlin, and Tanacross in the interior, at Unalakleet on Norton Sound, at Kotzebue, Kiana, and Shungnak. Unalakleet is the only area where natives are producing garden products for sale and their production is still on a small scale.

Further investigations are needed to determine more fully the areas where soil conditions are satisfactory so that gardening may be successfully carried on, where irrigation is possible and practical, and where soils are satisfactory if proper fertilizers are applied. Power equipment is needed where conditions are favorable for

gardening to subjugate land for garden sites, to prepare the land for planting, and in some instances to cultivate and care for the gardens. Additional qualified personnel is needed to instruct the natives in gardening.

Up to the present time the native population has done little in the production of livestock other than reindeer. There are areas of native population on the islands along the Alaska Peninsula and in the Aleutian Islands where the production of cattle, sheep, and goats is possible. Further studies are needed to determine the practicability of livestock production in the areas, the adaptability of the natives to a livestock economy, and the possibility of developing satisfactory markets for products to be sold. Should development appear feasible importation of foundation stock would be necessary.

Reindeer were introduced into the native economy by importations from 1891 to 1902. The industry developed rapidly to where the reindeer population was estimated at 500,000 head in the early thirties. From then on numbers steadily declined until now there are an estimated 40,000 head in Alaska. Virgin grazing areas, the lack of predators contributed to the rapid increase in numbers. Lack of markets, wolves, some overgrazing, deer going with caribou migrations, and lack of attention to herding were contributing factors in the rapid decrease in numbers.

Present herds are now located at Barrow, Wainwright, Point Hope, Kivalina, Kotzebue, Shungnak, Kewalik, Teller, Golovin, Unalakleet, St. Michael, Hooper Bay, Nunivak Island, Kodiak Island, Umnak Island, and Atka Island.

Herds are owned either by the Government or by natives. Native ownership includes individual and association ownership. Future development contemplates increased individual ownership. Funds are needed to assist individuals in becoming established with herds to prevent butchering of breeding stock while building herds to economic units. Funds will also be needed by the Fish and Wildlife Service to assure adequate control of wolves in areas where reindeer are grazed.

Alaska will be the principal market for reindeer meat for some time to come. Adequate cold storage facilities are needed to hold the meat from butchering time through seasons when the meat is not prime or when it cannot be safely transported so that a steady supply may be assured the markets. Low-cost power is essential in providing adequate cold storage facilities.

Mines

Natives have taken only a small part in the development of mines in Alaska, except as laborers in mines.

Reindeer at abattoir near Teller. Low-cost power is essential for providing adequate cold-storage facilities.

Generally they lack the knowledge of minerals which is required for independent prospecting and mining.

Mining of coal for village needs is becoming more important as better housing facilities are provided. The need will increase as Alaska develops. Coal is now mined by natives for their use near Barrow, Wainwright, Point Lay, and Nelson Island. The production at Barrow is greatest with 340 tons being produced in the operating year 1945–46; 761 tons in 1946–47; and 636 tons in 1947–48.

Coal deposits have been reported on St. Lawrence Island and near Point Hope, Kiana, and Unalakleet.

Coal has also been mined near the native village of Deering. This development was operated by white owners.

Further investigations of coal deposits near native villages are needed to determine the possibilities of development and the most practical locations of mines to supply local needs. Studies of transportation problems in connection with moving and storing the coal are also needed. Low-cost power for use in mining coal and improved transportation facilities should do much to improve the fuel supplies of native villages in areas where coal is found or where it may be mined and shipped at reasonable cost.

Kodiak Island, Shungnak, St. Lawrence Island, and Venetie show promise of mineral deposits. Investigations are needed in these areas to determine possibilities of development. Instruction should be provided also for interested natives to give them the necessary knowledge to prospect for and identify valuable minerals.

Sawmills

The native population has taken little active participation in timber operations other than as laborers in sawmills and logging camps.

One large mill has been in operation at Metlakatla for a number of years and is now in the process of being rebuilt. Production figures on past operations are not available.

Small mills are in operation or have been purchased

to go into operation at Hydaburg, Klawock, Kake, Noorvik, Shungnak, and White Mountain. The operation of these mills is mainly to produce materials at low cost for native housing, boat building, and other local needs.

Funds are needed for surveys and studies to determine where other small mills should be located to serve local needs of native people. More mills will be needed as the housing program develops.

A source of low-cost power for the operation of the sawmills would be of benefit in producing cheaper construction materials.

Fishing

Fishing has always been of prime importance to the natives of Alaska. In Southeast Alaska fishing and related industries not only provide more than half of the cash income of native people but also furnish a major portion of the food supply. In other parts of Alaska, on the Aleutian chain, north along the coast, and up the major rivers, fish and other sea foods are even more important as a source of food than in Southeast Alaska. Great quantities of fish are dried, smoked, or frozen for human consumption and for dog food. Fish in many of the areas in the north is the main source of dog food.

Three canneries are owned by native groups. These are located at Metlakatla, Hydaburg, and Hood Bay. The latter two have been financed by loans from the Government. The Hood Bay cannery was purchased in 1948 to go under the operation of the Angoon Community Association in 1949. It was under lease in 1948. The Metlakatla cannery was operated under a share lease prior to 1948. It was operated by the native group this year. Hydaburg has been under native operation for the past 10 years. All three hire experienced managers to operate the canneries for them. Comparative packs for Hydaburg and Metlakatla for the past 10 years are shown below:

TABLE 60.—*Comparative packs in two canneries*

Year	Annette Islands Canning Co., total number of cases	Hydaburg Co-operative Assoc. Cannery, total number of cases
1939	94, 211	41, 236
1940	102, 399	25, 397
1941	141, 827	43, 117
1942	100, 203	31, 917
1943	87, 769	23, 913
1944	74, 621	30, 137
1945	75, 147	26, 059
1946	96, 215	34, 939
1947	42, 201	16, 103
1948	74, 717	33, 819

Funds are needed for development of similar enterprises in other communities and for studies and investigations of other possibilities for development of fisheries by the native groups. A source of power at low cost is essential in the development of quick freeze and cold storage plants for handling fish and some other sea food products. Availability of low-cost power will be a determining factor in the selection of locations for such enterprises.

Wildlife Resources

Most of the native people in Alaska are very closely dependent upon the fish and wildlife resources of the individual communities.

The matter of fisheries has previously been discussed.

No data are available on the exact extent to which the native population is dependent upon other wildlife resources for their livelihood. However, they do catch various fur animals and use the fur for clothing and the surplus for sale. They also obtain considerable food and clothing from various species of birds. Seals, walrus and whale furnish an important part of the livelihood of the people of certain villages. Game animals are also used for food.

Additional information is needed as to the extent that the native population is dependent upon wildlife resources for their livelihood. A study should be made of the normal production of different areas with reference to fur and game animals. This could be used to determine the areas which various individuals and groups would need for their use in trapping and hunting to make an adequate living for themselves.

Information is also needed upon the effects of the proposed power development on wildlife resources of the areas involved and the economy of the natives related thereto.

Manufacturing

The native people of Alaska do very little manufacturing in the sense of industrial manufacturing as we commonly think of the term. They do, however, manufacture a great many articles for their own use and some for sale.

Articles manufactured mainly for home use include dogsleds and harness; kayaks, comiaks and other small boats; and many articles of clothing. Articles manufactured largely for sale through commercial channels include craft products of ivory, wood, and baleen; woven baskets and mats; articles of fur and skin clothing; certain types of dolls; and replicas of old native hunting and fishing equipment.

There is no yearly record of the total value of all articles manufactured by the native people. Reports were received from teachers and compiled in 1944 which showed a total production value of $677,395 of which $191,714 worth of products were used in the home, $285,191 worth were disposed of through local sales, and the remainder or $200,490 worth were sold through the Arts and Crafts Clearing House in Juneau. No similar records for later years are available.

The year 1944, a war year, was near the peak of craft production at high prices. Sales through the Arts and Crafts Clearing House increased to $212,500 in 1945, then dropped to $114,000 in 1946, and raised back to $127,000 in 1947. It is highly probable that the volume of manufacturing of crafts for home use remains fairly constant from year to year with changes in total volume being reflected in the volume of sales and prices. The lower value of sales in 1946 and 1947 as compared to 1944 and 1945 is due partially to less demand on account of the withdrawal of military personnel and partially to lower prices for articles sold.

More information is needed on total production of craft items in connection with the developing of markets for such articles. Studies should also be made of the possibilities for the development of a tanning industry to tan Alaskan furs for the manufacture of native products.

Wholesale and Retail

There are 40 group-owned stores operating in Alaska, of which 31 have been organized under the Indian Reorganization Act and 9 are operated as stock companies or village enterprises. These stores are generally in small communities where they have been established to serve and meet the needs of the communities in which other store facilities are inadequate or not available. Twenty-eight of the stores are members of the Alaska Native Industries Cooperative Association, a central buying organization, which was developed to purchase supplies and market products for the native stores. Two additional stores have made application for membership in this central organization and will be full-fledged members as soon as their applications are approved. The stores purchase supplies for the communities in which they are located and sell their merchandise for cash or exchange it for furs or other items which the native members of the communities have to sell. The stores sell the furs or other items which are accepted in barter to obtain cash for the further purchase of supplies.

A survey is needed to determine other native villages which are inadequately served at the present time and to give them assistance in organizing their groups and obtaining loans if necessary to finance the local stores. Additional credit funds are also needed for making loans to communities which need stores or which need to increase their purchasing power to meet the needs of the communities.

Utilities

Native villages of Alaska have practically no development of utilities. The people of Metlakatla have their own water and light plant and are arranging for the development of additional electric power. A few other villages have obtained light plants which they are operating to meet the village needs. Some have sources of water power which appear to be sufficient to operate small power plants that would meet village needs. Additional studies of power needs and possibilities of development are needed as well as funds to assist in making developments where investigations indicate that they are feasible. Surveys are also needed to determine the feasibility of the development of water supplies and sewage disposal systems for various villages. Government assistance in some villages will be necessary in providing funds for development of low cost power for villages to meet domestic and industrial needs.

Immediate Program

A proposed program for the economic development of the natives of Alaska has been worked out for the six-year period ending with the fiscal year 1954. This program includes the following:

1. The development of fisheries, canneries, cold storage, mild cure, and quick freeze units at various places for greater participation of the natives in the fishing industry.

2. The development and use of timber resources by natives, including establishment of small sawmills for production of lumber for home construction, village streets and docks, building of boats, and other local needs.

3. Continuation and expansion of the native store program to meet the needs of communities not adequately served.

4. Development of better housing facilities for natives either through new construction or the repair of present housing facilities.

5. The development of water supplies and sewage disposal systems for better sanitation and health.

6. Garden and agricultural development including reindeer and other livestock where practical.

7. Development of coal mines for native use to provide adequate and sure fuel supplies in areas where coal is available and can be mined and transported economically.

8. Study and development of other mining industries which might contribute to the income of native groups.

9. Development of better warehousing and storage facilities in native villages for the preservation of foods.

10. Further development of the native arts and crafts program, including the development of new designs typical of Alaska and utilizing Alaska products. This includes the establishment and development of training and work centers for native craft production. It includes ivory, gold, silver, lapidary, wood, skin sewing, and basketry work.

11. Settlement of land titles and handling of other land problems.

12. Assistance in placing natives in employment in industries which develop in the Territory.

13. Development of other small industries in the Territory which will provide gainful employment for natives and stabilize their economy on a standard of living comparable to that of other residents of the Territory.

14. Continuation and expansion of the credit program to provide funds for loans to tribes for the development of corporate or tribal enterprises and for relending to individuals to assist them in developing sound economic enterprises.

15. Development of electrical power for village and industrial use where practical.

The purpose of this program is to help the native people to help themselves in the development of their natural resources to the point where they can compete with and fit into the over-all economic program of increasing industrialization and development of Alaskan resources that will come with an increased Alaskan population. Much of the development must come through small industries which will give the people longer periods of gainful employment and supplement sources of income which they now have. Some of the development means better use of present resources, including preservation of food and production of garden produce to supplement other food resources and low cash income.

The program contemplates some appropriations by the Government which will be outright grants to assist in the rehabilitation of the native groups. It contemplates additional appropriations of revolving credit funds for loans for developing enterprises and industries. It also contemplates additional appropriations for personnel to train and work with natives in the expanded program of developing new commercial industries and improving the present ones.

It is important that the rehabilitation funds be appropriated on a no-year basis so they may be used until a project is completed. This will allow better planning and more economy in the expenditure of the funds. After 1954 the funds needed for loan purposes would remain fairly constant until the rehabilitation program was completed. It is anticipated that it would require 2 or possibly 3 years to complete all rehabilitation work after appropriations are made available. The program contemplates the production and use of local materials for home construction where such production will provide the materials at a lower cost than shipping them in. It is contemplated that a village receiving a grant from the Government for housing purposes would establish a repayment plan for individuals receiving benefits from the fund so that a permanent revolving fund would be established to meet future housing needs of the village.

Closely related to the economic development program are the educational and medical development programs which call for:

1. The construction of additional schools in areas where the number of native children justifies such action and the needs are not taken care of by Territorial schools.

2. Construction and operation of additional medical facilities where conditions are found to justify such action.

An estimate of funds needed for the construction of new educational and medical facilities for the period 1949 through 1955 (fiscal years) is as follows:

TABLE 61.—*Estimate of funds needed*

Fiscal year	School facilities	Medical facilities	Total
1949	$35,000	$588,000	$623,000
1950	1,120,000	2,239,500	3,359,500
1951	2,119,000	4,285,000	6,404,000
1952	5,270,000	2,420,000	7,690,000
1953	585,000	724,000	1,309,000
1954	405,000	686,000	1,091,000
1955	405,000	500,000	905,000
Total	9,939,000	11,442,500	21,381,500

NOTE.—These figures do not include operational costs.

The production and distribution of low-cost power in areas where Native Service installations are located would facilitate operation of the units and should reduce operating costs.

Long-Range Program

The long-range program of the Alaska Native Service for the economic development of the natives of Alaska is somewhat different to that of long-range programs of most agencies. Most long-range programs provide for development of services or production to a maximum point, and maintenance at that point thereafter making only such changes as are necessary to meet changing conditions. In working with the native people of Alaska it is anticipated that they will gradually fit into the developing economy of the country and that the need for a special service to assist them and look after their interests will gradually diminish. The Alaska Native Service is in the unique position of working itself out of a job. Just how fast this will be accomplished will depend upon several factors among which are how fast the natives adapt to the changing economy, how fast the economy of the Territory changes and develops, and what provisions are made for providing needed services to all people of a community by the same agency, and how fast such services can be extended to all communities. This may take 15, 20, 25, or more years.

It is not anticipated that the native people of all villages or communities will reach that stage of development where the services of the Alaska Native Service can be withdrawn at the same time. Rather it is expected that any withdrawal of services will be gradual, village by village or community by community, over a period of years. In the meantime the economic development program must be a continuation of that of the next 10 years, changing as needed to meet changing conditions.

The sooner the native population is provided with facilities, working conditions, and improved industrial and employment opportunities which will enable the people to maintain an improved standard of living comparable to that of other residents of Alaska, the sooner the Alaska Native Service will have fulfilled its mission. The development of Alaska's comparatively untouched natural resources such as timber, coal and some other minerals, agriculture, and certain fishing areas facilitated by the development and use of its hydropower may well hasten that day. Low-cost power has been proven the key to industrial development and to economies of labor and time for individuals. It is also the key to many of the comforts and luxuries of life.

Investigation Program

The following investigation program is needed for the Alaska Native Service:

Land Ownership and Use

1. Investigations to determine areas needed for natives' use and development.

2. Investigations of areas now under the Alaska Native Service that can possibly be released.

Agriculture

1. Soil surveys to determine areas adapted to gardening or needs for fertilizer to make land suitable for garden production.
2. Surveys of localities to determine suitability of feeds and climatic conditions for livestock production.
3. Investigation of individuals and groups to determine interest in livestock and gardening and suitability of such projects to native economy.
4. Investigation of possible markets and cost of marketing products produced for sale.
5. Investigation of the possibilities for irrigation of garden sites including those where low-cost power is available for pumping.

Minerals and Mining

1. Surveys to determine feasibility of coal mine development for native use at Tanunak, Unalakleet, and on St. Lawrence Island.
2. Surveys to determine practicability of mining for other minerals on Kodiak Island, Shungnak, St. Lawrence Island, and in the Venetie area.

Timber Products

1. Surveys to determine amount of accessible timber in areas where sawmills or other timber products plants are proposed to be located in interior Alaska.
2. Studies to determine practicability of installation of timber processing plants by natives.

Fisheries

1. Surveys to determine kinds and potentials of sea foods available in areas where canneries, quick freeze, mild cure, or other processing plants might be developed to provide longer periods of employment and greater income for natives.
2. Studies on the feasibility of construction and operation of processing plants by natives in areas where natives are congregated. This includes such places as Angoon, Hoonah, Haines, Kasaan, Kake, Klawock, Chanega, Tatilek, Atka, Tyonek, Alitak, Belkofski, Egegik, Gambell, Karluk, Mountain Village, Old Harbor, Saint Michael, Unalakleet, Yakutat, and White Mountain.

3. Studies to determine the effect of proposed power and pulp developments on fisheries and the native economy. In many areas, including interior Alaska, natives are dependent upon fish for a large portion of their food supply and as the principal source of dog food.

Wildlife Resources

1. Studies of average normal fur production of given localities to determine areas needed by members of native villages to provide an average normal income from furs and at the same time study procedure for protecting and conserving breeding stock, breeding grounds and introducing breeding stock into adaptable areas.

2. Study to determine the effect of power development upon wildlife and its relationship to native economy.

Manufacturing

1. Surveys and studies of localities where materials suitable for development of Alaskan craft products are available and can be developed profitably by natives.

2. Study of possibilities for developing a tanning industry for Alaskan furs for use in native skin sewing projects.

Wholesale and Retail Trade

1. Studies to determine localities where natives are not adequately served by store facilities at reasonable prices and where new stores should be developed.

2. Studies of markets and possible markets for native craft products and other products produced by them, surplus to their needs.

Utilities

1. Studies of electric power needs of various villages for industrial and home use.

2. Surveys to determine flow of streams at prospective sites for power development near certain villages and determination of whether power plants should be diesel or hydroelectric.

3. Studies to determine feasibility of proposed small power developments for villages.

4. Investigation of possible sources of water supply for certain villages and plans for systems of distribution.

5. Study of plans for sewage disposal for native villages.

Shrimp travel operations near Petersburg, Alaska.

Markets

1. Investigation of market possibilities for livestock and agricultural products produced in excess of local needs.

2. Investigation of markets for processed sea foods.

3. Investigation of markets for timber products.

Recreation

1. Survey of areas as possible sites for development of hunting lodges or other recreational facilities.

2. Investigation of interest of natives in operating hunting lodges or other recreational facilities.

Power

1. Survey of hydropower development possibilities throughout Alaska and prospects of actual power generating facilities with studies of how industries of the native population may be geared to such development.

FISH AND WILDLIFE SERVICE

The wildlife resources of Alaska—fur animals, game birds, game animals, and above all commercial and game fishes—represent a greater proportionate wealth in the Territory than is the case with any one of the 48 States.

Most of the 586,400 square miles in the Territory are better suited to the production of wildlife than to other forms of land use; and the fisheries of the Territory—its principal resources—have established Alaska as one of the important seafood producing regions of the world.

Chief among the Alaska marine species forming the basis for elaborate industries are the salmon, which collectively yield high quality food products valued around 100 million dollars annually. Thus, salmon fishing is Alaska's most lucrative industry.

Ranking third (gold mining is second) among Alaska's basic industries are the furbearers—as raw material for the pelt and fur industry. This includes trapping as well as fur farming.

The Alaska Planning Council, however, rates even higher the value of wildlife as an economic attraction to tourist visitors. In 1941 the Council wrote: "Wildlife holds a very distinct place among Alaska's basic economic assets, and its perpetuation is, therefore, of the utmost significance to the future economic development of the Territory: First, as an attraction to an increasing number of tourist visitors, especially big game hunters, naturalists, and photographers . . ."

For these and other reasons, any comprehensive programs for the future development of Alaska's water resources for power or any other purposes will be closely watched by the Fish and Wildlife Service for possible effects, good or bad, on fish and wildlife resources. This, of course, is required of the Bureau of Reclama-

A haul of herring in Shelikoff Strait.

tion or any other agency constructing projects as well as the Fish and Wildlife Service in compliance with the Coordination Act as amended by Public Law 732. Review of hydropower and other developmental projects may require the full-time service of at least one person on the Fish and Wildlife Service staff.

Also, in connection with proposed development, the Fish and Wildlife Service urges caution in the approval of further land withdrawals for any purpose, but stands ready to cooperate with the National Park Service and the Bureau of Reclamation in the establishment of such sanctuaries or wildlife management areas in the vicinity of new reservoirs as may be deemed advisable. Such areas would preserve small sections of Alaska in their pristine state as places where everyone can have a chance to see the fauna of Alaska in their natural habitat.

In the beginning, of course, fishermen took fish in the most convenient manner possible and conservation was ignored. Ill-advised practices made themselves felt in as short a time as 10 years so that Congress in 1889 deemed it necessary to prohibit the erection of permanent gear or barricades in salmon streams. At the same time the Office of the Commissioner of Fisheries was established and directed to make an investigation as a basis for legislation that would place the industry on a sound, sustained footing. This study discovered what has continually been emphasized ever since: fishery problems are so everlastingly complex, intricate, and variable that their solution is long and difficult.

Jurisdiction over Alaska's fur seals and fisheries was transferred from the Treasury Department to the Department of Commerce in 1903, to be administered by the Bureau of Fisheries. The Bureau was transferred to the Department of the Interior in 1939 and the following year was combined with the Bureau of Biological Survey to form the Fish and Wildlife Service.

Authority and Functions

Laws governing the administration of Alaskan fisheries derive from Congressional Acts, some of which make specific provisions for control, while others delegate certain broader fields to the Secretary of the Interior for his supervision. The act of 1906 prohibited wanton waste of fish, assessed a small case pack tax, required submission of statistics by fishery operators and gave the Secretary authority to prohibit commercial fishing in streams. The other more important act upon which regulations are based is the "White Act" of 1924 which prohibited all commercial fishing between 6 p. m. Saturday and 6 a. m. Monday, established the principle that escapement should equal catch, and gave

the Secretary rather broad powers to make regulations he felt necessary to conservation. The Secretary's authority and responsibility is discharged through the Branch of Alaska Fisheries of the Fish and Wildlife Service.

It is a function of the Fish and Wildlife Service to determine the best means of managing the fisheries of Alaska through research and observation and, with that knowledge, to formulate regulations and enforce them. A considerable volume of complex regulations had gradually evolved to control and preserve the various fisheries and they are amended endlessly to meet changing needs and conditions. Fishermen, operators and resident Alaskans are consulted annually in an effort to secure the benefits of as wide experience and knowledge as possible.

Current Organization, Responsibilities and Activities

The Fish and Wildlife Service as a whole has widespread duties that are national and even worldwide in scope, and is concerned with practically every important item of wildlife as well as fish in the United States; Alaska's fisheries are but one of its concerns. The Branch of Alaska Fisheries is the subdivision of the Service immediately concerned with management and enforcement in Alaska commercial fish and fur seals. It is advisedly assisted with scientific research conducted by the Alaska Investigations of the Branch of Fishery Biology. Chiefs of these Branches have headquarters at Washington, D. C., but actual administration of the management work in Alaska is performed by the Regional Director at Juneau. Under the Regional Directors are fishery field agents who administer surrounding districts from headquarters at False Pass,[1] Chignik,[1] Kodiak, Naknek,[1] Anchorage, Cordova, Yakutat,[1] Juneau, Sitka, Craig, Wrangell, and Ketchikan.

The scientific staff is headquartered at the Fish and Wildlife Service office and laboratory building at 2725 Montlake Boulevard, Seattle, Wash. Formal biological field studies are currently being made on the sockeye salmon of Bristol Bay, the sockeye runs at Karluk Lake on Kodiak Island, the pink salmon of Southeastern Alaska generally and the three major herring fisheries. Related miscellaneous fishery problems are also investigated by the staff as they arise. A comprehensive program of physical stream survey coupled with barrier removal and spawning ground improvement is being conducted jointly by fishery engineers and biologists. These activities are directly under the authority of the Chief of the Branch of Fishery Biology

---

[1] Seasonal only

but, of course, their findings are integrated with the management functions of the Regional Director.

A technological research laboratory (Branch of Commercial Fisheries) at Ketchikan constantly experiments with means of improving or inventing products derived from the waters of Alaska. Food processing, storage, by-product development, quality standardization, and seafood utilization are subjects coming within the laboratory's scope. This work is supplemented to some extent by related studies at the Seattle laboratory. This same branch is also now conducting fishing exploration in Alaska waters to determine the potential yield of presently unfamiliar grounds. Two large trawlers commenced their studies with a preliminary trip in 1948 to the Bering Sea and Western Alaska.

A somewhat different organization pertains to the Pribilof fur seal operation, which is independent of the Juneau Regional Office. The Superintendent and his staff have seasonal headquarters at both Seattle and the Pribilofs and work directly under the central office in Washington, D. C. All activities covering fur seals are, of course, subject further to the terms of the international convention with Canada.

The halibut fishery is outside the purview of the Fish and Wildlife Service, except in matters of enforcement, as it is managed and regulated by the International Fisheries Commission established under treaty with Canada. All other commercial fisheries in Alaskan territorial waters, however, are subject under law to regulation by the Fish and Wildlife Service.

Future Plans and Estimated Costs

Management

The severe decline in the salmon resources of recent years leaves no question but that efforts to protect and restore the runs must be greatly intensified if the fishing industry and thereby the economy of Alaska is to be preserved at anything like its present level. The distressing lag of actual production behind potential is due in large part to unsound and overly intense fishing practices, the result in turn of inadequate law inforcement and scarcity of scientific knowledge. It will be impossible to rehabilitate satisfactorily Alaska's salmon unless personnel and equipment to do the job are markedly increased. It is reassuring that substantial improvement has been possible in this regard during the last 2 years through larger appropriations of funds by the Congress so that a good nucleus has been formed for expanding into the necessary fields.

Pending reorganization of the Alaska staff establishes two classes of field agents concerned with fisheries: enforcement and management. The eventual stationing of one of each of these agents in most of the fishing districts and the permanent staffing of the Yakutat and Yukon-Kuskokwim Districts will require doubling the present force of 12 men. This necessarily requires a correlative increase in clerical and administrative personnel, and it is intended eventually to assign clerical help to those several field stations now without such assistance.

It is also desirable to expand further the number of temporary, seasonal, enforcement personnel from 90 to a minimum of 130 so that most of the principal spawning streams can be assigned individual watchmen to prevent poaching during the time of the runs. Each man must be equipped with an outboard motor and boat and camping gear.

Accurate, factual data become of increasing importance as management of the fisheries becomes more capable and more precise. In fact, statistics on the catch are absolutely indispensable to an understanding of the numerous factors constantly affecting the highly complex and ever-changing salmon industry. Collection, compilation and analysis have become so necessary and will be so involved as to require the services of a trained statistician to do the job properly.

Experience has shown that counting weirs in streams are the most practical means of effecting adequate escapement in that area. Prior to 1932 an elaborate weir program was an established part of salmon management in Alaska. Only five units have been operated in recent years, due to lack of funds, but two new weirs were installed in the Ygashik and Naknek Rivers on Bristol Bay in 1949. A complete weir program, however, requires that racks also be placed across the other three Bristol Bay rivers, plus 10 on other key streams throughout Alaska. It is estimated that the original cost of installing and operating a project of this nature would be almost $200,000, although the annual expense should be only one-third that amount once the initial equipment is in place.

As a result of vessel and airplane acquisitions from war surplus supplies, the Service now has a reasonably adequate patrol fleet; transportation is no longer the severely limiting factor it once was. However, funds as recently available have restricted use of this equipment below the optimum considered desirable from an enforcement standpoint, and they must soon be increased to raise vessel crew wages commensurate with those prevailing in the maritime industry. Fast but livable speedboats of the type needed for patrol of inshore waters are not available from war surplus sources and must be purchased new. Early replacement of the Service's present fleet of outmoded small craft is essential as several units are badly deteriorated.

Fur seals flourish at the rookery at St. Paul, Alaska.

A total of 11 new 45-foot speedboats is required, costing about $20,000 each at present prices.

Other items of transportation in current need are a large and fully equipped hangar that can accommodate the fleet of 19 planes based at Anchorage. The severity of winter weather, the huge investment in aircraft and our dependence on their condition and reliability make obvious the necessity for adequate storage and servicing facilities. The use of commercial aircraft in the interior has grown so fast that Government planes are seriously handicapped by the resultant lack of accommodations. A much smaller hangar is also required at the Juneau airport for the three planes assigned to Southeastern Alaska, likewise without cover at present. It is estimated that the Juneau hangar will cost somewhere near $15,000 but the big Anchorage installation will come to nearly a quarter million dollars.

The efficiency of the field personnel at the various stations would be greatly promoted if they were provided with trucks in good running condition for carrying out local assignments. Four are in urgent need at the present time because of distances involved and all stations should be so equipped eventually.

INVESTIGATIVE PROGRAM

The future management of Alaskan wildlife resources may dictate the future economic welfare of the people. The depletion of wildlife resources in Alaska has followed the same pattern as in the States. Proper management of wildlife based upon scientific knowledge of the species and environment offers a real opportunity for increased development of the resources.

Wildlife

The Pribilof Island fur seal herd is an outstanding example of successful management. Management of some other species has not yet met with the same success. The fur seal herd has been increased from 132,000 animals in 1910 to 3,837,000 in 1948. The annual harvest has also been steadily increasing. Research and investigation should provide the knowledge necessary to manage other important game and furbearing animals to their maximum population consistent with the environment and relative value directly or indirectly to the welfare of the people. A few of the basic problems which will require investigation and research before the proper management of wildlife can be practiced are now apparent, other problems will arise with management and development.

Restoration of Wildlife to Former Ranges

The depletion of wildlife has followed closely the development of the Territory and the present range of many kinds of wildlife has been greatly reduced from the original range. Factors which govern the distribution of wildlife should be studied and where possible and desirable from the economic, social, biological, recreational, or aesthetic standpoint, efforts should be made to restore the wildlife to the original ranges. The caribou is an example. This species is no longer found on the Kenai Peninsula where it formerly was abundant. Similarly caribou have been severely depleted in numbers over wide areas in the Territory. Studies are necessary to determine the factors limiting the caribou range. Life history investigations including migration, food and cover requirements, predatory and other factors of mortality are essential as a basis in restocking the Kenai and other former ranges not now occupied by the caribou. Such studies will undoubtedly entail several years' work by competent biologists working in the field following the caribou in all their migrations throughout the year.

Stocking of Native Species

Basic life history and distribution studies of the species and the environment should be made on a number of the more important furbearers and big game animals to obtain information for use as a guide in stocking suitable range not at present occupied. For example, the mountain goat now occupies a limited range on higher elevations along the coast of South and Southeast Alaska. Studies should be made to determine the maximum available range in the Territory and determine the proper methods of stocking. Baranof Island has been successfully stocked with goats and other islands of Southeastern Alaska may prove equally suitable.

Management of Introduced Animals

Research should be initiated to follow closely the progress of animals which have been introduced such as the elk, bison, and muskox. Once an introduction is successful proper herd management is essential. The continuous public demand for the introduction of new forms of wildlife necessitates the need for factual data on the range and the species requirements. Introductions of any species to a new environment should be undertaken only after thorough research has shown the adequacy of the range, the possible affect of the introduction on native species and environment.

Wildlife Threatened by Extinction

Alaska provides the home for a number of species of wildlife which have decreased to a population level where they may not recover. Studies should be conducted at least to the extent that the necessary protection is provided and the known management measures are taken before the populations reach a critical level. Investigations on the trumpeter swan might have revealed information necessary to avoid the danger of extinction which has threatened this species for the past 3 decades.

Migratory Waterfowl

Investigations on the breeding range, nesting areas and migration of the thousands of migratory waterfowl in Alaska have not been extensive. Banding studies (Lower Yukon, 1941; Hooper Bay, 1942; Innoko River, 1948) are limited to a few hundred birds in a few isolated areas. Almost nothing is known about the extent to which ducks and geese, raised in Alaska, provide the hunting for the waterfowl hunters in the Mississippi and Central flyways of the States.

Investigations should be completed in the Territory to provide the minimum essentials to proper management of the waterfowl for the welfare of the hunters on the North American continent. Nesting, resting, and wintering range of all species of ducks and geese found in Alaska should be determined. The important nesting areas should be studied over a period of years during times of high and low water levels and high and low populations. Migration pattern by dates and location of species should be investigated through banding and aerial surveys. Factors affecting nesting mortality should be known for the important nesting areas.

Sea Mammals

The Alaskan waters contain sea mammals that furnish an important source of food and clothing to many of the northern native people. The conservation of these oceanic forms of wildlife such as the hair seals, walrus, and whales has been given little consideration

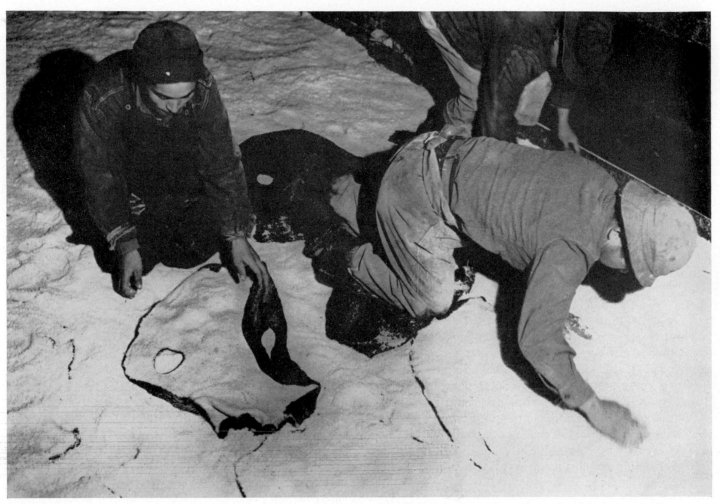

Seal skins are salted, shipped to the States for tanning, then returned to furriers in Alaska for templating, cutting, and sewing into finished garments.

because of lack of information on the range, habits, population, and harvests. The use of modern firearms and equipment, together with the demand for such items as ivory and sperm oil may result in unnecessary destruction and depletion of oceanic wildlife. Investigations on the life history, distribution, and population status should be made to provide the necessary basic information for proper management and harvests.

Harvest of Wildlife

The Alaskan Game Commission is continually confronted with the difficult task of establishing regulations pertaining to the taking of game and furbearers. Studies relative to the populations and allowable harvest should be continuous to establish facts upon which to base the setting of seasons for hunting and trapping. Lack of adequate information may result in an excess harvest that may curtail the harvest for many subse-

quent years. Likewise closed seasons (where justifiable hunting and trapping could be allowed) may result in losses of valuable fur and game from starvation, cyclic disturbances, or predation. Discriminatory harvests of certain sex or age groups may increase the take without affecting the breeding stock.

Utilization of Game and Fur Resources

The increase in population of Alaska together with the growing demand for outdoor recreation from both Alaskans and nonresidents will necessarily bring heavy pressure on fur and game species of wildlife. The demand for food and clothing for the natives is an ever present critical problem. The proper utilization of all parts of a bird or animal carcass for food or clothing is imperative. Studies on utilization of fur, carcasses, and other products should be made. For example, the 1948 harvest of seal skins provided the carcasses of over 70,000 seals, a by-product which should have maximum utilization without waste. Natives and some whites have been known to kill an excess of caribou causing undue waste. Usable food is wasted in hunting walrus for the ivory trade and allowing the beheaded carcass to go unused. The methods of harvest require study to avoid losses. For example, losses of oceanic mammals from "sinking" after being shot represents a serious loss and expense to the native. New techniques require development to avoid losses of this type. The byproducts of the entire fur, fish, and game industry require a thorough study to avoid waste.

Research is Good Business

The future of Alaska will depend to a large extent upon the management and utilization of the natural restorable resources. Fur and game represents a large percentage of the food, clothing, and revenue from a restorable resource. Investigations have not been adequate to provide accurate information on the annual harvest of wildlife to determine the importance to the public welfare. Research and investigation must precede proper wildlife management. The monetary expenditure for research is not the sole criterion for a job to be done, but if modern industry finds it is necessary to spend about 3 percent of the gross sales on research then it can be assumed that a like amount may be required to manage properly the wildlife. The Fish and Wildlife Service receives a limited amount ($25,000) of funds from Federal Aid to Wildlife Restoration, a portion of which is devoted to research. No other wildlife research funds have been available. None of the license fees for

Alaska furrier cutting seal skins to be sewed into garments.

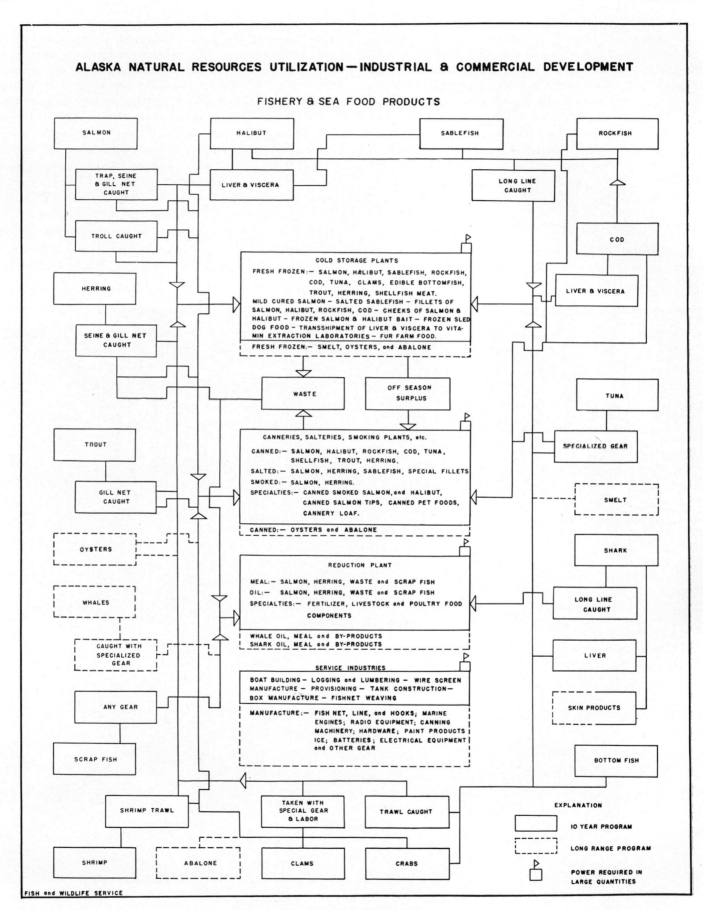

ALASKA NATURAL RESOURCES UTILIZATION—INDUSTRIAL & COMMERCIAL DEVELOPMENT

FISHERY & SEA FOOD PRODUCTS

WILDLIFE & MARINE FISHERIES GROUP

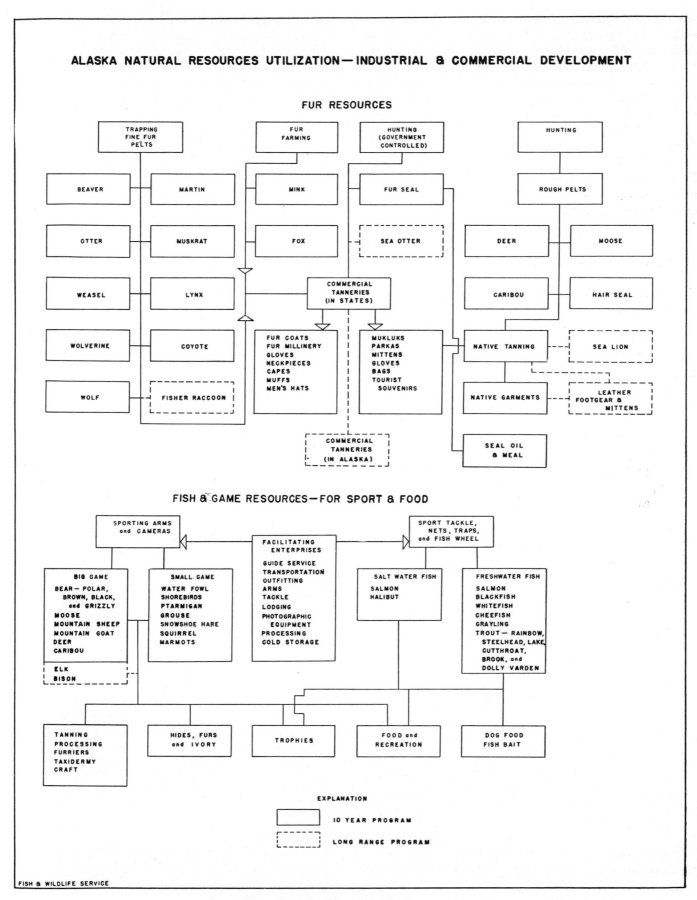

ALASKA NATURAL RESOURCES UTILIZATION — INDUSTRIAL & COMMERCIAL DEVELOPMENT

FUR RESOURCES

FISH & GAME RESOURCES — FOR SPORT & FOOD

EXPLANATION

10 YEAR PROGRAM

LONG RANGE PROGRAM

FISH & WILDLIFE SERVICE

WILDLIFE & MARINE FISHERIES GROUP

trapping and hunting is used directly for the management of fur and game. The shipment of furs from Alaska in 1947 amounted to approximately 7 million dollars. The value of game for food, clothing, and recreation can be conservatively estimated at 8 million dollars. The total combined estimated value of game and fur would be approximately 15 million dollars per year and at 3 percent would yield $450,000, the amount which could reasonably be spent annually in research and investigation of problems affecting the development of the resource. Investigation and research is good business and essential to the proper development of the fur and game resource.

BUREAU OF LAND MANAGEMENT

The development of Alaska's natural resources is fundamental, both from the values that these resources can contribute immediately to the economy and well-being of the Territory and the United States, and from the additions to the security and wealth they can contribute over a long period of time. Existing international unrest lends impetus to the immediate need for Alaska's development because of its strategic location and vital importance to national security. Abundant and inexpensive power must be available for this needed industrial development of Alaska. As shown in the foregoing report, Alaska has abundant potential hydroelectric power resources that only await development to be made available for industrial expansion. Considerable other direct and indirect values will also be realized by such developments. Inexpensive electric power as well as irrigation water will aid in the development of agriculture and, likewise, food production and general security.

One of the fundamental purposes for the existence of the Bureau of Land Management in Alaska is to facilitate the development of the Territory. In general, the Bureau is responsible for the administration and disposition of the public domain. It is the desire of the people, as expressed through Congress, to transfer the ownership of these lands to private individuals for development and productive use as rapidly as possible. However, as a public resource, it is desired that the land be placed in its most productive use. Some types of land, therefore, should remain in public ownership and be administered for certain public purposes. Other lands, suitable for agricultural, industrial, municipal, and residential uses, are transferred to private ownership for their development and use. The construction of multiple-purpose dams and the provision of electric power and irrigation water will greatly aid the development and highest productive use of the land.

To promote the best possible use of the public domain and to insure its fair disposal, Congress has developed laws regulating the disposal of public lands. Homestead laws have been enacted to encourage and regulate the transfer of unappropriated public domain to private ownership for agricultural development and use of the land. Other laws have been enacted to facilitate and regulate the transfer of land to private ownership for business, residential, recreational, and health uses. The Bureau has been designated to administer these regulations as well as to administer the use of the public domain remaining in public ownership.

The various homestead laws permit male citizens of the United States who are 21 or more years old or who are heads of families, to select, develop for agricultural use, and acquire up to 160 acres each of unappropriated public domain. Good intention must be demonstrated by the construction of a habitable house on each entry, by 3 years of residence on the land, and by the cultivation of at least one-eighth of the total area by the end of the third year. After these conditions have been met, an application for title to the land may be accepted. Some requirements are modified, particularly for the war veterans.

Examination of the unappropriated public land by the Bureau of Land Management, study of its physical characteristics, and determination of its suitability for various uses is not required by law, but is highly desirable prior to settlement upon the land. Such research not only may save settlers costly mistakes, but provides needed guidance and a sound foundation for public land administration. As previously indicated, limitations of time and personnel have allowed such examinations to be made in only a few areas and represent only a very small proportion of the area where settlement will probably occur in the immediate future. Such studies are also needed to assist in public land development programs such as the hydroelectric and irrigation development program as proposed by the Bureau of Reclamation. Likewise, these examinations are essential to foresee the future need for land to be reserved for public recreational and other purposes.

In spite of its limited numbers of available trained personnel, a vigorous program of land classification has been proposed for the next several years. This program calls for the detailed classification of over 3,000,000 acres and reconnaissance studies on about 6,000,000 acres of land in the next 6 years. The study and classification of these lands will provide much needed guidance to prospective settlers as well as a better foundation for public land administration. Likewise, such information will be available for use of the Bureau of Reclamation in its planning for development of specific reclamation projects.

ALASKA'S LANDS

Alaska's primary resource—its land—is at the present time virtually an unknown, and nonmeasured asset. Specialists of the Alaska Agricultural Experiment Station, Office of the Commissioner of Agriculture, and others have made observations in various localities. The land in a few areas has been examined in detail by the Bureau of Land Management and the Soil Conservation Service, but these and the reconnaissance observations represent a very small proportion of Alaska's total land area.

Land Ownership, Present Use, and Suitability for Agriculture

The very large majority of the land of the Territory is in public ownership. Information is not available to show the exact amount of land in each type of ownership. However, of Alaska's gross area of over 375,000,000 acres, about 365,000,000 acres were in Federal ownership as of June 30, 1947. Of this, about 265,000,000 acres were vacant, unappropriated, and unreserved.

Detailed examinations of lands have been conducted in eight areas by the United States Bureau of Land Management and in two areas by the United States Soil Conservation Service. These examinations were conducted to evaluate the physical characteristics of the land in terms of their limitations upon potential use of the land, and, in so doing, to provide a guide for future land settlement and for public administration of the lands involved. Reports on some of these investigations have been completed and have been published. Others, because of their recency, are not as yet in completed form and, consequently, data obtained from them represent tentative estimates only. In an attempt to summarize the data, some regrouping of the land suitability classes was necessary.

A total of 1,206,142 acres has been included in these land examinations. Of this, 327,822 acres or 27 percent were tentatively found to be suitable for Alaska general type of farming. This class of land is considered to be physically suitable for cultivation and the production of vegetables, grains, forage crops. Local areas will be subject to major or minor limitations.

On 417,211 acres, or 35 percent of the area examined, the land is tentatively considered suitable principally for grazing; however, in some instances it may be adaptable for the limited production of forage crops.

Land tentatively considered to be unsuitable for agricultural use included a total of 461,109 acres or 38 percent of the total area examined.

Because of its physical characteristics, present inaccessibility, and relatively small economic demand, most of Alaska's land area is in its natural wild state and therefore directly contributes to the economy of the Territory only through its production of natural products. In 1939, only 623 farms embracing a total of 1,775,752 acres were enumerated by the Census of Agriculture. In the same year, the Census of Population listed only eight incorporated towns of 1,000 or more population. Numerous small villages exist as well as rural homesites, business sites and industrial sites. However, the actual total use of Alaska's 365 million acres of land is very slight. The potential value of Alaska's land resources is almost unlimited. These values will be realized as the population pressure and the demand for land is increased, inaccessibility is overcome by extension of transportation facilities, reclamation projects are built to provide electric power and irrigation water, and mechanical power is made available for land clearing and drainage. Alaska awaits general development of its public facilities before its vast land resources can more materially contribute to its economy.

SOUTH CENTRAL ALASKA REGION

Anchorage–Cordova Division

As mentioned, the Bureau of Land Management has conducted two detailed surveys of land within this geographic division. In addition, a survey of the Matanuska Area was made by the Soil Conservation Service in 1946. Other than for the land included in these surveys, little information concerning land use or ownership is available.

Anchorage Area

A total of 60,800 acres was examined in this area to determine their physical suitability for settlement and to provide a guide to settlement and public land administration. Of the total area in 1947, about 41,200 acres were included in military reservations; 18,000 acres were in private ownership; and about 1,500 acres were vacant and unappropriated public domain.

The privately owned land is primarily used for residential and commercial purposes. A small proportion of the land is used for farming. In 1939, the Census of Agriculture enumerated 23 farms with a total acreage of 2,120 acres.

Of the 60,800 acres of land examined, 16,314 acres were tentatively considered to be suitable for Alaska general type of farming with local limitations; 19,630 acres suitable for grazing or limited crop production;

and 24,856 acres unsuitable for agricultural use at the present time. Undoubtedly, the highest use of any land in the vicinity of the city of Anchorage will be for the rural residential and business uses because of the rapid growth of the population of the city.

Wasilla Area

This area was examined in 1947 to determine the physical adaptability of the land for settlement use. A total of 121,089 acres was included in the survey.

The present ownership of the land, estimated as of November, 1948, is as follows:

	Acres	Total acres
Privately owned land:		
Patented	5,880	
Patent pending	11,915	
Total private land		17,795
Federally owned land:		
Reserves	16,661	
Unappropriated	86,633	
Total federal land		103,294
		121,089

The suitability of the land examined for agricultural uses was tentatively found to be as follows:

	Acres	Total acres
With local limitations suitable for Alaska general farming	37,920	
Production limited forage crop principally suitable for grazing	30,858	
Unsuitable for agricultural use	52,311	
Total		121,089

Matanuska Valley

The Matanuska Valley was examined in 1946 by the Soil Conservation Service to determine the physical characteristics and adaptability for agricultural use of some 317,510 acres of land. This survey indicates the use then being made of this land as follows:

	Acres	Total acres
Cleared for crop production	4,781	
Seeded Pasture	68	
Slashed for clearing	733	
Grazing or native clovers	6,342	
Urban uses	279	
Total land used		12,203
Total land unused		305,307
Total area examined		317,510

The suitability of this land for agricultural use was classified as follows:

	Acres	Total acres
Tillable	59,435	
Suitable for pasture or hay	156,257	
Unsuitable for agricultural use	101,818	
Total area classified		317,510

Kenai Peninsula Division

As discussed, the Bureau of Land Management has conducted two detailed surveys of land within this geographic division. Other than for the land included in these surveys, summarized information concerning land ownership and use is not readily available.

Kenai Peninsula

A gross area of 333,800 acres of land was examined to determine the physical characteristics of the land and its suitability for settlement.

The ownership of these lands, as of February, 1946, was estimated as follows:

	Acres	Total acres
Privately owned land:		
Patented	14,750	
Patent pending	11,450	
Total, private		26,200
Federally owned land:		
Reserves	11,200	
Unappropriated	296,400	
Total, Federal		307,600
		333,800

Approximately 163,000 acres of the public domain have been withdrawn from entry pending enactment of regulations by Congress for planned group settlement. This reservation also includes a large proportion of the unappropriated public domain in the Kenai River Area.

Similar to other areas, the large majority of the land is not being used at the present time. In 1945, some 41 operating farms were enumerated. These farms embraced a total of 5,658 acres, of which 305 were under cultivation. At that time, little of the nonfarm land was grazed, the livestock population consisting of 54 dairy cows, 58 beef animals, 23 horses and colts, and 7 sheep. Numerous small tracts of land are used as rural residences and somewhat less than 500 acres are used for municipal purposes.

The study of the physical characteristics of the land indicated its tentative suitability for agricultural use as follows:

	Acres	Total acres
Suitable for Alaska general farming	41, 415	
Limited crop and livestock production	90, 760	
Limited crop and grazing	72, 533	
Limited suitability for grazing	34, 815	
Unsuitable for crop production or grazing	91, 354	
Water area	2, 923	
Total classified		333, 800

Kenai River Area

An area of land through which the Kenai River drains was examined in 1947 to determine its physical suitability for settlement. A total of 79,388 acres, of which 2,968 acres were water surface and 76,420 acres of land area, were studied. The ownership of these lands, February, 1948, was as follows:

	Acres	Total acres
Privately owned land:		
Patented	0	
Patent pending	5, 697	
Total, private		5, 697
Federally owned land:		
Reserves	6, 443	
Leased	670	
Unappropriated	63, 610	
Total, Federal		70, 723
Grand total		76, 420

(A large proportion of this area has been withdrawn from entry pending enactment of regulations by Congress for planned group settlement.)

At present, there is very little use being made of the land in this area; the principal present use is for a few scattered rural residences. Other than for home gardens, there is virtually no present agricultural use of the land.

For potential use, the land was tentatively found to be as follows:

	Acres	Total acres
Suitable for Alaska general crop production	2, 048	
Suitable for Alaska crop production with local limitations	23, 521	
Suitable for grazing and limited forage crop production	25, 415	
		50, 984
Unsuitable for agricultural use		25, 436
Total		76, 420

Portions of the Kenai Peninsula and Kenai River area containing about 163,000 acres and known as the Kenai-Kasilof Withdrawal Area have been examined for their agricultural suitability by the Soil Conservation Service.

YUKON–KUSKOKWIM REGION

Tanana River Division

Several detailed surveys have been made of areas within this geographic division. The Bureau of Land Management has studied the physical characteristics of land within four areas, and the Soil Conservation Service has examined one area. Other than the information available from the field notes and preliminary reports on these surveys, no summarized information is available concerning present land use, ownership, or land suitability for the rest of the land in the Yukon-Kuskokwim Region.

Big Delta–Goodpaster Area (Estimates)

The physical characteristics of about 165,000 acres of land in the Big Delta-Goodpaster drainage basins were studied in 1948 to determine their suitability for settlement.

The land in this area is owned at the present time almost entirely by the Federal Government. About 1,000 acres are in private ownership and the remainder, about 164,000 acres, are in various forms of public ownership.

Less than 10 rural residences and homesteads are located in the area. Their use of the land is primarily for residential purposes with very little agricultural use being made of the land. As the livestock population is very limited, little or no grazing use is made of the land.

The suitability of the land was tentatively found to be as follows:

	Acres	Total acres
Suitable for general Alaska crop production	25, 000	
Suitable for grazing and limited crop production	25, 000	
Unsuitable for agricultural use	115, 000	
Total, classified		165, 000

Salcha River Area (Estimates)

Approximately 65,000 acres of land in the lower Salcha River basin were studied to determine their physical suitability for settlement.

The land included in the study is practically all in unappropriated public domain. This type of Federal ownership was estimated to include about 64,500 acres of the total area. The remainder, or 500 acres, were owned by five or six private land holders.

Other than residential, no use is being made of the land.

The suitability of this land is very limited for intensive uses. It was tentatively estimated that about 500 acres are suitable for general crop production; 1,000 acres for grazing and limited forage crop production, and approximately 63,500 acres are unsuitable for agricultural use because of their physical characteristics.

Chena–Fairbanks Area (Estimates)

The lower drainage basin of the Chena River was studied and classified for its suitability for settlement. Potential agricultural use was tentatively found to be as follows:

	Acres	Total acres
Alaska general crop production	7, 450	
General crop production with some limitations	20, 550	
Principally grazing and limited forage crop production	11, 550	
Limited grazing, woodland and other extensive uses	16, 250	
Unsuited for crop production, grazing, or forestry	19, 500	
Total		75, 300

Nenana–Fairbanks Area (Estimates)

Approximately 80,150 acres of land surface and 2,950 acres of water surface, comprising the portion of the lower drainage basin of the Nenana River, were studied and conclusions reached as follows:

	Acres	Total acres
Suitable for Alaska general crop production	3, 080	
Suitable for general crop production with some limitations	19, 070	
Principally suitable for grazing and limited forage crop production	23, 940	
Suitable for limited grazing, woodland, and other extensive uses	30, 600	
Unsuited for crop production, grazing, or forestry	3, 460	
Total		80, 150

Dunbar Area (From Tentative Soil Conservation Service Data)

This area includes a total of 32,437 acres of land bordering the Alaska Railroad right-of-way in the vicinity of Dunbar. It was withdrawn from entry in June 1948 to allow study and classification for agricultural uses prior to settlement. Consequently, it is in reserved public ownership. There is no present agricultural use being made of the land.

The physical characteristics of the land for agricultural uses were classified as follows:

	Acres	Total acres
Suitable for cultivation with minor permanent limitations	17, 464	
Suitable for cultivation with major permanent limitations	594	
Suitable for occasional cultivation due to major permanent limitations	621	
Suitable for grazing (including muskeg swamps)	221	
Unsuitable for agricultural use	13, 262	
Total		32, 162

Forestry and Fire Control

The Bureau of Land Management, through its Division of Forestry, is responsible for the management of the forest and other natural resources of the public domain lands in Alaska. It is also responsible for the protection of the vegetative resources from forest fires.

Although these responsibilities have been vested in the Bureau (formerly the General Land Office) for many years, it was not until 1940 that funds were provided for the establishment of organized fire protection, and until 1946 before forest management policies and practices were initiated. Funds provided to date have met only the bare operational requirements of fire presuppression and timber sale supervision. The funds have not been adequate to undertake forest surveys, fire damage appraisals, and all phases of forest research. These studies, while essential to sound forest management, have never been initiated on any of Alaska's public domain land. It is for this reason that any figures or data presented on behalf of Alaska's interior forest lands must be based on invalid estimates.

It is assumed that 225,000,000 acres of the public domain bear some form of vegetation. Of this, 125,000,000 acres are believed to bear forest growth of varying density and species, and the balance consists of extensive grasslands, brushlands, and tundra. Estimates of the gross timber volume vary from 70,000,000,000 board feet to 350,000,000,000 board feet. The latter estimate is based on 85,000,000 acres of sparse forest bearing four cords per acre (gross, 340,000,000 cords) and 40,-000,000 acres of dense forest bearing 9 cords per acre (gross, 360,000,000 cords).

The vast grass and tundra areas constitute potentially valuable grazing lands for domestic stock. Pioneer attempts have already been made, especially within the Aleutian Island and Matanuska Valley areas. Although only partially successful, these attempts have been indicative of what may be accomplished under more favorable economic factors (better intra-Territorial transportation routes, lower freight rates, increased Territorial demand for meat, hides, wool, et cetera) and with more extensive research into forage values of native vegetation, stock-carrying capacities of local ranges, and possible improvements to range conditions. Today, and in the future, the grass and tundra lands will support large populations of reindeer, caribou, bison, and other wildlife. There is a great need for intensive research in wildlife management to the end that the game population can be increased to equal more nearly the carrying capacity of the range and thereby assure food to the natives and residents of Alaska as well as a continued income to the Territory as derived from big-game hunters and other sportsmen.

The forests of Alaska are broadly separated into two types: the coastal forests, and the interior forests. The coastal forests are the extension and northern limit of the big timber found along the coast in the Pacific Northwest. Western hemlock comprises about 70 percent of the merchantable volume of the Alaskan coastal forest; Sitka spruce, 24 percent; western red cedar and Alaska yellow cedar, the balance. The coastal forests are confined to the seaward slopes of the Coastal Range and are largely included within the two national forests, Tongass and Chugach, which are under the administration of the United States Forest Service. The greatest potential use of these forests is now being realized with the recent award of a 50-year contract for 1,500,000,000 cubic feet of pulpwood, which will support one pulp and paper mill of 550-ton capacity in perpetuity. There is sufficient timber in the Tongass National Forest to support five such mills.

The interior forests primarily consist of white spruce and white birch, with smaller amounts of northern black cottonwood, tamarack, aspen, black spruce, balm-of-gilead, alder, and willow. The forests are typically found as narrow belts of timber along the major streams and their tributaries. Low-lying benchlands and plateaus between such streams are usually forested. Timberline varies throughout Alaska but is usually between 1,500 and 2,500 feet. The forests do not ordinarily occur in large unbroken stands; rather, they are broken by areas of swamp and muskeg, of greater or lesser extent, which make their utilization most costly and definitely seasonal in nature.

The interior forests are primarily valued for consumption within Alaska, and not for export purposes. Except for white birch which has a definite export possibility, the other species are of generally inferior value and could by no means compete with Pacific Coast timber. White spruce, which is the only species utilized today, has inferior mechanical properties but is of major

988410—52——18

importance to Alaska. It supplies most of the fuelwood, houselogs, and lumber used by Alaskans (not including residents of incorporated cities and Government projects). It is found throughout Alaska; it is the species found at the limits of tree growth in latitude, longitude, and altitude. Small though the trees may be, they make possible the development of Alaska because they are found where needed. Prospectors would be unable to live and work without spruce for fuel, cabins, and timbers. Trappers could not exist, nor could the wildlife and fur-bearers. Homesteaders are of vital importance to Alaska because they develop the basic need of agriculture. They are typically imbued with the necessary pioneer spirit but just as typically have a minimum of cash assets. Were it not for the white spruce, available under free use privilege, they would be unable to build their homes, barns, corrals, and obtain their fuelwood, because imported forest products would be too expensive for their limited means. White spruce is thus considered not only the major commercial species of interior Alaska but also the major factor which allows her other natural resources to be exploited and developed in behalf of the United States.

No technical data can be supplied regarding tree sizes, volumes per acre, et cetera. It is presumed that the white spruce will average 8 to 12 inches in diameter and 70 feet in height over much of Alaska. However, individual stands of spruce attain diameters of 36 to 54 inches and heights of 90 to 110 feet. Acreage volumes vary from 2,000 board feet per acre to 12,000 board feet. White birch, except for the Cook Inlet region, is usually small and may average 7 to 8 inches in diameter and 50 to 70 feet in height. In the better white birch stands found in the Cook Inlet region, the birch may attain diameters of 30 inches and 90 feet in height. These latter stands are now being considered for utilization and probable export to the Pacific Coast markets.

In Alaska, residents may legally cut from the public domain up to 100,000 board feet of forest products each year for their own personal use in developing their land claims. The widely scattered population of Alaska, coupled with the small number of personnel in the Division of Forestry, make it impossible to know just how much free-use wood is actually cut each year. The reported annual cut has averaged about 11,000,000 board feet of all forest products—including lumber, houselogs, posts, poles, and cordwood. The 1947 reported cut by commercial operators was 28.9 million board feet of sawtimber and cordwood and 6,990,125 linear feet of houselogs and poles. Here, too, it is known that all of the commercially cut wood has not been covered under formal sale permit.

Until forest surveys of at least reconnaissance accuracy have been obtained, and other basic forest management data compiled, it cannot be argued that the interior forest have any greater potential types and degrees of utilization than those now enjoyed. It is believed that the white birch can be successfully entered upon the export market. This will require the establishment of sawmills, dry kilns, and remanufacturing plants. Woodworking plants and possibly a small veneer plant will undoubtedly follow. It is believed that Anchorage and vicinity will become the hardwood center of Alaska. Local observation indicates that the interior forests are capable of rather large annual increment, as a result of the long summer daylight period. It may therefore be shown that certain areas could well be used in perpetuity by small chemical plants and possibly pulp plants.

The greatest destructive force suffered by the interior forests is that of uncontrolled forest fires. The long daylight hours, the semi-arid climate (typified by low precipitation and low relative humidity), and the shallow-rooted trees cause a long fire season of medium to high fire danger and extraordinarily heavy losses to trees within burned areas. Although lightning is a considerable causative agency in certain areas of Alaska, most fires are man-caused. Since most of Alaska's residents and travelers are found along the river valleys and lower benchlands, it is obvious that most fires occur within the rather restricted zone of tree occurrence previously mentioned.

Forest fires have been a major destructive factor since the days of the early gold rushes. Subsequent stampedes to other portions of the Territory are clearly marked by the more recent burns. It is not known what annual losses may have been suffered, but it is estimated at 3 to 8 million acres. In 1940, when the Alaskan Fire Control Service (now the Division of Forestry of the Bureau of Land Management) was organized, the fire loss was 4,500,000 acres. Active fire suppression, public education, and the war-year restrictions brought a marked decrease within the next few years—losses of 110,000 to 117,000 acres per year. The 1946 and 1947 fire seasons reflected the lapse of military restrictions on travel and civilian activities in Alaska, as well as the postwar interest in Alaska's development potentialities, by increasing the annual losses to about 1,500,000 acres.

Such vast and repeated burns over the estimated 125,000,000 acres of vegetated public domain, have in many areas completely destroyed all vegetation; in others, have changed cover composition; and in all, have caused vast losses of public resources which are now so urgently needed in developing this last frontier and northern outpost of the United States.

BUREAU OF MINES

That the mineral resources of Alaska have added considerably to the national wealth, being exceeded only by the value of fishing products, is demonstrated by the following table:

TABLE 62.—*Alaska's mineral production for years 1880–1947*

Gold	$636, 516, 000
Copper	226, 569, 000
Coal	25, 252, 000
Silver	14, 144, 000
Other	36, 892, 000
Total	939, 373, 000

Alaska with a land area roughly one-fifth that of continental United States is as yet largely unexplored. The Geological Survey has been engaged for nearly half a century on studies in Alaska, but most of these studies were of a general nature and only an exceedingly small proportion of the total land area has been geologically mapped. At the present rate of progress it will be scores of years before even preliminary work will be accomplished.

Due to a lack of transportation, labor, power and other factors entering into a remote mining operation, special emphasis was placed in the past on gold production. The facts in hand are still too meager to justify even wild guesses as to the value of other mineral resources. However, it has been amply demonstrated that many of these other mineral products have already been found in commercial quantities at widely separated points and have contributed notable amounts to Alaska's output of minerals.

During the recent World War, the United States was hard pressed to obtain minerals to meet the high demands of military and civilian requirements. The post-war period has not lessened these demands. Recent appraisals by the Bureau of Mines and the Geological Survey have indicated the deficiency of a number of important industrial minerals essential to our national security and economy.

Space does not permit discussion in detail of each of the various minerals of which the distribution of some of the better known deposits are indicated.

Among the critical and strategic minerals found in Alaska are:

1. *Chromite.* The United States is almost wholly dependent on imports for its supply of chromite. Among known domestic deposits some of the best quality, though not the largest, are those of the Kenai Peninsula, Alaska. Chromite likewise is known on Knik River, Baranof Island and Cleveland Peninsula.

2. *Tin.* Tin occurs in the York district on the Seward Peninsula and in the central Yukon Valley. Some

the Territory, making a total to June 30, 1948, of $13,602,259.20.

Funds expendable on forest highways in Alaska are secured under the authority of the Federal Highway Act and amendments thereto. The following tabulation shows the amount expended for the fiscal years 1928 to 1948, inclusive, regular and emergency funds:

TABLE 64.—*Funds expendable on forest highways in Alaska*

Fiscal year	Regular funds	Emergency funds	Other funds	Total
1928	$510,248.43		$40,832.64	$551,081.07
1929	542,191.99		39,764.27	581,956.26
1930	434,000.54		3,388.70	437,389.24
1931	672,407.25		[1] 32,311.41	704,718.66
1932	789,701.71		25,000.00	814,701.71
1933	304,014.00			304,014.00
1934	267,829.56	238,447.05		506,276.61
1935	315,015.83	210,552.29		525,568.12
1936	327,565.38	364,360.72		691,926.10
1937	430,870.40	168,612.25		599,482.65
1938	597,932.06	39,094.69		637,026.75
1939	782,779.04			782,779.04
1940	401,477.08		6,555.60	408,032.68
1941	355,402.62		43,444.40	398,847.02
1942	222,108.45		19,658.98	241,767.43
1943	158,101.71		377,582.38	535,684.09
1944	211,575.17		[2] 131,286.17	342,861.34
1945	261,349.69		167.89	261,517.58
1946	303,552.82		30.90	303,583.72
1947	437,797.26		36,551.00	474,348.26
1948	510,701.23		42,568.34	553,269.57
Total	8,836,622.22	1,021,067.00	799,142.68	10,656,831.90

[1] Includes $4,670.00 refund to cooperator.
[2] Includes $1,500.00 refund to cooperator.

During World War II funds were made available from defense access funds for the improvement of some sections of the forest highways upon certification from the Army or Navy as to their importance in the war effort. A total amount of $585,160.51 of access funds were expended on forest highways in Alaska.

Forest highway funds are expended exclusively on the forest highway system which was selected in the early 1920's and originally consisted of 21 routes and a total mileage of approximately 384 miles. Subsequent revisions approved by the Secretary of Agriculture, on the joint recommendation of the Territorial Road Commission, Forest Service, and Public Roads Administration, have from time to time changed the system as originally selected and the Alaskan forest highway system now consists of 18 routes, with a total mileage of 356.3, of which 274.3 have been improved to date. Forest highway construction projects are programmed annually by the Secretary of Agriculture after joint recommendation of the Territorial Road Commission, Forest Service, and Public Roads Administration. The following tabulation shows mileage ap-

proved, improved and remaining to be improved, by routes, as of June 30, 1948:

TABLE 65.—*Mileage approved and improved by routes*

Route number	Route name	Approved (miles)	Improved (miles)	To be improved (miles)
1	Tongass Highway	49.8	22.1	27.7
2	Glacier Highway	57.9	43.3	14.6
3	Seward Highway	33.5	33.5	
4	Cordova Highway	20	10.4	9.6
5	Kenai River Highway	19.7	19.7	
7	Mitkof Highway	17	10.5	6.5
9	Salmon River Highway	12.1	12.1	
11	Sitka Highway	12.9	8.7	4.2
12	Crow Creek Highway	7.8	7.8	
13	Palmer Creek Highway	11.9	11.9	
14	Moose Pass Highway	45.5	45.5	
16	Wrangell Highway	13.6	9.6	4
17	Skagway Highway	7	2.3	4.7
18	Texas Creek Highway	11.7	11.7	
26	Point Agassiz Highway	8	4.6	3.4
30	Afognak Lake Highway	4.5	4.5	
31	Douglas Highway	11.6	4.3	7.3
32	Copper River Highway	11.8	11.8	
	Total	356.3	274.3	82

The principal value of the forest highway up to the present day has been in the opportunities they have afforded the public to settle and make use of the adjacent land. The rough terrain and dense forest cover, particularly in Southeast Alaska, preclude any settlement without roads. Before the forest highways were constructed there were no settlements outside of the incorporated towns and villages. As roads were constructed, the settlers followed and in the 10-year period immediately before the war a considerable settlement was in progress, particularly adjacent to the larger towns. The settlement came to a standstill during the war because of restrictions on materials and manpower. After the war the construction of permanent homes, summer homes, small businesses, etc., is again progressing at a rapid rate.

In addition to the resumption of the normal development, interrupted by the war, a wood pulp production development program is beginning in Southeastern Alaska which will materially affect road construction within Tongass National Forest. This forest covers practically the entire Southeastern Alaska which consists of the islands and a comparatively narrow strip of mainland adjacent to the sea coast. Most of the timber is therefore accessible by water and the transportation of the timber to the mills will therefore probably always be done by the comparatively cheap water route and forest highways will not be required for timber haul, but rather for access to mill sites, shipping routes, power sites, and sites for new communities that will be created.

The forest highways within the Chugach National Forest are located on the Kenai Peninsula; where there is a connected road system of approximately 110.6 miles. This system has heretofore been isolated and has served local traffic only. The Alaska Road Commission is at the present time constructing a road connecting the forest highway system with the Kenai Village-Homer Area. This project, together with the Turnagain Arm project which also is under construction at the present time, will give the forest highway system on Kenai Peninsula added importance, particularly if the Alaska Railroad abandons the section between Portage and Seward. The Turnagain Arm project when completed will connect the road system on Kenai Peninsula with the road system in interior Alaska and through the Alaska Highway with the road systems in Canada and the United States.

The Turnagain Arm project mentioned above is being constructed from funds made available through the Department of the Interior through an interdepartment cooperative agreement. Public Roads is responsible for the location, design, type and supervision of construction of the portion of the project extending between the southern terminus to Indian on the north side of Turnagain Arm. Construction of the section between Indian and Potter, the northern terminus of the project, has been assigned to the Alaska Railroad, subject to review by the Public Roads Administration. The Alaska Road Commission of the Department of the Interior has the over-all control of funds.

The Public Roads Administration became active in the interior of Alaska for the first time during the war when the Alaska Highway was constructed jointly by the United States Army and Public Roads. After the completion of this project, in 1943, the Public Roads was not active in interior Alaska until this year. Through a cooperative agreement with the Department of the Interior, the Public Roads Administration is responsible for the preliminary engineering, preparation of plans and specifications, bids and contracts, and the supervision of construction of a large improvement program involving the hard surfacing of portions of the major interior routes; namely, Glenn Highway, Richardson Highway and the Alaska portion of the Alaska Highway. Funds for this program have been made available to the Alaska Road Commission of the Department of the Interior which under the agreement exercises general supervision of programing, design and construction.

It appears that the road construction program in Alaska which heretofore has lagged because of insufficient funds, will proceed at an accelerated pace in the next few years.

ALASKA COMMUNICATION SYSTEM

1. Mission

The Alaska Communication System, operated by the Signal Corps, United States Army, provides the long lines telephone and telegraph service from Alaska to the States and between key towns in Alaska. It serves (a) the military, (b) all Federal agencies, (c) all Territorial and other Government agencies, and (d) the general public. This latter includes coastal service to and from ships at sea, press service to newspapers and radio broadcast stations. ACS has provided the arterial communication services for Alaska since 1901.

2. Organization and Operation

(a) The headquarters of the Alaska Communication System is in the Federal Office Building, Seattle, Wash. The majority of communication to and from the States and Canada is routed through ACS Seattle Communications Center. Operating directly under the Commanding Officer are 32 different ACS stations and eight branch offices in Alaska to serve the military and civil customers. ACS offices are located at the following points: Adak, Anchorage, Barrow, Bethel, Big Delta, Cathedral Bluffs, Cold Bay, Cordova, Craig, Curry, Fairbanks, Flat, Unalaska, Haines, Healy, Juneau, Ketchikan, Kodiak, Kotzebue, Naknek Airbase, Nome, Northway, Petersburg, Seward, Shemya, Sitka, Skagway, Umnak, Valdez, Whittier, Wrangell, and Yakutat. Branch offices are located at Fort Richardson, Ladd Field, Eielson Field, Annette Island, Naval Base Kodiak, Naknek Village, Nome Airbase and Yakutat Village.

(b) Col. Fred P. Andrews, Signal Corps, USA., is the Commanding Officer of ACS. The Deputy Commander for ACS, with headquarters in the Anchorage area, is Lt. Col. M. R. Kunitz, Signal Corps, USA. The Sector Commanders in charge of various operational areas in Alaska are Maj. Robert R. Wingfield, Anchorage; Maj. Robert D. Terry, Fairbanks; Capt. Charles M. Macali, Adak; and Capt. Svend C. Hansen, Juneau.

3. Facilities of ACS

(a) Alaska Communication System provides arterial communications over long lines telephone, overseas radiotelephone, radioteletype, and submarine cable telegraph. It interconnects at Seattle with the facilities of the American Telephone and Telegraph Co. and the Western Union for communication to all points in the United States, and at Edmonton, Canada, with the Canadian telephone and telegraph companies for communications throughout Canada.

(*b*) Services include long distance telephone, telegraph, telegraph money orders, press service, and radio broadcasts.

(*c*) Means available include radio, landline, submarine cable, VHF—these over a gradually expanding network offering several routings.

(*d*) ACS collects and distributes government and commercial traffic to and from approximately 150 small outlying connecting stations in various parts of the territory.

4. Improvement to ACS Services During the Period July 1947 to July 1948 by New Installations

(*a*) Installation of a new broadcast transmitter in Seattle for the relay of live broadcast programs from the States to key towns in Alaska.

(*b*) Initial establishment of limited intra-Alaska broadcast service.

(*c*) Established rates for broadcast program service from United States and intra-Alaska broadcast service.

(*d*) Reduced rates on money transfer service by making provision whereby supplementary messages may be filed with transfer messages and including provision whereby money transfers may be forwarded beyond original station of destination where necessary.

(*e*) Radiotelephone facilities were established between Sitka and Seattle on September 2, 1947.

(*f*) Rural landline telephone service for subscribers along ACS circuits on the Alcan Highway between Fairbanks and the Canadian Border (opened September 1, 1947).

(*g*) Additional carrier equipment was installed on the lines between Anchorage and Fairbanks, providing additional voice channels for use of the military and civilian populace stationed at Fort Richardson and Ladd Field.

(*h*) Provided positive telephone service between Petersburg and Wrangell by installing voice carrier equipment on the cable.

(*i*) At the request of the Weather Bureau, a telephone circuit through ACS and the Ketchikan Public Utilities switchboards connecting the Weather Bureau on Annette Island, was completed February 10, 1948. This circuit is used on a call basis and provides a ready means of communications for the public in Ketchikan to receive the latest weather reports upon request.

(*j*) On June 3 the ACS completed installation and final tests of an 11-pair submarine cable between Ketch-ikan and Pennock Island. This cable connects with the single channel submarine cable extending to Gravina Island, thus providing telephone service for the Forest Service between Gravina Island and Ketchikan. The laying of the multichannel cable between Ketchikan and Pennock Island makes available circuits for use by the Ketchikan Public Utilities in providing telephone service to the residents of Pennock Island.

5. Improvement of Existing Services

(*a*) Obsolete and nonstandard transmitting equipment was replaced at Ketchikan, Anchorage, Nome, Kodiak, Sitka, Wrangell, Kotzebue, and Flat.

(*b*) New radiotelephone transmitter was installed at Adak, improving Adak-Seattle telephone service.

(*c*) Installed remote receiving facilities at Wrangell and Petersburg to improve radiophone between these points and Juneau and Ketchikan.

(*d*) Installed a new transmitter at Juneau to improve the Seattle-Juneau radiophone circuit.

(*e*) Improved Juneau and Ketchikan ship-shore radiophone facilities by installation of new transmitters and terminal equipment.

(*f*) On the current trip of the cable barge *Lenoir*, which started on May 28, work is being performed by the barge crew and other specialized technicians to generally improve and extend cable, telephone and radio facilities in Southeastern Alaska. This will result in generally improved communications in the area. One of the primary accomplishments will be the extension of telephone facilities via cable and radio, permitting increased intra-Alaskan and Alaska-to-the-States service.

The Alaska Communication System is capable of handling a considerable increase in traffic with its present equipment. Any sudden increase in communications, such as expected from the pulp mills or new developments, can easily be absorbed.

The system is continually being face lifted. Obsolete equipment is replaced with new as fast as it becomes available, thus providing the best service possible.

ALASKA RAILROAD

During the summer of 1948, the Alaska Railroad explored the possibilities of creating additional rail traffic near or within its operating area. The study was directed toward establishment of new ventures or an expansion of those already in existence, but of such modest scope that their rail tonnage was insignificant.

From over 100 suggested enterprises 38 were selected

for investigation. A few of these, such as coal and cement are primary sources possessing characteristics which commit them economically to rail traffic. Of course, all possibilities enumerated, plus many other types of activities must be present to ultimately attain a balanced economy. Still it is not beyond the realm of possibility to create and develop all these various types of establishments simultaneously. It is equally difficult to select those which should be given precedence over the balance. For instance, if reasonably priced cement were available it would make possible lower-cost housing. This in turn would produce a tendency to stabilize employment, attracting a more permanent class of labor. Thus the chain continues, each link enhancing the value of the other types as they themselves become realities.

To most observers, the futility of effectuating a program establishing commercial services, industrial fabrication, or extractive production is obvious since communication, transportation, and power are either missing or inadequate even in the most advanced portions of the Territory.

Therefore, it is necessary to begin with these fundamentals and only when they are assured can it be said that the first step toward a stabilized economy has been taken. As such evidences of permanence appear, venture capital will lose its reluctance to enter Alaska in direct ratio. However, these basic elements are more or less predicated upon the availability of another essential—low-cost power. Power is a vital characteristic of all progressive economic systems throughout the world. It is particularly critical in the Alaskan economy as labor and skilled craftsmen are at a premium and the distances to markets are vast. The woefully inadequate makeshift attempts to overcome this lack of power is one unavoidable observation to be made throughout Alaska. It is the outstanding deterrent blocking reasonable exploitation of Alaska's resources from Seward to Fairbanks. For example, the proposed cement plant at Windy must, before it can get into operation, create a 2,500-kilowatt power plant for its own use in manufacturing processes and the townsite for its employees. This represents a capital investment (if written off at the same rate of amortization as the balance of the plant) of approximately 20 cents per barrel over power charges which accrue to the same product in the continental United States. Moreover, this power capacity would have to be geared to the maximum peak load of this industrial installation and must, therefore, represent considerable over-capacity during slack periods. Multiplying this situation by all enterprises—mines, manufacturing plants, and commercial institutions—which are or should be part of this economy would, at even a conservative estimate, require twice the capital investment and operating expenses a single integrated system would have to assume.

Of course, the enormous spread between the local cost of manufacturing cement and its Alaskan sales price is largely accounted for by costs which accrued through handling, water and land-borne freight, et cetera. A differential which will enable this industry to privately generate such power as necessary and still show a distinct price advantage is necessary to accelerate the building of Alaska. However, much of the benefit of this production will be lost as the products fan out into the present and new areas for an uneconomic application will be inherent due to lack of power and power equipment at the point of use.

Another great resource which is retarded in reaching its proper stature is Alaska's coal industry. Beginning with excavation of coal at the mine, the absence of low-cost power has permitted certain inefficiencies to become a part of the system—all the way from digging to washing, grading, and loading. Moreover, absence of low-cost electricity has precluded the next logical step in utilization of Alaska coal; namely, that of processing coal to extract and refine its volatile oils. This process would presumably offset, in part, transportation costs on various petroleum products—from asphalts to aviation fuels—now imported.

Digressing from the strict realm of commerce and industry, attention should be called to the major problem of the Alaska Railroad. This is the difficulty in obtaining (and retaining) suitable personnel, owing mainly to inadequate housing, previously mentioned and related again to the matter of high building cost particularly of cement. If building costs were revised downward and adequate housing provided, it would solve one problem, but create another. More dwellings would impose an impossible burden upon municipal functions in all towns along the railroad, particularly Anchorage and Fairbanks. In these latter cities a well-known overload now strains electrical generators, the school system, the water supply, et cetera.

Another digression having an important bearing on commerce and industry is the matter of agricultural produce. This vital need necessitates imports which in many instances are too expensive, long delayed, and lacking in freshness. However, local supply is accorded little favor because of the high moisture content, particularly in root and tuber crops. Both quantity and quality could be increased and the shortage of locally produced beef, lamb, and pork nullified if these products were processed and the poor storage qualities for winter forage was banished through artificial curing. Standby electrical produce driers would rectify many of the troubles inherent in the present agricultural development program. Hence, low-cost power would mean greenhouses, curing establishments;

the result being an over-all reduction in costs of food-stuffs.

In this category there are three additional types of activities capable of exerting a beneficial influence on the distribution system. These are "feeder-transportation" lines to facilitate movements of people and goods to and from certain areas such as the Southwest Kenai area. This would encourage development of that area as well as create a source of rail revenue, not now existent. Such a feeder-transportation system would embrace trucks and buses designed to transport people, freight, cargo, express, mail, et cetera, on a regular schedule geared to anticipated growth rather than the existing need. Such a function would permit operation of both mines and farms in areas now lying idle. Presumably this would result in increased payrolls as well as produce a supply of certain vegetables more nearly in line with local demand.

Warehousing is another needed facility. Creation of suitable merchandise warehousing where trade goods and other expendable items could be imported under the more favorable rate structures would, to a large extent, remove the plague of maritime strikes, or at least their disastrous consequences.

The third element regarding a portion of the general subject "community planning" is shopping centers. Here again, planned facilities offering a well-rounded variety of supplies and services in new areas would encourage more logical development of residential sites and would, in a measure, assist in establishing the residential character of a community as well as maintaining it. These activities exhibit a sufficiently attractive financial return to justify private capitalization. Benefits of these activities would permeate into virtually every phase of social and economic life. The latter projects are only indirectly dependent upon the thread of low-cost power, which is both the foundation and keystone of this entire program, yet their value pales into insignificance without it.

The third set of enterprises which must enter the Alaskan picture eventually are of necessity all small, at least at their inception. All are predicated upon the majority of the forementioned factors and facilities being present in a substantial degree. Of course, the desiny of such establishment, besides dependence upon proper capitalization, management, et cetera, must rest with conditions and circumstances beyond the control of the individual enterprises. These minor industries, like the more important ones previously mentioned, have been covered in greater detail by individual reports available through the general manager's office (A. R. R.) in Alaska. However, the following summaries will suggest the complete dependence all such establishments must have upon the fundamental facilities enumerated, particularly power.

Acetylene

Because of operating conditions, the vast quantity of heavy-duty machinery and equipment in Alaska are subjected to an extremely high incident of breakage. This and the remoteness of most scenes of operation suggest a high ratio of welding equipment with acetylene and oxygen and it is necessary that the cylinders be imported from the States and the empties returned—both operations being conducted at considerable expense and loss of time.

The Alaska Railroad has an acetylene generating plant, but the exclusive requirements of the railroad have never quite justified operating this unit. However, other demands for acetylene (plus that of the railroad) would make this a profitable enterprise when combined with certain other related types of activity.

In subsequent chapters of this report other activities may occur to the reader which might be combined with this, for instance, oxygen, ice-making, welding, et cetera. Such a consolidated headquarters for these "service industries" should be located on the railroad just north or south of Anchorage, as this is the center of the market as well as the most likely source of steady labor.

Alabaster

In the search for low-cost building material, alabaster should not be overlooked since gypsum is available in several localities and the process necessary to achieve a building material of many favorable characteristics is relatively simple. Alabaster provides a strong, light, self-insulating structural surface capable of supporting tremendous weights and impervious to chemical reaction and moisture.

Antimony

Antimony has been prospected in numerous areas, particularly in central Alaska where a large deposit was located just north of McKinley Park at Stampede.

Lesser quantities have been found just eastward of the Big Delta area. Antimony's broadening application to the munitions field, matches, linotype metal, bearings, battery plates, et cetera, calls attention to the desirability of developing these deposits further, (1) by increasing their accessibility through passable roads (concentrates are now being brought out by air); (2) that a sample custom mill be established for further refining of this concentrate, thus avoiding the tremendous expense of transmitting so much bulk ore to refineries in the States.

Beidellite

This particular clay is found in enormous quantities on the north side of Richardson Highway, south and east of Fairbanks. The quantity in the almost pure state may be of commercial significance since the two principal deposits in the United States—one at Beidell, Colo., and the other in Central Louisiana—both require some refinement and both are limited in quantity. Samples of this material should be submitted to oil companies, the largest potential users. Exploration of the cosmetic field would also be in order as beidellite makes an excellent "mud pack." It also makes an exceptionally fine soap for mechanics and others whose vocations bring their hands in contact with oils and greases as it is a most effective solvent for petroleum and petroleum products.

Beef

The lower southwest portion of the Kenai Peninsula is literally covered with a natural forage—"redtop" and clover. This luxuriant growth is—according to the Department of Agriculture and the natives of this area—an excellent fattening food for cattle. Its principal drawback is that it does not store well and cannot be cured, largely due to the excessive rainfall in the area during the ripening period.

To some extent, "redtop" is stored in underground silos for a wet winter silage. Heat generated by the moisture, prevents it from freezing except in the area which is exposed directly to the weather. Production of beef, however, is not wholly contingent upon this storage. In addition to Peninsula-bred cattle, young animals might be shipped into the region early in the spring for summer feeding and would, in all probability, be ready for market before the winter freeze-up. The present Alaska market, for this beef will be inaccessible to the area until the Kenai road, now under construction, is completed into Anchorage. Predatory animals—now common in the vicinity—might make some inroads on this type of livestock if permitted to graze without protection.

Berries

The unusual quality and profusion of various berries in the Tanana, Dunbar, Kanai, Matanuska, and other areas, suggests that a de-luxe market for these unique products could be developed through clubs, hotels and delicatessen stores in the United States.

The types of berries which would be particularly adaptable for this market are blueberries, strawberries, cranberries—both high and low bush—and to some extent the sauces made from rose hips and other variations peculiar to Alaskan agriculture and culinary arts.

Blocks

Both cement and pumice blocks are now manufactured in Alaska but in almost every instance production methods are antiquated, hence expensive. These organizations should be financed on a more adequate basis, since pumice, sand and gravel exist in vast quantities throughout Alaska. Components to make an excellent cement are also present. Manufacture of cement in Alaska would provide impetus for block manufacture, as the cost of imported cement runs between $50 and $60 per ton, which is high enough to dampen the ardor of almost anyone for block construction. Moreover, present facilities of the block manufacturers is so limited that sills, lintels, chimney squares, and other supplement cement, pumice, and other preformed structural shapes are not available in any quantity or at any price.

Bricks

This building material is probably the least used of any in Alaska construction. Bricks were once made in a small hand plant south of Anchorage, and an old wall constructed some 40 years ago stands on the north side of Fourth Avenue near the city hall, enduring proof that frequent earth tremors do not impair its structural desirability. However, not a vestige of the brick plant or kiln survives. Presumably the small demand and the wealth of other materials for building houses and cabins terminated this venture before it was fairly started. Presumably even today the manufacturer of bricks for fireplaces, fire-brick and a few other uses could not be made into a profitable venture if required to stand or fall on these items alone. However, a modest establishment equipped to make and kiln numerous types of ceramic products such as the above plus tile—glazed and field—could undoubtedly find a place for itself in the present building-supply business. This is particularly true if this venture were supplemented by and combined with wallboard, insulating, and perhaps roofing materials.

Canneries

Many types of marine life have not been commercially developed and because of their relatively small potential are not of interest to the large packing organizations. These specialties, such as clams and crabs, could be developed by private individuals along Cook Inlet and perhaps Prince William Sound, thereby providing a substantial livelihood for a considerable number of workers.

The chief weakness of those now spasmodically engaged in this type of activity lies in the fact they do not have a sufficient consumer demand for goods packed under their labels or trade names. The superior quality and other unique characteristics of certain clams and crabs would appeal to the point of demanding a premium if these products were properly packaged, labeled, and presented to the small exclusive market represented by leading hotels, exclusive clubs and delicatessen stores in the States.

What has been said of crabs and clams could also apply to halibut cheeks, kelp and perhaps a wide variety of seafoods.

Produce Drier

If an agricultural community is to be established, particularly in the lower Kenai Peninsula, it is essential that growers of farm produce be insured against a certain but unpredictable loss which occurs owing to difficulty of drying certain produce during harvest seasons.

For instance, the lavish yield of potatoes possible in this area could be dried by spreading them out on the floor of farm buildings. Enough of the surplus water—inherent in the Alaskan potato—can be removed and a potato with storing qualities realized. However, large scale drying of potatoes is impossible without facilities especially designed for this purpose. Moreover, these facilities would not be continually necessary for the vagaries of climatic conditions are such that frequently vegetables can be air-dried without artificial heat being applied. But, the threat of a prolonged rainy period will preclude any conservative agriculturist from developing his lands along the line of commercial crops until standby equipment is available in the event of adverse weather.

The foregoing also applies to the curing of winter forage, necessary for the dairy industry to flourish. Importation of baled hay is prohibitive in cost and storage space for such forage limited.

Therefore it is recommended that the Department of Agriculture, having already made tremendous contributions toward the advance of Alaskan agriculture, be encouraged to study the matter of a subsidized produce drying establishment in the vincinity of Homer where it would be possible to use the readily available coal as a cheap and adequate supply of fuel. In addition, the growing season could be extended by starting various plants and vegetables in greenhouses, cold frames, et cetera.

This institution would of necessity require a large capital investment and could scarcely be looked upon as a self-sustaining project since its facilities could not reasonably be expected to yield a revenue in those years in which it was not used. Likewise the agricultural interests in the community could hardly be expected to pay on a scale that would support the facilities during inactive years in order to have them available during the emergency periods. However, to make Alaska self-sustaining from an agricultural and dairy products point of view would undoubtedly more than justify this form of subsidy.

Financial Institutions

Alaskan economy is plagued by under capitalization. Never in its history has there been the proper ratio between the volume of business and the amount of capital involved. Absentee ownership, the under-estimated capital investment costs, and a number of other factors have undoubtedly contributed to this, but the underlying ailment has always been greater than the speed with which capital surplus could be accumulated. To remedy this situation in part, it is suggested that at least one building and loan association be started in Anchorage and another in Fairbanks. The nature of this organization should be such that it can hypothecate its capital through the "Fannie May" operations of RFC. Thus such organizations could, with a modest capital investment, provide a favorable return to the investors and long term mortgage money for residential construction.

However, these building and loan associations would have to operate in conjunction with another very vital but missing factor in the financial structure of Alaska, namely, a title insurance company. The present method of bonded abstracts is not adequate for the purpose it attempts to serve. Instead, a regular title and guarantee company should be subsistuted. In view of the relatively short history of real estate transactions in Alaska, the problem of tracing titles and identifying property should be comparatively simple. Moreover, by bringing to light those parcels of land, the titles of which are clouded, would make possible the clarification of such titles at this time while most of the involved parties are alive, rather than wait until some future date and have each problem unnecessarily complicated by the death of or the inability to locate the key principals. Such a title company operating on a conservative basis would make possible the additional vital factor of remote secondary markets for mortgage paper.

Two additional types of financial institutions urgently needed in the Territory, but not necessarily related in any manner to those just mentioned, are savings banks and personal loan companies—the latter, of course, to include financing of personal property plus signature loans, which are beyond the realm of straight commercial banking functions. Either or both of these types of activity could well be included within the framework of the existing financial institutions but it is not necessary that this be done if the type of business contemplated is not within the reasonable scope or philosophy of the extant banks.

Fish Waste

The necessity for utilizing all available labor during the short salmon season has caused the cannery operators to overlook or ignore one of the principal byproducts of their business, principally waste.

Narrowing margins of profit owing to declining salmon runs will eventually call more widespread attention to the desirability of utilizing this byproduct for manufacture of fertilizer, meal, and fish oils.

Foundry

At various times small foundries have been established in Alaska. One operated for a period of years as a part of the Alaska Railroad. It is not clear why these infant units did not survive but presumably it was lack of volume demand. Today, however, Alaska has expanded to the point where a small foundry, properly operated, should be a successful venture owing to the quantities of heavy construction and mining machinery imported into the area as well as the extension of municipal facilities which require manhole covers, frames, gates, et cetera. In addition, rehabilitation of the railroad will permit greater speeds, thus requiring increased tonnage of brake shoes and other expendable castings. Moreover, the residential construction industry has a tremendous potential so an expanding market exists for soil pipe, grates, and miscellaneous other cast products. Raw materials such as scrap iron are generated by the railroad and other commercial enterprises in excess of such a foundry's needs. There is also a definite possibility that pig iron may be produced in the future. No satisfactory fuller's earth is available at this time but nominal quantities might be imported without excessive cost being added to the foundry operation.

Graphite

Graphite—imported into the United States because of the domestic shortage—is to be found in Alaska in enormous quantities. Presumably, if demand for graphite remains at its present level the small domestic supply and the foreign sources would be satisfactory. However, since it has taken on new significance in connection with atomic energy and its generation, the necessity of exploring the possibilities of a further supply within the jurisdiction of the United States Government is evident. One or more of the several deposits should possibly be examined with a view to supplementing commercial demand, plus underwriting any emergency demand in the event of military requirements which is certain to develop with another world catastrophe.

Hotels

Development of tourist trade in Alaska depends not so much on the magnificent attractions in scenery and wild life as on the provision for accommodating the tourist with the reasonable necessities: transportation, communication, quarters, and food. Likewise these facilities must be so coordinated that no blind spots will exist in the system. The best method of regulating this business would consist of licensing each participant and inspecting the services rendered so that uncontrolled individual operators might not nullify all that is done to promote this industry. A single instance of "bad will" can offset a shipload of "good will" in the tourist trade.

The principal contribution is good hotel accommodation. Several excellent hotels exist now but they are independent of one another and not adequately connected by transportation to form any semblance of a tourist route. Furthermore, these establishments do not at present have the capacity to care for the present volume of guests. Ultimately these hotels will form a loop, one part of which will pass through northwest Canada and the balance swing southward from Fairbanks.

Ice Plant

Ice-making machinery, installed in conjunction with other types of service equipment heretofore mentioned, would undoubtedly find a ready market for its production during summer months. This market would come principally from the icing of refrigerator cars, and demands of local hotels, restaurants, and clubs. At this time such a function would not—if operated on an exclusive basis—be a profitable enterprise, for the total local market for ice is not sufficient to keep equipment operating on a full-time basis.

Insulation

The need for insulating practically all types of structures is so apparent that the principle is accepted without question by most of the local residents. Bulk or cubic requirements of most insulation materials has precluded its importation to some extent—an importation largely unnecessary due to the volume of local products which could be converted into suitable insulating materials.

Mineral-wool and asbestos or materials from which they could be made are found in many readily accessible areas. It is desirable, then, to examine the possibilities of combining this activity with other enterprises wherein the creation of building materials is contemplated. Perhaps the most likely establishments would be those engaged in making gypsum board, pumice blocks, or ceramic products. Such consolidations are recommended because some of the equipment used in these processes could be adapted to the manufacture of insulating boards, sheets, and pads; also the identical market absorbing the products would utilize delivery equipment and thus minimize the distribution expenses and the sales effort.

Lead

The diminishing world supply of lead and the increased demand for this commodity suggest development of new sources for both commercial and strategic use. Some lead deposits are known in Alaska, but their potentialities have not been determined. Known lead deposits, particularly at Galena and Groundhog Basin, become of ever increasing importance. The United States Geological Survey has compiled some data on these and other deposits and improved techniques in refining lead-bearing ores may increase the possibility of development.

Leather

Another byproduct of the fishing industry which has received too little consideration is the possibility of converting fishskin into commercial leather. Preliminary tests on tanned salmon skins have proved they may be of considerable value to the American leather trade, particularly the novelty phases of this business. In addition, hair seal, both with and without the hair

in place, has established a certain limited demand as upholstering material and a material for ladies' coats. It would seem that either or both of these sources of leather should be further explored to determine whether or not the characteristics of each are of sufficient value to establish a profitable industry. Present indications are that this is well within the limits of possibility.

Machine Shop

The necessity for a privately-owned machine shop is demonstrated by the increasingly large volume of requests to the railroad to machine a wide assortment of metal shapes. Obviously this imposition on the railroad's facilities only reflects a small percentage of the total demand, the balance being satisfied either by replacing equipment in its entirety or obtaining parts from the original manufacturers. Obviously, if a small foundry and welding shop is created the necessity for a flexible and universal machine shop becomes automatic.

Oil Reclaiming

The premium paid for new petroleum products in Alaska suggests that oil reclaiming could flourish providing the founding and the reprocessing expense is not such that the advantage in the price differential is absorbed. Presumably the large amounts of oil used or which will be used in the Diesel engines of the railroad and the certain percentage of automotive lubricants now in use would justify the millwrighting of a small reclaiming plant. It is not recommended that any further capital investment be made in this type of equipment but rather that an inquiry be directed as to the cost of operating the equipment which is now lying fallow in Anchorage. Presumably if this can be accomplished without inordinate expense it could be a source of substantial revenue, at least until such time when it might be supplanted by cheaper petroleum products extracted from oil and shale. This process might also develop a byproduct which, mixed with beidellite, could be used as a means of controlling dust on the many streets and highways, which is so objectionable and likely to continue offending for many years before the streets and roads are included in a hard-surfacing program.

Roadhouses

The Alaskan roadhouse is a vital link in the day-to-day commercial life of Alaska as well as in the development of the tourist, hunting and fishing businesses.

The ever-expanding highway system will, to a large measure, rely upon such establishments to supply motorists with all manner of traveling services and accommodations. It is therefore desirable that the proper distribution of these services is observed and some control over their operation be exercised by a Territorial licensing board, as previously mentioned.

It may be essential to subsidize roadhouses in certain areas by assisting them to procure supplemental revenue like postmasterships, weather reporting stations, et cetera. For it is clear the new highways must come before the users and when the highways are used there must be facilities along them to provide the needs of the initial travelers—these facilities must of necessity have a capacity in excess (at least at first) of the demands that are made upon them.

Smoked Salmon

Improvements or changes in the regular commercial salmon industry are far beyond the scope of any superficial survey. However, there is a place for salmon specialties—smoked salmon, squaw candy, salmon sticks—and even regular salmon if carefully selected for high quality, and then fastidiously hand-packed. This de luxe merchandise has been sampled by experts in the specialty food lines, particularly those serving the high grade delicatessens, clubs, and the exclusive hotel trade. In every instance these experts have agreed that the quality is such that over-market prices could be demanded and obtained, but they point out that in order to appeal and to cultivate this market, de luxe packaging and a recognized brand must be the basis of any successful exploitation.

Smelter

The need for a custom smelter or sample mill has often been stressed by the operators of small mining claims, but Geological Survey and Bureau of Mines experts have always contended there is not enough volume of business to justify such an institution. While this is true as of today, there is a real possibility that there would be enough business if such a service were available to the small operators. It is the contention of these operators that they cannot develop their properties because of the high cost of transmitting ores to United States refineries, and that if such a service were provided at central points—central eastern Kenai Peninsula and in the Curry-Healy areas—that both would have a sufficient volume of business to make the venture entirely profitable.

Wallboard—Asbestos

This product should be related to other building material activities, preferably combined with those interests now creating a pilot plant in the Chickaloon area, an organization wherein gypsum board and gypsum plaster are the immediate objectives. Undoubtedly the same group which undertakes the manufacture of pumice blocks and mineral wool insulation, et cetera, could profitably explore the possibilities of a composition wallboard which embodies a fireproofing percentage of asbestos. The staff and equipment necessary for fabricating dry wallboard certainly can be adapted to the manufacture of asbestos insulating materials with very little additional investment and the market apparently is sufficient at this time to justify such adaptation.

Wood

Lumber and lumber products along the railbelt differ considerably from those of the southeastern Panhandle and western Canada. The stands of lumber are, for the most part, inferior in quality, and many special problems are created for the lumberman who proposes to operate there. Nevertheless, demands for railroad ties, piling, and boxing, emphasizes the need for creating these products in this locality. It should be recognized that either lumbering or lumber products manufacture nevertheless must be approached with full recognition of the extraordinary procedures which are an integral part of any such business in this area.

For instance, oversized dry kilning equipment and creosote and other pressure treatment equipment would be vital in order to make the products acceptable to local users.

Birch could be used locally in many cases, particularly for flooring, furniture frames, and trim. There is even the possibility that automatic turning equipment could compete in the export market for a portion of the spool, coat hanger, handle, and similar specialty and novelty items. There is also the possibility of developing the novelty and gift trade outlets for the unusual products now being developed in Seward and Copper Center, since the grain of the birch in these areas, particularly in the burls, make very fine dishes, plates, laminated cutting boards, bookends, candlesticks, and lamp bases. The current price at which these are sold in Alaska are favorable enough that these could enter the competitive market in the States and absorb the transportation bill necessary to get them here.

Skiing facilities near Anchorage.

NATIONAL PARK SERVICE

Alaska's recreational resources are abundant and of great variety. They are of world-wide fame and constitute one of the Territory's greatest assets. Its mountains rival and surpass those of Switzerland; the fiords equal those of Norway; glaciers, ice caps, and volcanoes are of unsurpassed magnitude and beauty; the rivers, hot springs, forests, lakes, fresh and salt water game fish, historical evidences, and primitive frontier developments all loom as recreational attractions. Its refreshing summer climate and its fame as the "Land of the Midnight Sun" add greatly to the pleasure derived by the tourist.

The recreation industry looms large in the over-all economy of Alaska. During 1948, the number of visitors to Alaska outnumbered the permanent population of the Territory. With the provision of much needed facilities and the stimulus of an increased population, the value of this industry can be expected to expand many fold. The industry already supports a substantial portion of the population, and upon expansion it can logically support a much greater number. Reservoirs having recreation potentialities to be developed in connection with the water resources program will create new opportunities, reflecting an increase in the value of the industry.

Far too little has been done so far toward the development of facilities to make these resources available to the people of the Territory and the thousands of visiting tourists. The National Park Service and the United States Forest Service have provided pioneer facilities in certain areas under their jurisdiction. In the Tongass National Forest of Southeastern Alaska and the Chugach Forest of Southwestern Alaska some basic recreational facilities have been provided. In a few instances communities have provided small municipal recreation parks. Of the five areas under the administration of the National Park Service, two of which are the largest areas in the entire National Park System exceeding even Yellowstone, basic facilities for recreational use have only been provided at Mount McKinley National Park and Sitka National Monument. Nothing has been accomplished at Katmai, Old Kasaan, and Glacier Bay National Monuments in spite of repeated and continuing attempts to secure the necessary funds. The insufficiency of appropriations in recent years also has retarded the accomplishment of much needed developments in McKinley National Park.

The development of Alaska's water resources as contemplated by the Bureau of Reclamation will, undoubtedly, create numerous impoundments, some of which may have recreational value. Likewise, heretofore inaccessible regions will be opened by construction roads to exploitation for recreational purposes such as hunting and fishing. However, it appears that many of these new reservoirs will probably remain too far removed from population centers to justify developments for recreation, although others closely related may have great recreational value. All reservoirs within the scope of the program will obviously have to compete recreationally with many of the hundreds of natural lakes that now exist within the Territory. This is particularly true in the southeastern and southwestern regions where the natural scenic attractions are greatest and where the future population increase is likely to occur. Therefore, the geographical position and accessibility of the various projects will, in a large measure, be one of the governing factors justifying recreational development.

Alaska's superb hunting and fishing opportunities are sure to attract great numbers of sportsmen if the region is made accessible. The potential magnitude of sports fishing alone is indicated by the often heard claim that in the United States more money is spent on fishing tackle than on equipment for any other sport, including golf and boating.

For the most part, it is doubtful whether the recreational potentialities of water resources development will have an appreciable effect upon the national parks and monuments in Alaska under the administration of the National Park Service. The exception may be Mount McKinley National Park in the vicinity of which the Bureau proposes to impound waters of the Nenana River which forms the easterly boundary of the park. Impoundment of these waters will create reservoirs of considerable magnitude along the boundary possibly flooding some park land and altering the present recreational pattern in the area. The National Park Service would be opposed to any proposals to flood park lands and would require investigation of every possible alternative before any park values are sacrificed.

Very little is known about the specific areas in which these projects are to be undertaken and whether or not they will be readily accessible. An analysis of popula-

tion trends of the region in which each will be located will be a factor in determining the value of recreational developments.

A comprehensive study of the proposed projects will be needed before any conclusive recommendations can be made as to the recreational possibilities of the individual projects and the over-all program. This study and the resulting recommendations must be based on factual knowledge. It should consider population trends, availability of land for facilities, accessibility, location, evaluation of scenic qualities, economic values, cost of recreational facilities, and effects upon the wildlife, history, and archeological resources. This investigation will serve as a basis for the allocation of recreational benefits and will assist in determining the policy to be followed in developing and administering those areas having recreational potentialities.

CIVIL AERONAUTICS ADMINISTRATION

In the year 1939 when the Civil Aeronautics Administration first came to Alaska for the purpose of developing a Federal Airways and Communications System as aids to aerial navigation, we found that aviation was being conducted here under extremely adverse conditions.

There were approximately 150 small airports scattered throughout the Territory, none of which could meet the standards of a Class I airport as approved by our organization. These airports were either constructed with Territorial funds, by mining interests, by private individuals or a combination of two or more of these groups. There were no communication aids to aircraft other than those developed by small aviation companies for their individual interests. Weather reporting was also most unsatisfactory and entirely inadequate to properly serve the pilots who were attempting to give Alaskans a mode of transportation.

During the period from 1939 to 1948, and assisted primarily with funds allotted for national defense, the Civil Aeronautics Administration has established a broad Federal Airways and Communications System which now not only serves Alaska but is a vital connecting link in the International Airways System serving the Orient.

In general, this system is considered reasonably complete insofar as Federal aids to air navigation are concerned. Weather reporting stations both on and off the airways system are now reasonably sufficient to meet the needs of both airline and personal aircraft pilots. It is true that improvements and refinements to these systems are constantly being made and no doubt will continue to be made for many years to come.

Transportation in Alaska has been developed under conditions in the reverse order to transportation growth in the continental United States. In the continental United States, the oxcart, the road, the automobile, the highway, and finally the airplane has been the order of transportation development. Here the airplane took the lead. This is largely due to the fact that surface transportation in Alaska is extremely difficult and expensive. The construction of roads and highways requires the outlay of vast sums of money. This kind of money was not available locally as the population was not able to supply it. Neither did there appear to be sufficient justification for the expenditure of Federal funds to construct these roads over treacherous swamps and across or around glaciers in order to serve a sparse population. Consequently in 1939 the only road of any consequence extended from the coastal town of Valdez to Fairbanks in the interior, a distance of approximately 368 miles. A small roadway system was in operation in the Anchorage area extending to Palmer and the Willow Creek mining area for a distance of 100 miles. Shorter systems existed in the Seward area and in a few mining districts; however, none of these were interconnected.

During the past nine years and primarily as a result of the national defense program, this road system has been extended somewhat. As a means of serving the more remote locations, however, the road network is still grossly inadequate. It is our opinion that this condition will persist until such a time as the airplane can demonstrate the importance of a particular section of the country from a commercial, industrial or agricultural standpoint.

During this 9-year period very little work has been done by the Territory of Alaska to construct new and to improve existing airports off the Federal Airways System. Federal funds are not directly available for this purpose except through the Federal Airport Act which permits the construction of airports within Alaska on the basis of 75 percent Federal to 25 percent local or Territorial funds. Unfortunately the Territorial Legislature has not as yet seen fit to avail themselves of an available $10,000,000 in Federal money to improve old and construct new fields so vital to the growth and development here.

Agriculture

The agricultural possibilities within the confines of Alaska are somewhat problematical.

A relatively small amount of farming and gardening is being conducted in the Anchorage, Palmer, Homer, and Fairbanks areas with some truck gardening at Unalakleet and in the southeastern area around Yakutat and other locations to the southeast.

In the Anchorage and Palmer areas the growing season is approximately 108-110 days with only a moderate yearly precipitation of 14-16 inches which is not normally sufficient to mature crops properly. The dry season usually occurs in the spring and early summer when rainfall is necessary for proper germination. Therefore, an irrigation system is considered essential to improve the growing of vegetables and small grains in these areas. Water is available from reasonably shallow wells; however, at present the excessive cost of electric power and the lack of an adequate rural electrification system eliminates any possibility of this type of irrigation being conducted on a commercial basis by pumping. If electric power could be made available at a cost of several mills per kilowatt-hour rather than 6 to 11 cents, the picture would be completely reversed.

There are certain areas around Anchorage where one would expect the growing of such crops as potatoes, carrots, turnips, celery, lettuce, radishes, cabbage, cauliflower, and broccoli to be relatively ideal. It has been found from experience, however, that soil conditions are not necessarily the determining factors but growth is hampered by cool winds blowing down across the fields. Fields that have similar soil conditions in close proximity have produced in abundance. Other areas, particularly in the interior which appear to have excellent top soil characteristics for growth of garden vegetables are of little value due to the permanently frozen ground below the surface.

In certain spots such as Unalakleet on the Bering coast and Yakutat along the Gulf of Alaska where one would suspect that the growing of garden produce would not be possible or at least not profitable, excellent results have been obtained in almost pure sand. It appears, therefore, that much pioneering work is yet to be done before a particular piece of ground can be condemned as unfit for the production of certain vegetation.

Fruits, vegetables, and grains such as apples, plums, figs, cherries, corn, beans, tomatoes, melons, and similar produce requiring hot weather cannot be grown successfully outside of hothouses or greenhouses. There seems to be a possibility, however, that with low-cost electric power the growing of many farm products could be carried on commercially by the chemical process and they could be placed on the market on a competitive basis with produce shipped or flown in from the States.

Many present producers of garden vegetables can find an immediate market for a limited supply of their products. Lack of cold and cool storage facilities, however, prevents the storage of excess stocks for winter consumption. Any attempt to increase production without this cold storage would only result in glutting the summer market. Production of food stuffs for export use is not considered inasmuch as the cost of production in this climate could not compete with California produce even if the transportation costs were eliminated.

Across Knik Arm to the north and northwest of Anchorage lies a completely undeveloped area of approximately 40 square miles. Even though the near edge of this area is but 1 or 2 miles from Anchorage it is completely inaccessible except by way of the Matanuska Valley or a distance of nearly 100 miles. This area could be made available for the growth and expansion of the city of Anchorage and for farming purposes if a causeway were constructed across Knik Arm. The growth of Anchorage is already hampered by Knik Arm on the north and west, by the military reservations to the northeast and by the Chugach Range to the east and southeast and Turnagain Arm on the south.

In the vincinity of Cairn Point just north of the city only about one-half mile of water remains at low tide. A highway and railroad could be placed on a causeway constructed at this location. It would shorten the route to Fairbanks by some 30 or more miles and would open up an area much of which has rich agricultural possibilities. By constructing a causeway at this point it appears that a deep water harbor area could be formed where ocean going vessels could come and go during all seasons of the year. At present the fresh water flowing in from the Matanuska and Knik Rivers creates large blocks of ice which choke this channel during the winter months. This ice is carried back and forth as the tide ebbs and flows and prevents vessels from using the present docking facilities for 5 or 6 months each year. This fresh water could be shut off by causeway gates late in November or early December when the river flow is relatively small and this should clear the channel of ice hazards.

The tide in Cook Inlet averages in the neighborhood of 30 feet. A causeway might be utilized for low-cost power production by taking advantage of the drainage trapped behind the causeway.

Mining

Mining of gold and other minerals in Alaska has been curtailed on account of inadequate transportation and the high cost of industrial power. As air and surface transportation improves and a system of low-cost electric power is made available such as only the Bureau of Reclamation can make possible, the search for strategic minerals will increase. The exploration of mining areas will be initiated by the establishment of local off-airway airports of Class I size or larger. If the mining area thus explored proves to be of sufficient economic value, highways will be constructed to connect these areas with arterial highways.

The Territory of Alaska is known to hold large quantities of different minerals. Only a relatively small portion of the area has been explored to date.

The smelting and refining of ores could be carried on here providing an ample source of low-cost power could be provided. At present these ores are shipped out to the States.

Miscellaneous

The lumbering in the Anchorage area and most of the interior of Alaska will never be conducted on a scale of any appreciable size. This is due primarily to the small sized growth of timber in this part of Alaska. Nevertheless, the growth of spruce south of the Chugach Range and particularly in the Matanuska Valley area offers an opportunity to produce a generous supply of small dimension lumber which can be used locally in constructing new homes. This small scale lumber industry would be greatly augmented by a source of low-cost electric power. The result would mean the increase of much needed lumber for general construction and home building, clearing of lands for agricultural purposes and the employment of additional labor to carry on this work.

Summary

In summarizing the outlook for future growth and development within the Territory, we have reached the following conclusions:

1. The Federal Airways and Communications System will keep pace with all scientific improvements which may be used in perfecting all aids to aerial navigation in the interests of safety and efficiency. The present system is capable of supporting a large increase in air travel, both foreign and domestic.

2. A source of low-cost electric power will open the way for a sound economic growth of commercial, industrial, agricultural and private interests within the confines of the Territory. Without such a source of power the growth of the Territory will be severely hampered.

3. Transportation both air and surface must continue to grow and expand in such proportions as to adequately serve the population. Reduced rates rather than continuously increasing rates are essential.

4. The Federal Airways System must be augmented by a series of local airports serving off-airway communi-

ties. The principal airway centers are Anchorage, Fairbanks, McGrath, Nome, Bethel, and Naknek. From these centers the surrounding areas will develop or remain stagnant largely depending upon the action taken by the Territory in the sponsoring of the Federal airport program. This is an extremely important point to be considered in the anticipated growth of interior Alaska.

5. A causeway across Knik Arm in the vicinity of Cairn Point near Anchorage will permit Anchorage to develop and expand so that it should become a great industrial city of perhaps several hundred thousand population helping to serve the vast Alaskan interior. We would further emphasize the fact that adequate transportation facilities, both ground and air, working together but neither one eliminating the necessity for the other, coupled with a plentiful source of low-cost power and a good communications system will create this increase in population so vital to National Defense and the growth and development of the Territory. The interior, as mentioned in the preceding paragraph, must also be developed if this goal set for Anchorage is to be achieved.

6. The International Airports at Anchorage and Fairbanks will become connecting links of a number of international airways systems, both foreign and domestically owned, that serve the entire world.

ALASKA DEPARTMENT OF HEALTH

The Territory of Alaska has health problems no different from those in the States except for the very high incidence of communicable diseases, including tuberculosis which is of epidemic proportions. Poor water supply, sewage disposal systems, and general unsatisfactory sanitation conditions seriously complicate all health programs.

Climatic conditions would not be detrimental to health provided housing conditions were adapted to the prevailing weather trends.

Many communities in Alaska cannot properly supply their citizens with good drinking water and modern sewage plants without further engineering in sanitary projects. With increased industrialization and population existing plants will become obsolete. Inadequate municipal water supplies have already resulted in emergency uses which are dangerous because of possibilities of pollution. Water-borne diseases such as typhoid and polio might arise.

Food habits of Alaskans are in a state of transition. Many Alaskans adequately nourished by food habits developed by trial and error over centuries are now poorly nourished owing to substitutions which do not meet nutritional needs. Transportation of fresh foods is dependent on air lifts which are still expensive. Alaska's agriculture is not yet adequate to take care of present population needs. Nutritional deficiencies contribute to Alaska's health problems.

The improvement of environmental sanitation and all types of sanitary engineering must receive immediate and effective attention. Local governments have not been able to cope with the problem which has become more acute with recent increases in population.

The Federal Government has a responsibility for establishment of improved water supplies which are adequate and safe, of sewage disposal units, and other sanitation facilities. In any comprehensive planning for future development, action by some Federal agency or agencies that can construct facilities, planned in cooperation with health engineers, for providing satisfactory municipal water supplies is imperative. Further increases in population are unthinkable unless this can be done.

In the States, several of the more recent multiple-purpose projects constructed by the Bureau of Reclamation have included as incidental or secondary benefits from storage of water for irrigation and power development the supplying of domestic and industrial water to municipalities. Such water, of course, is available over and above agricultural and power needs.

A notable example is Salt Lake City which will shortly have its municipal water supply more than doubled as a secondary benefit of the multi-million dollar Provo River project.

Such facilities are costly, even for cities the size of those in Alaska. The Alaska Department of Health knows what is needed and how to meet the needs but is limited by lack of funds. It is understood that the 10-year and long range program contemplated in this report by the Bureau of Reclamation outlines possibilities for construction of many potential multiple-purpose dams throughout the Territory. For a fraction of the total cost, extra capacity for municipal water might be included in the designing of these reservoirs; also the necessary aqueducts to convey the water to our cities. If necessary, filtration plants and modern distribution systems might be included.

With its knowledge of the difficulties that beset sanitation engineering in Alaska, the Department of Health in cooperation with city governments is prepared to undertake the planning of such projects with Reclamation engineers.

The climate, especially in the Arctic, is an ever-present problem. Permafrost, which exists in the entire Arctic region, can best be described as frozen ground which in summer thaws from the surface to a depth of but a few feet. Below the thaw, solid ice extends to depths of several hundred feet. In winter, the earth is solidly frozen up to the surface with concomitant external temperatures of minus 70° F.

The difficulties of laying water and sewer pipes are apparent, also, the sewage problem created by lack of drainage for cesspools.

Inspections have disclosed the continued improper discharge of community sewage on tidal flats, in small streams, and on beaches in most of the coastal towns—a situation far from healthful.

If such basic essentials for living are not properly met, it cannot be expected that many people will be attracted to live in Alaska, or at best long remain.

FOREST SERVICE

Alaska has two national forests comprising a total of 20,846,000 acres. The Tongass National Forest contains 16,046,000 acres and includes the greater part of the region popularly known as Southeast Alaska. The Chugach National Forest covers the timber belt on the shores of Prince William Sound and the east half of the Kenai Peninsula. Its area is 4,800,000 acres.

These national forests were set apart from the open public land area between 1902 and 1909. They have been placed under the administration of the United States Forest Service for development and management by methods that will insure continuous forest productivity. All of their resources are available for use. Standing timber may be purchased for manufacture in practically any quantity desired; lands valuable for agriculture, mining, industrial plants, homesites, and townsites may be patented under the general public land laws; areas needed for water-power development, fur farming, summer homes, residences, and other special purposes may be leased under appropriate laws and regulations, public recreation facilities are provided; hunting and fishing are fostered.

TONGASS NATIONAL FOREST, SOUTHEAST ALASKA

Place of the Timber Industry in Regional Development

Southeast Alaska presents an opportunity for the development of permanent pulp and paper manufacturing enterprises founded on sustained supplies of timber coming from forests that are almost entirely of outstanding pulping species and that are and will continue to be in the ownership and under the management of the Federal Government. The industry would have an almost year-round logging season, cheap log

transportation along protected sea channels between the woods and the mill, ocean shipping for inbound mill supplies and outbound paper products, water power for mill operation in an equable climate that permits of unhindered mill operation throughout the year. In view of these favorable features, the management plans for the timber resources of the Tongass Forest are being so drawn that these resources will contribute in the greatest possible degree to a permanent regional development of the industry.

TONGASS NATIONAL FOREST STATISTICS

Estimated merchantable timber stand of 78,500,-000,000 feet board measure.

Estimated allowable annual cut under sustained yield 1,000,000,000 feet board measure.

The allowable annual cut will support a pulp and paper industry with a daily production capacity of 3,000 tons, operating 300 days per year, and which will use 850,000,000,000 feet board measure of timber annually.

The additional cut of 150,000,000 feet board measure per year will be used to support associated major industries producing high-grade lumber, plywood, special cedar products and cedar shingles.

The Forest Service will insist that the plans of concerns entering this new field call for economically-sized and well-equipped plants, and for operations for a type that will promote continuous employment for skilled woods and mill workers and foster the building up of thoroughly modern industrial communities. While

TABLE 66.—*Estimated employment and population*

	Raw material requirements, thousand feet board measure per year	Production capacity per day	Timber industry total	Service Industries required	Total employment	Estimated population
Pulp and paper	850,000	3,000 tons	5,250	5,250	10,500	31,500
Lumber	85,000	285 thousand	390	390	780	2,340
Plywood	25,000	85 thousand	235	235	470	1,410
Shingles and cedar products.	40,000	135 thousand	375	375	750	2,250
Total					12,500	37,500

the timber of the Tongass Forest is regarded as primarily valuable for the support of a pulp and paper industry, the Forest Service estimates that approximately 15 percent of the possible yearly log output will be more valuable for such other uses as high-grade lumber, plywood, special cedar products, and shingles. The region thus offers an opportunity for an integrated system of timber industries making the best possible use of the forest resources.

Physical and Climatic Features of the Region

Southeast Alaska consists of a long, narrow strip of mainland and an adjoining archipelago of hundreds of islands, extending southeasterly from the main body of the Territory along the west side of northern British Columbia. The region covers an area about 350 miles long and 120 miles wide. The mainland strip and numerous islands are penetrated and separated by an intricate system of navigable straits, inlets, channels, canals, and bays, which give the region a total shore line of about 9,000 miles, and make a very large proportion of its forests readily accessible by tide-water transportation. The total land area of Southeast Alaska is about 34,391 square miles.

This region possesses a high relief and rough topography. The slopes, both on the islands and on the mainland, are mostly steep and heavily dissected, and the shore lines are largely bold and rocky.

Most of the streams are small, since either they are on the islands or their catchment basins are confined to the seaward slopes of the mountain range which parallels and adjoins the coast of the mainland.

There are no rail or motor road connections with the main body of the United States, except the stub pioneer motor road at the extreme north which joins the Alaska Highway. The nearest transcontinental railroad point is Prince Rupert, British Columbia, a Pacific Coast terminal of the Canadian National Railroad system, 95 miles from Ketchikan, the nearest Alaska town. Transportation to and from this region is largely by water, through the sheltered "Inside Passage," which lies back of the island groups that extend from Puget Sound to the north end of Southeast Alaska. Ketchikan and Juneau, the two largest towns, are 660 and 900 nautical miles, respectively, from Seattle. Year-long steamship service is provided from Seattle and from Vancouver, British Columbia.

The main sea channels are deep. Ocean-going steamers can transport materials to or products from the existing towns or other sites at which manufacturing industries, such as pulp and paper mills, might be located. The network of protected sea channels is admirably suited to the use of small craft. Small tugs with barges and flat scows are used extensively to transport coal, lumber, ore, canned salmon, and other products between local points and to and from Puget Sound. A railroad car ferry or barge service could easily be operated between the Southeast Alaska ports and the Prince Rupert terminus of the Canadian National Railroad. This would permit Alaska pulp,

paper, and other timber products to be shipped by a short route to the Middle Western States.

The markets of the Orient and Australia for pulp and other timber products are as readily accessible to Alaska as they are to the Pacific Northwest and British Columbia. Those of the Gulf States and other sections of the Atlantic seaboard can be reached by water shipments through the Panama Canal.

In general terms the winter climate is similar in character to that of Puget Sound but somewhat colder, and the precipitation is higher. The mean temperatures for the winter months at the various towns range from 29° to 35° F. Zero temperatures occur infrequently. The lowest recorded temperature in Juneau during a 30-year period of weather records was 15° below zero.

The precipation is extremely heavy, the yearly mean for Juneau being 81 inches; for Ketchikan 156 inches. There is no pronounced dry summer season as in the Pacific Coast States. Snow does not accumulate to great depths at sea level, much of the winter precipitation there being in the form of rain. The towns are practically free of snow the greater part of the winter.

The above statements apply only to low elevations near tidewater but most of the activities of this region are conducted on or near the coast lines. Winter temperatures decrease rapidly with increase in elevation and progress inland; precipitation is much heavier on the higher mountains; and at altitudes over 1,000 feet snow covers the ground for not less than 4 months of the year.

As the above information indicates, there are no climatic factors which prevent or seriously hinder the operations of woodworking enterprises throughout the year. The main seaways and most of the small inlets are free of ice throughout the winter, permitting water transportation at all times. The logging season is usually considered as covering 9 months, March 1 to November 30, but winter logging is practicable in many localities so far as weather is concerned. The short winter days are somewhat of a handicap, however, since the latitude is about that of Denmark or Southern Sweden.

The heavy rainfall of the average summer gives this region a very low forest-fire risk.

Population

The population of Southeast Alaska in 1940 was 25,240, including 6,500 native Indians. The estimated population in 1948 was 27,200. The principal industry is the sea fishery and its appurtenant service industries. Mining and lumbering are next in importance. The larger towns together with their present estimated populations are: Juneau 7,000; Ketchikan 7,000; Sitka 2,000; Petersburg 1,500; and Wrangell 1,200. All have community facilities that are at least equal to those of towns of similar size in continental United States. All can be reached by ocean-going steamers throughout the year. Satisfactory locations for pulp and paper mills are available in the vicinity of these towns.

Timber Resources

Southeast Alaska is within the extensive "Coast Forest", which occurs in the coastal sections of Oregon, Washington and British Columbia and along the southern shores of Alaska as far north and west as Afognak Island. As this Coast Forest pushes northward from the most favorable part of its range, in Washington, it gradually loses some of its species, the timber line decreases in altitude, the trees become smaller, and species of higher elevations gradually work down toward sea level.

As found in Southeast Alaska, the Coast Forest is predominantly a mixed stand of western hemlock and Sitka spruce. In many places western red cedar and Alaska cedar are associated with them. Anyone of these four species may be found occasionally in a pure stand of small extent. There is no Douglas fir. The forests have an almost tropical density of trees and underbrush. In the usual mixed stand, hemlock with some cedar forms a dense main cover, and this is overtopped by the more light-demanding spruce, which occurs singly or in small groups. Small bushy saplings of the shade-resistant hemlock and cedars, and blueberry, devil-club, and other shrubs form a dense understory. Down timber, which decays very slowly because of almost continuous saturation from abundant rainfall, is plentiful everywhere.

The forest cover extends from the edge of tidewater to an altitudinal limit of about 2,750 feet in the southern part of the region and 2,000 feet in the northern sections. At an elevation of about 1,500 feet the commercial timber gives way to stands of dwarfed, limby trees, which are classified as noncommercial. Because of the prevailing steep slopes the commercial forests form relatively narrow bands along the shore lines of the mainland and islands, rarely extending inland more than 5 miles, except along the valleys of the few large streams.

It is estimated that 75 percent of the commercial timber lies within 2½ miles of tidewater.

The forests of commercial value are broken into large blocks by frequent extensive noncommercial areas of "scrub" and peat "muskegs".

Volume of Standing Timber

The following represents a conservative estimate of the volume of commercial timber by species on the Tongass National Forest:

TABLE 67.—*Estimated volume of commercial timber, Tongass National Forest*

Species	Feet, board measure	Percent
Western hemlock	58, 000, 000, 000	74
Sitka spruce	15, 800, 000, 000	20
Western red cedar	2, 350, 000, 000	3
Alaska cedar	2, 350, 000, 000	3
Total	78, 500, 000, 000	100

Between 4 and 5 million acres of national forest land are estimated to carry timber of present or possible future commercial value. At least one-third of this area carries timber that is marginal in value at this time but should become usable in the future. There are also extensive areas of "scrub" timber that is considered unusable at present.

The average volume per acre of the stands that are classed as commercial under present conditions is between 15,000 and 20,000 board feet but individual logging units may have 40,000 board feet per acre over extensive areas. The majority of the merchantable trees are from 2 to 4 feet in diameter and from 85 to 140 feet high.

Character of the Forest

Overmature Timber

This class of forest consists of a mixed stand of open overmature hemlock and spruce and an understory that is largely younger hemlock, with some cedar. In its more advanced stages of overmaturity it contains about 75 percent hemlock and 25 percent spruce by volume, the spruce consisting of scattered exceptionally large trees. The overmature hemlock is 3 to 4 feet and the spruce 4 to 6 feet in diameter. The younger trees of the stand range from 8 inches to 2 feet in diameter, and are tall, well-formed, clean-boled, and sound.

This combination of overmature and young timber constitutes about half of the commercial timber of the region and must be relied upon to furnish a corresponding portion of the wood supply for mills. It will yield primarily pulp timber, but much spruce saw timber of large size, cedar shingle timber, and long hemlock piling can be segregated from the pulpwood output. Perhaps half of the timber logged from this class of forest will come from the younger understory hemlock.

Mature Timber

Mature timber includes mixed stands of the principal species of the region which have not yet begun to open up and let in the young growth. The trees range in diameter from 2½ to 4 feet and are of good quality. Although not so prevalent as those of the overmature forest, extensive areas of this mature timber are scattered throughout the region. Their heavier yield per acre and smaller amount of defect than the mixed overmature-young growth stands give them a high value from a logging cost standpoint.

Young Growth Timber

Stands of even-aged young growth timber, varying from a few acres to several square miles in size, are frequently found throughout the region. These even-aged stands are the result of windfalls, landslides and in some cases fire. They usually contain a much larger percentage of spruce than the virgin forest which they supplanted. On areas of average site quality and in stands 100 years old or more the trees range from 1 to 2 feet in diameter and from 90 to 150 feet in height. They are clean stemmed, well-formed and sound. Extensive cutting will not ordinarily be done in this class of timber in the near future except for small areas that occur in stands of older material.

Timber Uses

Western Hemlock (Tsuga Heterophylla)

This is an excellent wood for a great variety of lumber uses and is superior to eastern hemlock as a pulping wood. It is widely used for long piling in Alaska wharves.

The high value of western hemlock in pulp and paper manufacture has been fully established by the mills of Oregon, Washington, and British Columbia. It is the foundation of the extensive bleached and unbleached sulphite pulp industry which has been developed there in the last 15 years. Much of the bleached output goes into rayon and cellophane which require the highest grades of pulp. As unbleached sulphite and mechanical pulp, western hemlock also provides most of the principal raw material for the newsprint industry of that region.

Sitka Spruce (Picea Sitchensis)

This species supplies most of the present sawmill requirements of Southeast Alaska, and the trees yield a good percentage of clear lumber that can be exported profitably.

Sitka spruce is manufactured into all of the usual forms of lumber and into airplane stock. It is an excellent all-purpose pulping wood, comparing favorably with white spruce, the standard pulpwood of eastern North America.

Western Red Cedar (Thuya Plicata)

Western red cedar is used for siding and other specialized lumber items, shingles and poles. It is also usable for sulphate pulp. The species does not occur north of Frederick Sound in the vicinity of Petersburg.

Alaska Cedar (Chamaecyparis Nootkatensis)

Not much Alaska cedar is now cut as it is not well known in the markets. Its qualities and field of usefulness have not yet been studied carefully, but results obtained in local use indicates a high value for specialized purposes. It has a fine texture, is easy to work, has a bright yellow color, takes a beautiful satin finish, and is extremely durable. It is considered valuable for pattern making, furniture, toys, turned articles and cabinet work. A pronounced "cedar" odor makes it valuable for clothes closets and chests. It is used locally for boat-building and telephone poles. Battery separators have been made of it in British Columbia. Alaska cedar occurs throughout Southeast Alaska.

Scrub

The term "scrub" is used to describe the open stands of dwarfed, defective trees, with dense undergrowth, which occupy more poorly drained soils than those of the forest types. Many of the trees are highly defective, have a rapid taper, and in general present a scrubby and unhealthy appearance. All of the coniferous tree species of the region are usually present. Clumps of fairly good trees are scattered through the scrub stands and may sometime be logged in the form of cordwood for pulp.

Muskeg

The muskeg type consists of a vegetable cover of moss, grass, herbs, and a few isolated stunted trees, growing on peat accumulations often 5 feet or more in thickness. It covers extensive areas of swamp ground in this region and carries practically no commercial timber.

Silviculture Features

Sitka spruce, the most important species of this region is a rapidly growing, light-demanding tree. It reaches its best development when growing in mixture with other species, which it always overtops. Western hemlock, its principal associate, has fair growth properties and is shade-enduring, a quality enabling it and the more light-demanding spruce to form dense mixed stands. The preliminary studies made to date indicate that the two are an excellent combination for the production of pulpwood, and that the aim of the forester should be to reproduce both species but increase the proportion of the more valuable spruce.

The original forest cover in this region was doubtless almost pure spruce but such stands gradually tend to give way to hemlock. Areas recently uncovered by receding glaciers show spruce as the predominant species with hemlock just beginning its invasion. Over most of the region the forest growth is older, the hemlock now forms the major portion of the mixture. It is thought that under forest management this natural tendency toward pure hemlock can be checked and the proportion of spruce in the regrowth on the cutover areas materially increased through the use of cutting methods that favor the latter.

Research facilities so far available to the Forest Service have not been sufficient to provide comprehensive studies of various methods of cutting in Alaska forests. Clear cutting with reserved seed trees is the method now used in the sawtimber operations which characterize logging here, and ordinarily the areas so logged show ample reproduction. Due to the windthrow danger seed trees on the clear cut areas are not left as scattered individuals but in fairly large groups, a practice which causes little interference with logging operations. If further study should show that favorable results can be obtained by individual tree or group selection methods of cutting on certain classes of sites, such methods may be adopted for those sites.

It appears at this time that the disposal of logging slash on pulpwood cutting areas need not extend further than lopping and scattering of tops so that they lie close to the ground. Even these simple measures may be found unnecessary on the average logging area. Due to the wet climate, the fire hazard is usually so low that expensive slash disposal work is ordinarily not required from that standpoint.

Preliminary studies of yield in the forests of Southeast Alaska indicate that the rotation should be 75 or 80 years and that the crop produced in this period will have a volume per acre well above the average volume now found in the virgin commercial forest.

With an estimated commercial stand of virgin timber on the Tongass Forest of 78.5 billion board feet, and allowing an average of 78 years as the rotation period during which this virgin timber may be entirely removed under sustained-yield forest management, approximately 2,000,000 cords of wood of 500 board feet each can be taken from the forest each year in this period. If the entire output of timber were devoted to pulp manufacture it would be sufficient to produce 1,000,000 tons of sulphate pulp a year plus substantial quantities of lumber, plywood, cedar shingles, and cedar poles.

Water Power Resources

The Tongass Forest possesses an abundance of water power in units of suitable size for individual plants. The best sites range from 5,000 to 30,000 horsepower in capacity and can be very economically developed for a year-round supply. A typical power site has a high "hanging lake" a short distance inland that provides excellent water-storage facilities, requires short conduits to connect the lakes with powerhouses located at tidewater, and the power can be used for paper manufacture where developed so that transmission lines are unnecessary. In many cases power from a number of sites can be concentrated readily at one industrial plant by the use of short transmission lines.

A survey has been made by the Forest Service, Geological Survey, and the Federal Power Commission of the principal known power sites of this region. The sites covered have a total year-round capacity of about 800,000 horsepower. Fifty power sites with an aggregate capacity of 22,000 horsepower have been developed and are now in use.

All water power sites are publicly owned and can be leased under the Federal Water Power Act for periods up to 50 years.

Limestone and Coal

High calcium limestone deposits are available at tidewater points in Southeast Alaska. Coal can be obtained most readily from mines on Vancouver Island or in Western Washington.

Logging Methods and Costs

The methods of logging required in Alaska are similar to those used in Western Washington and Oregon. Machine logging with donkey engines and wire rope has proved to be the most practical means of moving logs from the stump on the usual logging area in this region because of the rough topography and wet ground.

Ground-skidding and high-lead systems are now used, but one of the overhead systems will probably prove most economical for extensive pulpwood operations.

A large percentage of the timber can be logged directly into tidewater by the use of two and three donkey engines working tandem. Log flumes, short railroads, or motor-truck roads will be required to transport the timber from the donkey yarding engines to tidewater in the longer valleys. Log driving is not practicable in the short turbulent streams.

Timber is commonly handled in full-tree lengths or as very long logs from the stump to the mill. After being placed in tidewater it can usually be towed in the form of flat rafts through the protected waterways, but Davis-type rafts are required in winter for tows in the wider, more exposed channels. The cost of towing logs is about 2 cents per 1,000 board feet per mile. Timber supplies for a plant can thus be drawn cheaply from a very extensive region.

Floating logging camps, which can be towed from one cutting area to another, are in general use. Similarly, donkey engines and all other logging equipment are moved on scows and floats. The average cost of sawlogs, exclusive of stumpage, delivered at the sawmills just prior to the war was about $10 per 1,000 board feet. It is estimated that on the basis of labor and equipment costs of 1948 the total cost of unpeeled pulpwood logs delivered at local mills would not have exceeded $10 per 100 cubic feet (equivalent to $20 per 1,000 board feet).

Existing Forest Industries

Practically all of the timber manufactured in Southeast Alaska is purchased from the national forest. The amount taken yearly from the forest under commercial sales is now about 80,000,000 board feet. Most of this goes into lumber, but about 20 percent is used in the round for fish-trap and wharf piling. Juneau and Ketchikan each have a modern, electric-driven sawmill of 100,000 board-feet capacity per 8-hour day. Sitka has an efficient mill of 35,000 board-feet capacity, and smaller mills are found in other communities.

Alaska has no operating pulp or paper plants at this time. The nearest mill is the newsprint plant of Pacific Mills (Ltd.), located at Ocean Falls, British Columbia, 296 miles south of Ketchikan.

Forest Management Policy

The following is a condensed statement of the main objectives and timber-use policies which have been

988410—52——19

established for timber management on the Tongass National Forest:

Objectives

1. The development and maintenance of a permanent pulp and paper manufacturing industry based on a sustained yield of the timber resources.

2. The furnishing of a permanent and convenient supply of timber for local consumption, with such an additional supply to the local sawmills for sale in the general lumber markets as may be needed to justify efficient milling facilities and provide year-long operation.

Timber-Use Policies

The productive forest land will be divided into pulp-timber allotments and local-use allotments.

Pulp-timber allotments will be laid out to supply the timber needs of pulp and paper mills of economical operating size in each section of the region. Sustained yield timber management will be practiced on each allotment or group of allotments.

Local-use allotments will be laid out on the basis of the suitability of the timber for the common local uses and its accessibility to points of consumption.

National Forest timber must be given at least primary manufacture in Alaska. Other things being equal, preference will be given to such industries and applicants as contemplate the most complete manufacture in Alaska.

The establishment of minor wood-using industries, especially those using western red cedar and Alaska cedar, will be encouraged.

Small sales will be encouraged so far as is consistent with the investment required.

Preservation of Scenic and Recreational Values

Scenic and recreational values rank high in much of the national forest area, predominate over considerable areas, and must be adequately safeguarded.

All timber management plans will be carefully coordinated with plans for the preservation of the scenic and recreational resources of the Forest.

Timber sales will not be made in locations where the scenic and recreational values are predominant. Along heavily traveled narrow sea channels and in other locations where justified, cutting will be either excluded entirely or permitted only under some form of selective logging which will prevent unsightly scars or openings in the timber cover, or exposure of the remaining stand to probable windfall. Within the boundaries of timber sale areas strips of timber will be left standing along the shorelines of important recreation lakes and fishing streams and along main roads.

General Conditions Applying to Larger Timber Sales

The stumpage alone is offered for sale from the national forest, the land being retained by the United States for the production of successive forest crops. The maximum amount of timber that will be placed under contract to one firm and the period of time allowed for its cutting will be determined by the Forest Service in consideration of the purchaser's logging and manufacturing investment, practical operating methods, and markets.

The timber of the unit to be offered for sale is appraised by a forest officer on the basis of its value for manufacture into the timber products for which it is best suited and practicable of manufacture within the region. The timber is then advertised for sealed bids for a period of not less than 30 days, the advertisement naming the appraised stumpage rates as the minimum that will be considered. It is awarded to the highest bidder who can make a satisfactory showing of ability, financial and otherwise, to carry the proposed operations through to completion.

The timber is paid for in relatively small advance installments as cutting proceeds and on the basis of a scale or measurement of the cut material made by a forest officer.

The bid stumpage rates in every long-term sale apply for a limited period only and are subject to readjustment at stated intervals throughout the life of the contract to bring them into conformity with the then current value of stumpage in Southeastern Alaska. The proposed stumpage reappraisal interval for large pulp sales is 5 years following an initial 10-year period of no readjustment.

National forest timber is sold for use and cannot be held for speculation or other purposes. Hence long-term contracts specify a definite date by which substantial logging must begin.

Timber is sold on the basis of the unit customarily used in the industry concerned. Thus, sawtimber is sold by the board foot, and piling and poles by the linear foot. Pulptimber will be sold by the cubic foot with the unit being 100 cubic feet of solid wood (excluding bark and rot), an amount approximately equal to a cord or to 500 board feet.

Alaska contracts usually provide for "clear cutting" the merchantable timber on the sale area with the ex-

ception that not to exceed 5 or 10 percent of the volume will be reserved for natural reseeding purposes. Seed trees must be protected against injury from logging operations. Some form of selective cutting may later be required in situations where such system of cutting proves to be feasible.

The Forest Service reserves the right to require the disposal of logging debris to the extent of lopping the tops and scattering the brush so that it lies close to the ground and away from seed trees and clumps of reproduction. Satisfactory precautions must be taken against the escape of fire from logging operations.

There must be no logging interference with salmon spawning streams.

CHUGACH NATIONAL FOREST— PRINCE WILLIAM SOUND AND KENAI

The timbered areas along the shores of Prince William Sound and in the east half of Kenai Peninsula above Seward have been set aside as the Chugach National Forest. Its area is 4,800,000 acres. The principal species are western hemlock and Sitka spruce but the tree growth is smaller than that of Southeast Alaska since this is the northern limits for the species.

The products of the Chugach Forest supply local needs, being the closest source of supply for the lightly timbered and nontimbered sections of Alaska farther to the north, that is, the interior and the Arctic-Bering Sea areas. The chief demand is for lumber, heavy-sawn timber and piling. The largest sawmill with a capacity of 60,000 board feet per day, is located at Whittier, a gateway of the Alaska Railroad into Interior Alaska. A few smaller mills, ranging up to 10 or 15 thousand feet in daily capacity, supply part of the local demands at Seward and other towns in or near the national forest.

National Forest Administration

The national forests of Alaska are administered by the Forest Service, United States Department of Agriculture, with a regional forester and staff resident in Alaska. Only important matters involving questions of general policy need be referred to Washington; most national forest business is handled locally.

The office of the regional forester is at Juneau. The Tongass Forest is divided into three divisions, with headquarters at Juneau, Ketchikan and Petersburg. The Chugach Forest has two divisions, with headquarters at Cordova and Seward. Each division is in charge of a supervisor. The regional forester and the supervisors have assistants for handling specialized lines of work.

A fleet of seagoing launches is maintained for field transportation.

Principal Provisions of the Sale Agreement Covering the Recently Awarded Ketchikan Pulptimber Unit

1. The total amount of timber placed under contract is an estimated 1,500,000,000 cubic feet (roughly equivalent to 7,500,000,000 feet board measure). This volume is based on the requirements for a 50-year supply of a sulphate or sulphite pulp mill having a daily capacity of 150 tons for the first 10 years and 525 tons daily for the remaining 40 years.

2. The agreement covers a period of 50 years.

3. The sale areas within which logging units are to be laid out to supply the timber for the pulp plant have been definitely designated.

4. The Forest Service has also designated the specific logging units, estimated to contain a 20-year timber supply for the plant, which are to be cut first. Units to be logged after the above have been cut will be selected currently by the pulp mill operator, as logging progresses, in advance of the plant needs, by 5-year periods. The selections are subject to the approval of the regional forester.

5. Insofar as conditions on the sale area will permit, the logging units to be selected and approved periodically throughout the sale period will be of such character that, with respect to the cost of logs delivered at the plant, the purchaser's pulp manufacturing operation will not be in a disadvantageous position in comparison with similar enterprises in the Puget Sound region.

6. The purchaser agrees to install in Alaska a pulp mill of not less than 150 tons daily capacity within 3 years from the date of execution of the timber sale agreement; and to enlarge the plant to a capacity of 525 tons daily within 10 years of the date of the execution of the agreement.

7. The bid rates of the successful bidder constitute the stumpage rates to be paid for an initial 10-year period of operation. These rates are:

> $0.85 per 100 cubic feet for timber cut for manufacture of pulp.
>
> $1.50 per thousand feet board measure for cedar.
>
> $2.00 per thousand feet board measure for sawlogs of hemlock and other species.
>
> $3.00 per thousand feet board measure for spruce sawlogs, including high-grade spruce logs intended for pulp manufacture.

The rates to be charged throughout the life of the sale agreement will be subject to readjustment at 5-year intervals after an initial period of 10 years, to make them conform to the then current value of the stumpage. The rates will be fixed by such reappraisals, which shall give consideration to the estimated cost for the Alaska plants of manufacturing and shipping as compared with the costs for similar enterprises on Puget Sound.

8. In addition to payments for stumpage, the purchaser will make deposits with the Government to defray the cost to the Forest Service of work to be done on the cutover areas to improve the future stand of timber. The rate will be 10 cents per 100 cubic feet or an equivalent amount for timber scaled by other units of measure.

9. Timber will be paid for as cutting proceeds in installments of $10,000 to $40,000.

10. At least three-fourths of the purchaser's yearly pulpwood requirements are to be taken from the areas under sale to him. The remainder may be taken from areas outside this proposed agreement under sales made to independent loggers or the pulp company.

11. Strips and blocks of timber having special scenic value in connection with water courses, lakes, recreation sites and highways are reserved from cutting.

12. The logging units are to be clear cut with the exception that not to exceed 10 percent of the merchantable timber volume within an actual cutting area is to be left for reseeding purposes, but this provision may be modified at dates of reappraisal of stumpage rates.

13. The merchantability of the trees and of the logs which must be cut are closely defined in the agreement.

14. The purchaser must take adequate precautions against the starting of forest fires and must assist in their suppression.

15. Woods operations will not be permitted to interfere with salmon in spawning streams or to injure spawning beds in any way.

16. To the extent that local laborers have the necessary skills and are available, the woods and other crews for the purchaser's operations are to be recruited from among all residents of Southeast Alaska.

17. A surety bond of $50,000 is provided for performance under the agreement.

U. S. DEPARTMENT OF AGRICULTURE— AGRICULTURAL DEVELOPMENT IN ALASKA

Agriculture in Alaska will develop along with industry, mining, recreation, fisheries and other commercial activities. As the population grows, there will be need for increased agricultural production. Es-

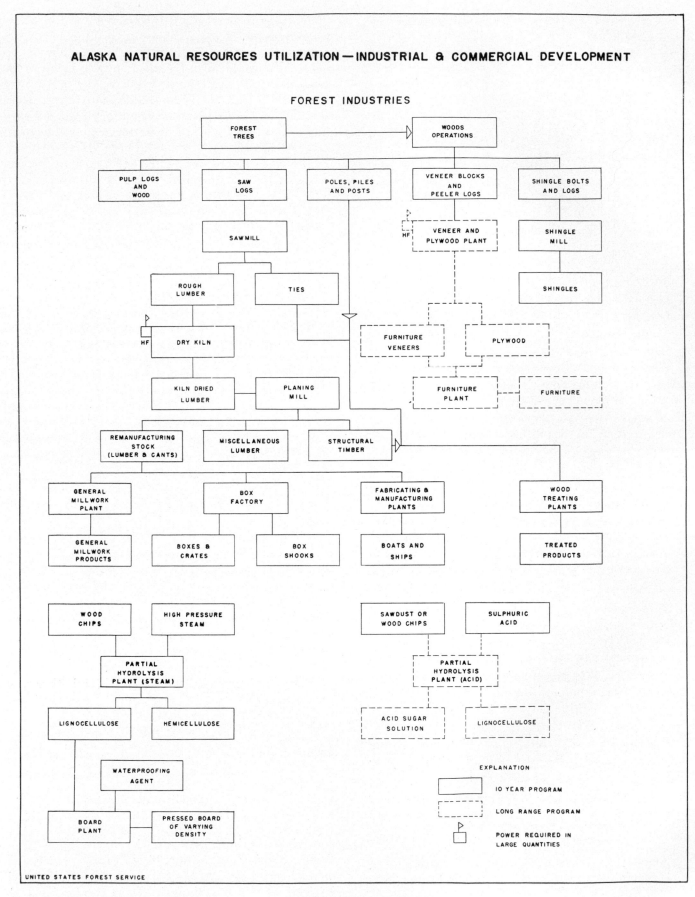

ALASKA NATURAL RESOURCES UTILIZATION — INDUSTRIAL & COMMERCIAL DEVELOPMENT

FOREST INDUSTRIES

MECHANICAL GROUP

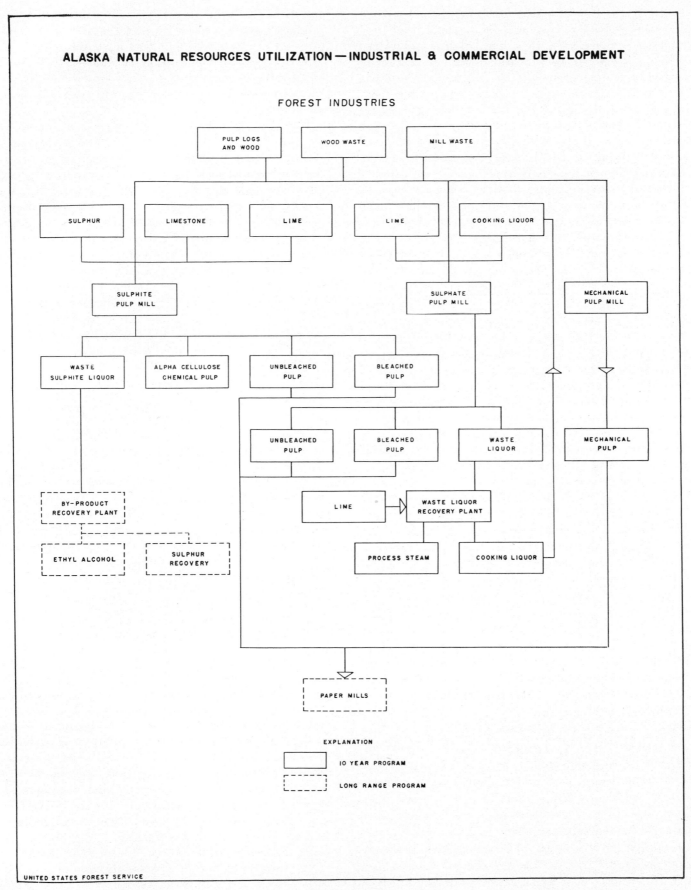

ALASKA NATURAL RESOURCES UTILIZATION—INDUSTRIAL & COMMERCIAL DEVELOPMENT

FOREST INDUSTRIES

FIBER GROUP

pecially in the immediate future it can be anticipated that military food requirements will remain high.

But there must be a very fine balance maintained between the rate of agricultural development and industrial development in Alaska. Payrolls for industrial workers in population concentrations are necessary if there is to be a market for Alaska agricultural products. The number of Army personnel at Alaskan bases and Army policy with respect to procurement of those food products which can be produced in Alaska will be of primary immediate importance in the rapidity and stability of agricultural development. Because of the short growing season and other factors, many farm families now and in the future will rely upon work off the farm for a part of their income.

From a technical viewpoint, research at the Experiment Stations and also farm experience have proved the possibility for further development of specialized farming enterprises in Alaska. In many instances specialized enterprises on the same farm have been combined in the farm economy to increase the income and and make better use of farm equipment and labor.

These specialized enterprises which have been given study at the Experiment Stations and used on the farms in Alaska are: Market gardening, dairying, meat animals including beef cattle, sheep, hogs and poultry; small fruits, grains, annual grain and legume hay crops, and perennial cultivated grass and legumes for hay and pasture. Better grain and forage crops, including pastures, are of basic importance to successful livestock and poultry enterprises.

Closely related to all these enterprises is the necessity for technical knowledge concerning soil classification, soil analysis, soil management and plant response. The scientific study of soils is a comparatively new phase of research work in the various agricultural areas of Alaska. It will become increasingly important in the agricultural development of the Territory. There are wide differences in climate and considerable variation in soil formations over the broad expanse of Alaska. Because of these variations, farm enterprises adapted to one area may be uneconomical in other areas. Excessive precipitation and lack of suitable soils in Southeastern Alaska make production of hay and grain difficult. Over much of Alaska the native grasses have been used extensively for hay. In the area extending northward from Homer, on Cook Inlet, through the Matanuska, Susitna, and Tanana Valleys to Rampart on the Yukon River, early maturing cereal crops ripen, even though the growing season is quite short, but artificial drying may be necessary to condition the grain properly for storage. These crops include wheats, oats, rye, and barleys. The seasons are too cool for corn to mature. The demand for grains for poultry

and livestock feed is increasing more rapidly than their production in Alaska because of the difficulty and expense of clearing land and putting it into cultivation. There is no doubt that eventually many of the varieties and strains of grains tried at the experiment stations will find wide use in Alaska farming areas where they are adapted.

Experiments with perennial cultivated grasses and legumes indicate that improved winter hardy, high-yielding strains of these valuable forage plants, adapted to both hay and pasture, may eventually be developed, but as yet this goal has not been attained. This lack is an important current handicap to livestock production, including dairying. Good pastures are especially important as a source of nutritious, low-cost feed.

Applications of barnyard manure and of commercial fertilizers to stimulate quick plant growth and increase the nutritional value of the hay and pasture is accepted practice on most of the farms. Only limited tests have been made on soils in Alaska to indicate their fertility. As soil analyses are completed on the various soil classifications, they will undoubtedly indicate that the use of barnyard manures, green manuring crops, and commercial fertilizers will become increasingly important in a good soil-management program.

There will be some farms in all agricultural areas in Alaska devoted entirely to the growing of market vegetables, an important limiting factor being the extent of the market. Because vegetable and potato production provide employment for only a comparatively short period, a large percentage of such enterprises will likely be combined with dairying, poultry production, or other livestock activities to provide a year-round income. In some areas the farming enterprise will be only a part-time occupation. Farm income will be supplemented by either year-round or seasonal non-farm work.

Livestock and Poultry

Because of the rapid increase in civilian and Army personnel in Alaska, there is a shortage of dairy products. It is doubtful if the production of fluid milk will reach the market saturation point for this population for many years. At present, only fluid milk is marketed. Very little butter, cottage cheese, or buttermilk are produced in Alaska and only very small amounts of whole milk are used in ice cream. A major portion of the feed concentrates for both dairy animals and poultry are imported from the States at high cost.

Poultry husbandry has been slow in developing in Alaska. Good housing is essential. Most of the grain used for feed is now imported at high cost. In the long run, local production of at least grain for scratch feed may become desirable if the enterprise is to be economic.

Poultry combines well with vegetable production, or with root crops such as potatoes, rutabagas, carrots, etc., and provides a year-round income to pay current obligations throughout the year. Experimental work at the Fairbanks and Matanuska Stations, as well as practical experience of farmers in Alaska, show that poultry can be an economic enterprise. As the country develops there will be room for expansion of this enterprise.

Sheep and cattle have been produced for many years on various islands of the Aleutian chain. There is considerable room for expansion of this industry in that section, especially on islands where harbor facilities are available.

To date very few beef cattle have been produced on the mainland of Alaska. The same may be said of sheep. Weather conditions prevailing from Kodiak Island north along Cook Inlet through the Big Susitna River valley are less severe than in much of the area of the intermountain States. Feed and water are abundant on the south slopes of the mountains above timberline throughout this entire area. On the extensive tide flats, along the southern Alaska coast and extending along Cook Inlet and on river deltas, some grazing is possible. With this abundant summer range, there is still the necessity for cleared land in the valleys on which to produce winter roughage for a long winter feeding period.

There are extensive highland areas in interior Alaska, north of the Alaska Mountain range, suitable for grazing, but only during a limited midsummer period. Valley land will have to be cleared on which to produce feed for the long winter feeding period. Because of severe winter temperatures and deep snow, it will be necessary to supply shelter. Predator control will be an important problem. Despite these limitations, it will be possible to produce some beef cattle and sheep in parts of Alaska.

Hogs have been produced in all the agricultural areas of Alaska for many years. At present, most of the hogs produced are in areas near Army bases or cities where garbage is available as the major portion of the feed. As more land is cleared for seeding pasture and grains and a system of hogging off crops is practiced, more pork will be produced for family use and for local market consumption.

nical assistance, and other aids. The high cost of clearing warrants thorough exploration of feasible ways and means for improving methods and reducing costs.

Barnyard manures, green manuring crops, and commercial fertilizer have been used on Alaska farms with excellent results. Bacterial action in Alaska soils is very slow, due to low prevailing soil temperatures and the short growing season. Barnyard, or green manures, supplemented by applications of such commercial fertilizers as soil analysis and plant response results indicate, will improve conditions for plant growth. Sound crop rotation practices will assist materially in increasing crop production and maintaining or even increasing soil fertility. Where livestock and poultry are major farm enterprises, production of feed crops, especially grasses and legumes, and use of barnyard manure will help to maintain soil productivity. Where crops such as market vegetables are produced, careful tillage, rotation, fertilization and other soil conservation and management practices must be applied, to maintain soil tilth, and to avoid deleterious soil erosion.

To produce farm commodities at a minimum of cost it will be necessary that labor saving equipment be used wherever possible. The best farm practices, including crop rotations and soil and moisture conservation measures, must be used. High producing animals, poultry, and seeds must be secured. Seeds of adapted varieties may be produced locally if properly conditioned for storage. Long range farm planning will be necessary. Farm records must be kept consistently, so that unprofitable farm practices, animals, equipment and enterprises can be eliminated. Only by keeping records and analyzing the farm business can a farmer expect to build a sound farm economy. Competition in agriculture is just as keen in Alaska as it is in the States.

Irrigation of some crops will be practical in certain seasons. Especially is this true where market vegetables are the major enterprises. In some agricultural areas, the gravelly character of the subsoil would preclude the use of water carried by ditches from streams. Where sufficient ground water is available for pumping at economical levels, the use of sprinkler irrigation by pipes laid on the surface has produced excellent results during the dry season. To whatever extent irrigation by pumping is used, it will not be profitable unless there is an abundant supply of low-cost electric power.

Other Agricultural Production Problems

A most pressing requirement for agricultural development in Alaska is land clearing. Few farms have sufficient cleared land for economical production.

Obtaining more cleared acres will require assistance in the form of long term, low interest rate loans, tech-

Marketing

Farming is a business which usually requires the full time of the operator. Marketing is a specialized business. Few farmers are so favorably situated that they can spare the time to supervise the sale of their products satisfactorily. Usually the farmer's produce is sold through a cooperative marketing organization, or on contract to private buyers. As agricultural development becomes more stabilized in Alaska, better marketing facilities will undoubtedly become available. In order to protect their own financial interests, it will be necessary that farmers produce and deliver only the highest quality produce for marketing. This requires education as to market grades and quality. The progressive farmer will take advantage of every opportunity to secure information on the market requirements for his products. He will also take a personal interest in the organization through which his products are marketed. He must be willing to invest his time, thought and money in his marketing organization.

Agricultural Services in Alaska

Research and experimental work in Alaska will follow definite trends in agricultural development. Agricultural leaders in Alaska are agreed that this development will first be dairying, poultry, forage and grain crops, and market vegetables and fruits. Soils work will include soils classification, analysis of soil samples, and work in soil management and plant response. Research work on types of farm building, their insulation and heating; methods and equipment for harvesting, storing and preserving vegetables, forage crops, and grains will be the goals of research by agricultural engineers. Analysis of individual farm records to establish the most economical farm enterprises and farm management practices, and marketing problems, will be handled by agricultural economists. As agriculture develops, plant diseases, insects, and weeds will become more prevalent. Studies of these pests must be made and control measures recommended by plant pathologists, entomologists and agronomists. Studies of human and animal nutrition must be made on Alaska vegetables, fruits, grains, and forage crops by nutritionists. As yet animal and poultry diseases have seldom reached major proportions because of the scattered farms in the agricultural areas. When fuller development is reached, these diseases are certain to take a heavy toll of livestock and poultry unless given study by bacteriologists and veterinarians under Alaska conditions, so that preventive measures may be devised and and taken. Fur farming problems—breeding, feeding, diseases, and others—need to be attacked. All these are research problems the solution of which is necessary for the building of a sound agricultural future in Alaska. Such research is the function of the Alaska Agricultural Experiment Stations, currently under the jurisdiction of the United States Department of Agriculture.

The results of research are brought to the citizens of Alaska through the educational activities of the Agricultural Extension Service. This is a cooperative undertaking of the United States Department of Agriculture and the University of Alaska. Its work is carried on by agricultural agents, home demonstration agents, 4–H clubs, and in other ways.

Alaska soils need to be safeguarded against erosion damage by wind and water. To attack this problem the Alaska legislature in 1947 enacted a soil conservation district law. The law declared the Territory to be a soil conservation district, established the Alaska Soil Conservation Board and a conservation committee advisory to it, and provided that land occupiers may organize and operate local subdistricts of the Alaska Soil Conservation District for the purpose of attaining soil conservation and wise land use. Organization of the district followed, and early in 1948 the Board began its program. Several subdistricts have been organized, and others are in process.

The operations of the Soil Conservation Service in Alaska consist of assisting the district and its subdistricts in two broad categories of work: making available the services of trained conservationists, and a limited amount of equipment and conservation materials, for helping settlers and farmers plan, apply, and maintain conservation and wise land use on their farms; and the conduct of land capability surveys and investigation of potential agricultural areas and of applicable soil conservation and erosion preventive and control measures.

The agricultural conservation program assists soil conservation and agricultural development by making payments for performance of designated practices for farm improvement and soil conservation, including clearing. The program is locally administered through the Alaska Director of Extension.

Production and subsistence loans are made by the Farmers Home Administration to farmers and stockmen who are unable to secure adequate credit at reasonable rates from the other sources for the purchase of livestock, seed, feed, fertilizer, equipment and for other farm needs, under authority of Title II of the Bankhead-Jones Farm Tenant Act as amended. Long-term farm ownership loans are made to farmers and veterans, unable to obtain satisfactory credit from other sources, for the purchase of family-type farms, for the enlargement of undersized farm units and the development of farm units under authority of Title I of the Bankhead-Jones Farm Tenant Act as amended. Preference is given to veterans. Under present law, a first mortgage on the real estate must be obtained. This can be done only where title has passed to private ownership. Legislation is needed to authorize the creation of a lien through other means upon homestead entry and prior to passage of title. One cooperative loan association is also outstanding; this is to the Matanuska Valley Farmers Cooperating Association, a purchasing and marketing cooperative.

To guard against the introduction and spread of injurious plant pests, the Bureau of Entomology and Plant Quarantine maintains inspectors in Alaska for the inspection and treatment, if necessary, of plant materials transported by air and surface-borne carriers in international commerce.

Highly important to successful agriculture and rural living in Alaska is rural electrification, which is discussed in detail below.

RURAL ELECTRIFICATION IN ALASKA

The Need for Hydroelectric Power for Rural Electrification in Alaska

Alaska's lack of plentiful electric energy at reasonable cost is recognized by those familiar with the Territory as a grave obstacle to full development of the area. The Rural Electrification Administration is particularly concerned about the situation because of its adverse effect on rural electrification progress in Alaska. Expanded hydroelectric development is necessary if the full benefits of rural electrification in the Territory are to be realized.

This conclusion grows from several years of experience with the rural electric cooperatives which have been organized with REA financing to carry out rural electrification in Alaska. There are at present six of these cooperatives. The first two were established in 1942 at Kodiak and Palmer; the others, in 1947 and 1948 at Homer, Fairbanks, Auke Bay, and Anchorage. Electrification of several additional areas of Alaska through cooperatives is under consideration.

None of the Alaska systems for which REA loans were made in 1947 and 1948 has yet been completed. While several factors have impeded progress, perhaps the most difficult problem has been to secure dependable sources of low-cost electrical energy. For example, the Matanuska Electric Association of Palmer gets its wholesale power from the Anchorage Power System, which was originally designed to serve a population of approximately 3,500, and is now serving about 20,000. This situation has brought serious problems to the cooperative and its member-users—service interruptions, restricted use of power and inability to serve new consumers. The Anchorage situation is perhaps the most severe in the Territory, but Fairbanks and other Alaskan communities have similar problems.

The high cost of electric energy in Alaska results chiefly from the Territory's dependence on numerous, small generating plants. Electricity produced by such means is a costly commodity. The Matanuska Electric Association buys power from the city of Anchorage at 2 cents per kilowatt hour—more than double the average wholesale rate paid by REA borrowers in the States. As a result the retail cost of electric energy to Matanuska Valley consumers is so high as to discourage full utilization of the advantages of electric appliances and machines. A typical valley user pays an average bill of $25 to $35 per month to operate an electric water heater, deep-well pump, electric range, electric washing machine and small house-hold appliances.

REA financing of generating and transmission facilities in Alaska will probably be necessary in serving certain isolated rural sections, but this represents no solution to the problem of over-all power development in the area. As in the Territory's present generating plants, the cost of producing power with such facilities would be high. Alaska needs a coordinated hydroelectric development program to provide low-cost power for its rapidly expanding military, industrial and rural needs. Such a program is, of course, far beyond the scope of REA.

If this high-cost situation can be overcome, doing so will greatly aid the further development of agricultural and associated industries in many parts of Alaska. Matanuska Valley farmers are at present using only an average of 140 kilowatt hours of electricity per month. If abundant low-cost power were available, estimates based on experience in the States indicate that average use would rise sharply—perhaps to 1,000 kilowatt hours per month within a very short time.

Low-cost electric power could do much to relieve Alaskan farmers of the hazards of a short and uncertain growing and harvesting season. It would also encourage the establishment of basic industries along the lines of REA borrowers in Alaska to supplement the agricultural development and provide a well-rounded economy for the area. These possibilities are indicated in more detail in the following summary of the status of each of the REA-financed systems in Alaska:

Matanuska Electric Association, Palmer: Operates 113 miles of line serving 552 consumers. Recently received additional loan of $185,000 for new construction and improvement of existing lines. Purchases wholesale energy from the city of Anchorage at a flat rate of 2 cents per kilowatt-hour, but has received notice from city of termination of present wholesale power contract. Serves the Matanuska Valley, and is in position to serve gold and coal mining area in the mountains bordering on the valley.

Kodiak Electric Association, Kodiak: Operates 10 miles of line serving 530 consumers in and near the town of Kodiak. Generates own power in diesel generating plant. Has new REA loan of $310,000 to finance complete rebuilding of distribution system and installation of additional generating units. Serves Kodiak fishing industry, which is expected to increase greatly in importance in the next few years.

Homer Electric Association, Homer: Has REA loan of $217,000 to finance a generating plant and 43 miles of line to serve 198 consumers. System under construction. Substantial agricultural and industrial development of the Homer area is anticipated. The town is situated on Kachemak Bay on the Kenai Peninsula. A low bench near the elevation of the town offers land and climatic conditions suitable for crop production. The higher land appears capable of being used for grazing. The area is underladen with a sub-bituminous coal deposit of great size. Homer will soon be linked with Anchorage by the Kenai Road now under construction. Completion of this road should result in a rapid growth of population in the Homer vicinity as well as elsewhere along the highway.

Golden Valley Electric Association, Fairbanks: Has REA loan to finance construction of 59 miles of line to serve 129 consumers. System now under construction. Expects to be able to purchase wholesale power. The area of this system lies immediately adjacent to the city of Fairbanks in the Tanana Valley. Placer mining of gold has been carried on here for many years. The valley is an area possessing possibilities for further agricultural development.

Glacier Highway Electric Association, Auke Bay: Has REA loan of $230,000 for 45 miles of line to serve 251 consumers. System under construction with energization expected in January 1949. Will be able to purchase wholesale power. This system lies in the vicinity of Auke Bay north of Juneau. Many persons living in the area are employed in Juneau, either in Government offices or by privately-owned businesses. There are numerous summer homes along the co-op lines which are expected to be occupied on a year-round basis when dependable service is available. The area has lumber and fishing industries and is hopeful of a large scale wood pulp development which would result in a substantial increase in the population.

Chugach Electric Association, Anchorage: Has REA loan of $560,000 for 100 miles of line to serve 848 consumers. Lines cannot be energized until power source is available. Anchorage is a growing commercial center, and the Anchorage vicinity is recognized as vital in the defense of Alaska. The area proposed to be served by this cooperative lies immediately adjacent to

the city and has shared in the tremendous growth which the locality has experienced in recent years.

The Anchorage area and the Matanuska Valley have been looking to the development of low-cost hydroelectric power from Lake Eklutna that can serve not only immediate defense requirements but should also provide a base for developing and stabilizing the civilian economy in this area. A project at Lake Eklutna is urgently needed to meet conditions that can be classified as an emergency.

HEADQUARTERS ALASKAN COMMAND
OFFICE OF THE COMMANDER-IN-CHIEF
FORT RICHARDSON, ALASKA

NOVEMBER 19, 1948.

The Honorable
The SECRETARY OF THE INTERIOR,
The Department of the Interior,
Washington 25, D. C.

Attention: Bureau of Reclamation.

MY DEAR MR. SECRETARY: My responsibility as the unified commander of the armed services in Alaska requires that I examine all of the factors which affect the national military establishment within the Territory. It is quite evident that the over-all defense of Alaska depends upon two closely interrelated factors, the military facilities and installations available to the Armed Forces and the civil resources of the Territory.

To the extent that civil facilities are developed to a level which will permit a self-sustaining economy and a full development of the natural resources of the Territory, the expenditures for purely military works may be reduced. The benefit to the national economy of such a reduction in military expenditures is obvious.

A review of the various programs proposed for implementation by the Department of the Interior indicates that a number of these would, if implemented, strengthen the internal economy of Alaska, and thus tend to reduce the investment in military works without a corresponding reduction in defense capabilities.

Among these projects are the provision of housing and community facilities, the improvement of transportation, the development of hydroelectrical power, increase in agricultural development, and the encouragement of capital goods industry.

It is difficult to assign an overriding priority to any of these projects since the cumulative effect is necessary if Alaska is to be made self-sustaining.

One of the most critical needs, however, is the provision of additional housing and community facilities. The demand for housing has far outstripped private

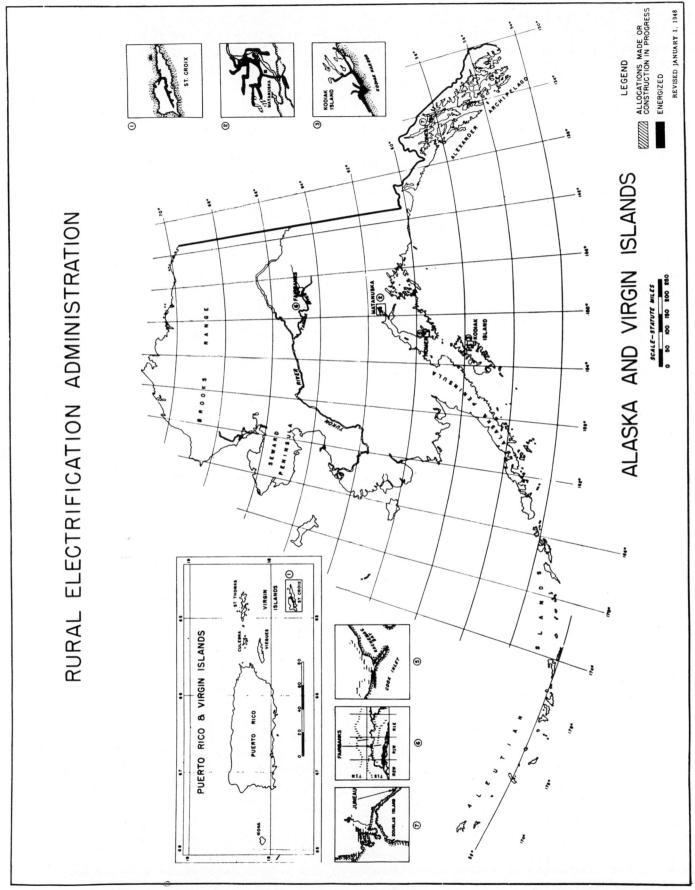

RURAL ELECTRIFICATION ADMINISTRATION

ALASKA AND VIRGIN ISLANDS

PUERTO RICO & VIRGIN ISLANDS

LEGEND

ALLOCATIONS MADE OR CONSTRUCTION IN PROGRESS

ENERGIZED

REVISED JANUARY 1, 1948

SCALE—STATUTE MILES
0 50 100 150 200 250

capabilities, especially in view of the high costs of construction in Alaska. Unless housing and related facilities can be provided at reasonable costs, all other efforts to reduce the cost of living in Alaska will be dissipated.

Since much of the present high cost of construction can be traced to high transportation costs and long delays in shipping, improvement in means of transportation and reduction in transportation costs is also vitally necessary. Improvement in the internal highway net in the central Alakan area is desirable from both the civil and the purely military standpoint. The provision of an alternate land line of communication to the United States is a vital matter. The blockade of Alaska, occasioned by the current shipping strike, merely hints at the disaster which would strike Alaska in the event the lines of communication were interrupted during the period of an emergency. Although improvement of the Alaskan highway would provide an emergency land line of communication, the only sure high tonnage link with the States is the construction of the proposed Alaska-United States rail line down the intermountain trough. Such a railroad would open up for development new areas presently inaccessible because of the lack of transportation, both in Alaska and in Canada.

I have been informed that almost 20,000,000 acres of Territory lands are arable and another 20,000,000 acres would serve as pasture lands. Improved transportation would open some of these lands almost immediately; however, the high cost of clearing land, the lack of suitable equipment, and the scarcity of fertilizers also currently impede improvement of the agricultural program.

Cheap and dependable power is a necessity for the development of any community. Only minor development of hydroelectrical power has taken place in Alaska and yet a potential exists which has been described as almost unlimited. A program for the development of hydroelectric power in the Anchorage area would undoubtedly result in a major improvement in the economic condition of this part of the Territory.

Finally, if Alaska is to be self-sustaining, domestic industry must be encouraged. In view of the current needs of the Territory, it would appear that action to develop at an early date indigenous sources of cement, fertilizer, and the production of petroleum from coal resources would produce the most striking results.

I have outlined these matters because of my knowledge that any increase in the economic development of the Territory of Alaska will result in a more adequate defense for the Territory and for the United States at a lesser cost in men, money, and materials. You may be assured that this command will support any practicable program to effect this end.

Sincerely,

(Signed) N. F. TWINING,
Lt. Gen., USAF,
Commander-in-Chief.

TERRITORY OF ALASKA
OFFICE OF THE GOVERNOR
JUNEAU

JANUARY 10, 1949.

Mr. JOSEPH MORGAN, *Chief,*
ALASKA INVESTIGATIONS OFFICE,
Bureau of Reclamation,
Juneau, Alaska.

DEAR MR. MORGAN: I am glad to have an opportunity to comment on the work of the Bureau of Reclamation in Alaska and the great good which I am confident will result from a federally organized effort under the Bureau to develop Alaska's hydroelectric power resources.

As we know, the Reclamation Act has never been extended to Alaska—one of the many discriminations of which our Territory has been the victim. We were gratified when Congress last year made it possible for the Bureau of Reclamation to make preliminary investigations in Alaska which should result, among other things, in the comprehensive departmental reconnaissance report on the development of the water resources of Alaska.

We are hopeful that the Congress will make it possible in the near future for the Bureau to operate, just as it does in the States of the West, in the Territory of Alaska where reclamation and power development are needed in order to enhance our opportunities for economic advancement.

Hydroelectric power constitutes probably Alaska's outstanding undeveloped resource. Its significance can be appreciated when its potentialities are considered alongside those of the mineral, forest, agricultural, fisheries, recreational, and other undeveloped resources of Alaska.

We are grateful for the work you have done and are anxious for progress on the work the Bureau of Reclamation proposes to do in this Territory. Not only is there every reason why Alaska should participate in the Bureau's program, but there is great need that the work be speeded because of the imperative necessity for rapid development of Alaska's potentialities, a development long delayed.

Sincerely yours,

(Signed) ERNEST GRUENING,
Governor of Alaska.

UNITED STATES
DEPARTMENT OF THE INTERIOR
OFFICE OF THE SECRETARY
Alaska Field Staff
JUNEAU, ALASKA

JANUARY 12, 1949.

MEMORANDUM

To: J. A. KRUG, *Secretary of the Interior.*
From: KENNETH J. KADOW, *Chairman, Alaska Field Committee.*

I have read with great interest the report on Alaska sponsored by and prepared under the general supervision of the Bureau of Reclamation. After careful consideration of the material presented therein, it is my opinion that this report accurately sets forth development potentials of Alaska's natural resources, points up many of its most important development problems, and may prove to be the basis for an orderly and comprehensive development of the Territory.

The report points out the definite need for integration of developmental activities, both public and private, and for coordination of governmental agencies. This need was recognized by your office when you recently appointed a personal representative in Alaska to coordinate and facilitate the various inter- and intra-developmental activities for the greatest public good.

Since this report is intended to provide "engineering and economic investigations as a basis for legislation . . ." to extend the reclamation laws to Alaska, I believe the contents herein satisfy that requirement, insofar as facts are now available.

It is my firm belief that the economic and social growth of Alaska cannot be satisfactorily accomplished without the development of its land and water resources. As I see it, cheap electrical energy is the "pass key" to present and future development needs.

I wholeheartedly endorse this report in its entirety and urge its early approval by the Department.

(Signed)   KENNETH J. KADOW,
Director.